7th grade

Heath
Mathematics

Walter E. Rucker

Clyde A. Dilley

D.C. Heath and Company
Lexington, Massachusetts   Toronto

About the authors

Walter E. Rucker Former Specialist in Education with the Curriculum Laboratory of the University of Illinois, has taught mathematics in public schools and is a coauthor of successful mathematics programs for elementary and junior high schools.

Clyde A. Dilley Professor, University of Toledo, Toledo, Ohio, is teaching methods courses in elementary and secondary mathematics. He has taught mathematics in public schools and is a coauthor of successful mathematics programs for elementary and junior high schools.

Illustrations George Hughes/Gwen Goldstein and Mark Kelley/Sharon Kurlansky

Photography Sharon Beals: 228, 231, 251, 317/Albert Bendelius, Shostal Assoc: 61/ Bettman Archives, Inc: 24, 122/Fred Bodin: 72, 133, 182, 206, 226, 258, 282, 288, 338/Bullaty-Lomee, The Image Bank: 266/Stuart Cohen: 32, 77, 160, 194, 195, 197, 239, 260, 269, 290, 291/Stephen Dalton, Photo Researchers: 171/Gerry Granham, Photo Researchers: 55/Hallinan, FPG: 47/Grant Heilman: 18, 19, 203, 323/Jon Huber, Editorial Photocolor Archives, Inc: 36/Ewing Krainin, Photo Researchers: 103/Ann McQueen: 81, 105, 167/Julie O'Neil: 46, 68, 69, 71, 94, 95, 101, 134, 165, 173, 175, 345/Photofile: 339/Marc Ribound, Magnum: 259/Deidra Delano Stead: Cover, 232, 280, 293, 294, 308, 321, 360/Alvis Upitis, The Image Bank: 17/E. V. Zeisman, Alpha: 215/Zimmerman, Alpha: 156

Contents

By now you have studied a great deal of mathematics. You've learned to add, subtract, multiply, and divide whole numbers, fractions, and decimals. These skills are often called the **basic skills** because they help us learn more about other topics in mathematics.

The first part of this book helps you find out which whole number skills you might need to review and then provides practice exercises for each of them. We used our computer (we call it "Clyde" around school) to generate these review and practice lessons. We hope you enjoy working with Clyde as much as we do.

HI!....

1

PRETEST

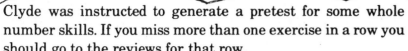

Clyde was instructed to generate a pretest for some whole number skills. If you miss more than one exercise in a row you should go to the reviews for that row.

Row	A	B	C	D	E	F	G	H	I
Go to Reviews	1, 2	1, 3	4, 5	4, 6	7, 8	7, 9	10, 11	10, 12	10, 13

PRETEST

A.
1. $\begin{array}{r} 25 \\ +43 \end{array}$
2. $\begin{array}{r} 60 \\ +34 \end{array}$
3. $\begin{array}{r} 46 \\ +81 \end{array}$
4. $\begin{array}{r} 32 \\ +72 \end{array}$
5. $\begin{array}{r} 72 \\ 23 \\ +43 \end{array}$

B.
1. $\begin{array}{r} 27 \\ +54 \end{array}$
2. $\begin{array}{r} 48 \\ +48 \end{array}$
3. $\begin{array}{r} 76 \\ +69 \end{array}$
4. $\begin{array}{r} 58 \\ +43 \end{array}$
5. $\begin{array}{r} 17 \\ 98 \\ +56 \end{array}$

C.
1. $\begin{array}{r} 73 \\ -28 \end{array}$
2. $\begin{array}{r} 80 \\ -17 \end{array}$
3. $\begin{array}{r} 94 \\ -36 \end{array}$
4. $\begin{array}{r} 82 \\ -58 \end{array}$
5. $\begin{array}{r} 71 \\ -37 \end{array}$

D.
1. $\begin{array}{r} 609 \\ -147 \end{array}$
2. $\begin{array}{r} 928 \\ -245 \end{array}$
3. $\begin{array}{r} 736 \\ -681 \end{array}$
4. $\begin{array}{r} 750 \\ -437 \end{array}$
5. $\begin{array}{r} 851 \\ -306 \end{array}$

E.
1. $\begin{array}{r} 32 \\ \times 3 \end{array}$
2. $\begin{array}{r} 14 \\ \times 2 \end{array}$
3. $\begin{array}{r} 71 \\ \times 6 \end{array}$
4. $\begin{array}{r} 90 \\ \times 7 \end{array}$
5. $\begin{array}{r} 61 \\ \times 4 \end{array}$

F.
1. $\begin{array}{r} 26 \\ \times 3 \end{array}$
2. $\begin{array}{r} 18 \\ \times 4 \end{array}$
3. $\begin{array}{r} 68 \\ \times 7 \end{array}$
4. $\begin{array}{r} 26 \\ \times 8 \end{array}$
5. $\begin{array}{r} 46 \\ \times 9 \end{array}$

G.
1. $5\overline{)33}$
2. $9\overline{)29}$
3. $7\overline{)46}$
4. $8\overline{)71}$
5. $6\overline{)49}$

H.
1. $4\overline{)328}$
2. $3\overline{)189}$
3. $8\overline{)640}$
4. $7\overline{)217}$
5. $2\overline{)166}$

I.
1. $6\overline{)78}$
2. $4\overline{)96}$
3. $7\overline{)91}$
4. $3\overline{)84}$
5. $5\overline{)80}$

REVIEW 1 Addition properties and basic addition facts

Clyde was instructed to search its data bank for two properties that help us remember addition facts. Here is the printout.

THE SUM OF A NUMBER AND ZERO IS THAT SAME NUMBER.

$$6 + 0 = 6 \qquad\qquad 0 + 3 = 3$$

YOU CAN CHANGE THE ORDER OF TWO ADDENDS WITHOUT CHANGING THE SUM.

$$3 + 4 = 4 + 3 \qquad\qquad 7 + 2 = 2 + 7$$

THERE ARE 36 PAIRS OF BASIC ADDITION FACTS SUCH AS $\begin{array}{r} 7 \\ +3 \\ \hline \end{array}$

AND $\begin{array}{r} 3 \\ +7 \\ \hline \end{array}$. IF YOU KNOW ONE FACT IN A PAIR AND THE COMMUTATIVE PROPERTY, THEN YOU KNOW THE OTHER FACT.

Clyde generated 30 practice exercises. Time yourself to see how quickly you can do them. Memorize the facts you missed. Repeat the exercise in a day or so to see if you have improved your speed and accuracy.

ADD.

1. $\begin{array}{r} 2 \\ +6 \\ \hline \end{array}$	2. $\begin{array}{r} 4 \\ +7 \\ \hline \end{array}$	3. $\begin{array}{r} 5 \\ +8 \\ \hline \end{array}$	4. $\begin{array}{r} 3 \\ +7 \\ \hline \end{array}$	5. $\begin{array}{r} 4 \\ +3 \\ \hline \end{array}$	6. $\begin{array}{r} 7 \\ +7 \\ \hline \end{array}$
7. $\begin{array}{r} 1 \\ +8 \\ \hline \end{array}$	8. $\begin{array}{r} 5 \\ +3 \\ \hline \end{array}$	9. $\begin{array}{r} 8 \\ +6 \\ \hline \end{array}$	10. $\begin{array}{r} 2 \\ +7 \\ \hline \end{array}$	11. $\begin{array}{r} 5 \\ +5 \\ \hline \end{array}$	12. $\begin{array}{r} 8 \\ +4 \\ \hline \end{array}$
13. $\begin{array}{r} 9 \\ +9 \\ \hline \end{array}$	14. $\begin{array}{r} 7 \\ +5 \\ \hline \end{array}$	15. $\begin{array}{r} 0 \\ +7 \\ \hline \end{array}$	16. $\begin{array}{r} 8 \\ +8 \\ \hline \end{array}$	17. $\begin{array}{r} 6 \\ +3 \\ \hline \end{array}$	18. $\begin{array}{r} 9 \\ +1 \\ \hline \end{array}$
19. $\begin{array}{r} 3 \\ +8 \\ \hline \end{array}$	20. $\begin{array}{r} 6 \\ +6 \\ \hline \end{array}$	21. $\begin{array}{r} 8 \\ +9 \\ \hline \end{array}$	22. $\begin{array}{r} 5 \\ +4 \\ \hline \end{array}$	23. $\begin{array}{r} 7 \\ +8 \\ \hline \end{array}$	24. $\begin{array}{r} 4 \\ +4 \\ \hline \end{array}$
25. $\begin{array}{r} 5 \\ +6 \\ \hline \end{array}$	26. $\begin{array}{r} 8 \\ +2 \\ \hline \end{array}$	27. $\begin{array}{r} 6 \\ +7 \\ \hline \end{array}$	28. $\begin{array}{r} 4 \\ +6 \\ \hline \end{array}$	29. $\begin{array}{r} 1 \\ +7 \\ \hline \end{array}$	30. $\begin{array}{r} 6 \\ +0 \\ \hline \end{array}$

COMPUTER CHECK

1. 8 2. 11 3. 13 4. 10 5. 7 6. 14 7. 9 8. 8 9. 14 10. 9 11. 10 12. 12 13. 18
14. 12 15. 7 16. 16 17. 9 18. 10 19. 11 20. 12 21. 17 22. 9 23. 15 24. 8 25. 11
26. 10 27. 13 28. 10 29. 8 30. 6

3

REVIEW 2   Adding 2–digit numbers

MEMORY RETRIEVAL—ADDING IN COLUMNS

	ADD ONES.	ADD TENS.

```
      72          72          72
    + 51        + 51        + 51
                ----        ----
                   3         123
```

ADD.

1.   53
   +16
	2. 21
	   +62
		3. 49
		   +40
			4. 13
			   +43
				5. 70
				   +15

6.   20
   +50
	7. 34
	   +83
		8. 82
		   +63
			9. 35
			   +72
				10. 34
				    +95

11.   84
    +70
	12. 76
	    +72
		13. 80
		    +80
			14. 36
			    +83
				15. 71
				    +56

16.   24
    34
    +60
	17. 43
	    23
	    +73
		18. 62
		    35
		    +81
			19. 32
			    45
			    +22
				20. 54
				    43
				    +71

COMPUTER CHECK
YOU SHOULD BE ABLE TO FIND EACH ANSWER IN THIS LIST:

4   56   69   70   83   85   89   99   107   117   118   119   127   129   139   145   148   154   160   168   178

REVIEW 3 Adding 2–digit numbers

MEMORY RETRIEVAL—ADDING WITH REGROUPING

ADD ONES, THEN REGROUP.

ADD TENS.

```
                           1                    1
     27              27                   27
   + 88            + 88                 + 88
                      5                  115
```

ADD.

1. 26
  +58

2. 17
  +37

3. 39
  +46

4. 51
  +29

5. 28
  +48

6. 38
  +35

7. 46
  +94

8. 73
  +28

9. 26
  +96

10. 55
  +59

11. 67
  +78

12. 69
  +62

13. 85
  +18

14. 77
  +66

15. 49
  +57

16. 28
  49
  +36

17. 85
  14
  +67

18. 46
  83
  +76

19. 24
  44
  +15

20. 65
  12
  +56

COMPUTER CHECK
YOU SHOULD BE ABLE TO FIND EACH ANSWER IN THIS LIST:
54 73 76 80 83 84 85 101 103 106 113 114 122 131 133 140 143 145 166 205

REVIEW 4 Basic subtraction facts

SUBTRACTION DATA BANK

IF YOU KNOW THE ADDITION FACTS AND REMEMBER THAT ADDITION AND SUBTRACTION ARE RE-
LATED, YOU SHOULD HAVE LITTLE TROUBLE RECALLING THE SUBTRACTION FACTS.

EXAMPLE:

$$\begin{array}{r} 5 \\ +9 \\ \hline 14 \end{array}$$

THIS ADDITION FACT HAS TWO RELATED SUBTRACTION FACTS,

$$14 - 9 = 5 \quad \text{AND} \quad 14 - 5 = 9$$

Time yourself to see how quickly you can do the 35 exercises below. Memorize the facts you missed. Repeat the exercises in a day or so to see if you have improved your speed and accuracy.

SUBTRACT.

1. 12 −4	2. 15 −7	3. 13 −8	4. 12 −9	5. 14 −8
6. 11 −7	7. 16 −9	8. 11 −2	9. 17 −8	10. 13 −4
11. 11 −6	12. 15 −8	13. 12 −7	14. 16 −8	15. 13 −9
16. 15 −6	17. 12 −3	18. 18 −9	19. 14 −6	20. 13 −7
21. 11 −8	22. 14 −9	23. 12 −5	24. 11 −9	25. 11 −3
26. 16 −7	27. 13 −5	28. 14 −7	29. 17 −9	30. 12 −8
31. 11 −5	32. 13 −6	33. 14 −5	34. 15 −9	35. 11 −4

REVIEW 5 Subtracting 2–digit numbers, one regrouping

MEMORY RETRIEVAL— 2–DIGIT SUBTRACTION

	NOT ENOUGH ONES, SO REGROUP A TEN.	SUBTRACT ONES, SUBTRACT TENS.
82 −53	7 8̸2 −53	7 8̸2 −53 —— 29

SUBTRACT.

1. 81   2. 73   3. 60   4. 94   5. 92
   −57   −58   −18   −78   −65

6. 74   7. 53   8. 62   9. 70   10. 56
   −19   −39   −37   −29   −37

11. 75   12. 92   13. 86   14. 62   15. 54
    −46   −75   −77   −13   −28

16. 92   17. 90   18. 82   19. 51   20. 52
    −56   −84   −69   −12   −34

COMPUTER CHECK
YOU SHOULD BE ABLE TO FIND EACH ANSWER IN THIS LIST:
6   9   13   14   15   16   17   18   19   24   25   26   27   29   36   39   41   42   49   55

Subtracting 3–digit numbers, one regrouping

MEMORY RETRIEVAL— 3–DIGIT SUBTRACTION

	SUBTRACT ONES.	NOT ENOUGH TENS, SO REGROUP A HUNDRED.	SUBTRACT TENS, SUBTRACT HUNDREDS.
4 2 7 −2 5 3	4 2 7 −2 5 3 4	³4̸ 2 7 −2 5 3 4	³4̸ 2 7 −2 5 3 1 7 4

SUBTRACT.

1.   617
−235

2.   524
−371

3.   447
−219

4.   571
−127

5.   962
−543

6.   663
−271

7.   806
−495

8.   807
−684

9.   974
−135

10.   454
−393

11.   228
−183

12.   883
−849

13.   174
−125

14.   445
−351

15.   419
−146

16.   960
−917

17.   486
−458

18.   870
−423

19.   245
−185

20.   721
−506

COMPUTER CHECK
YOU SHOULD BE ABLE TO FIND EACH ANSWER IN THIS LIST:

  28   34   43   45   49   60   61   94   123   153   215   228   273   311   382   392   419   444   447   839

REVIEW 7 Multiplication properties and basic multiplication facts

Clyde was instructed to search its data bank for three properties that help us remember the multiplication facts. Here is the printout.

MULTIPLYING BY ZERO PROPERTY

THE PRODUCT OF A NUMBER AND ZERO IS ZERO.

$$6 \times 0 = 0 \qquad 0 \times 3 = 0$$

MULTIPLYING BY ONE PROPERTY

THE PRODUCT OF A NUMBER AND ONE IS THAT SAME NUMBER.

$$6 \times 1 = 6 \qquad 1 \times 3 = 3$$

COMMUTATIVE PROPERTY OF MULTIPLICATION

YOU CAN CHANGE THE ORDER OF TWO FACTORS WITHOUT CHANGING THE PRODUCT.

$$3 \times 4 = 4 \times 3 \qquad 7 \times 2 = 2 \times 7$$

THERE ARE 36 PAIRS OF BASIC MULTIPLICATION FACTS SUCH AS $\begin{array}{r} 7 \\ \times 3 \\ \hline \end{array}$ AND $\begin{array}{r} 3 \\ \times 7 \\ \hline \end{array}$. IF YOU KNOW ONE

FACT IN A PAIR AND THE COMMUTATIVE PROPERTY, THEN YOU KNOW THE OTHER FACT.

Clyde generated the following practice exercises. Time yourself to see how quickly you can do them. Memorize the facts you missed. Repeat the exercises in a day or so to see if you have improved your speed and accuracy.

MULTIPLY.

1. $\begin{array}{r} 5 \\ \times 6 \\ \hline \end{array}$	2. $\begin{array}{r} 9 \\ \times 4 \\ \hline \end{array}$	3. $\begin{array}{r} 5 \\ \times 7 \\ \hline \end{array}$	4. $\begin{array}{r} 8 \\ \times 6 \\ \hline \end{array}$	5. $\begin{array}{r} 4 \\ \times 5 \\ \hline \end{array}$	6. $\begin{array}{r} 9 \\ \times 8 \\ \hline \end{array}$
7. $\begin{array}{r} 6 \\ \times 7 \\ \hline \end{array}$	8. $\begin{array}{r} 4 \\ \times 6 \\ \hline \end{array}$	9. $\begin{array}{r} 3 \\ \times 9 \\ \hline \end{array}$	10. $\begin{array}{r} 7 \\ \times 9 \\ \hline \end{array}$	11. $\begin{array}{r} 8 \\ \times 8 \\ \hline \end{array}$	12. $\begin{array}{r} 7 \\ \times 4 \\ \hline \end{array}$
13. $\begin{array}{r} 5 \\ \times 5 \\ \hline \end{array}$	14. $\begin{array}{r} 9 \\ \times 6 \\ \hline \end{array}$	15. $\begin{array}{r} 7 \\ \times 8 \\ \hline \end{array}$	16. $\begin{array}{r} 4 \\ \times 8 \\ \hline \end{array}$	17. $\begin{array}{r} 6 \\ \times 6 \\ \hline \end{array}$	18. $\begin{array}{r} 5 \\ \times 8 \\ \hline \end{array}$
19. $\begin{array}{r} 9 \\ \times 9 \\ \hline \end{array}$	20. $\begin{array}{r} 1 \\ \times 8 \\ \hline \end{array}$	21. $\begin{array}{r} 7 \\ \times 7 \\ \hline \end{array}$	22. $\begin{array}{r} 0 \\ \times 9 \\ \hline \end{array}$	23. $\begin{array}{r} 5 \\ \times 9 \\ \hline \end{array}$	24. $\begin{array}{r} 4 \\ \times 4 \\ \hline \end{array}$

COMPUTER CHECK

24. 16
13. 25 14. 54   15. 56   16. 32 17. 36 18. 40 19. 81 20. 8 21. 49 22. 0 23. 45
1. 30   2. 36 3. 35   4. 48 5. 20 6. 72 7. 42 8. 24 9. 27 10. 63   11. 64 12. 28

9

REVIEW 8

Multiplying a 2–digit number by a 1–digit number

MEMORY RETRIEVAL— MULTIPLICATION IN COLUMNS

	MULTIPLY ONES.	MULTIPLY TENS.
74 ×2	74 ×2 ― 8	74 ×2 ― 148

MULTIPLY.

1. 32 ×3	2. 41 ×2	3. 20 ×3	4. 11 ×7	5. 21 ×4
6. 23 ×1	7. 64 ×2	8. 73 ×3	9. 81 ×8	10. 72 ×3
11. 90 ×6	12. 41 ×7	13. 81 ×6	14. 82 ×2	15. 91 ×4
16. 80 ×3	17. 50 ×5	18. 61 ×6	19. 52 ×4	20. 74 ×2

COMPUTER CHECK
YOU SHOULD BE ABLE TO FIND EACH ANSWER IN THIS LIST:

23 60 77 82 84 96 128 148 164 208 216 219 240 250 287 364 366 486 540 648

**Multiplying a 2–digit number
by a 1–digit number**

MEMORY RETRIEVAL— MULTIPLICATION WITH REGROUPING

	MULTIPLY ONES AND REGROUP.	MULTIPLY TENS AND ADD.
54 ×3	1 54 ×3 ‾‾2	1 54 ×3 ‾162

MULTIPLY.

1. 29
   ×3

2. 13
   ×5

3. 13
   ×7

4. 23
   ×4

5. 37
   ×2

6. 15
   ×6

7. 64
   ×9

8. 83
   ×7

9. 46
   ×8

10. 46
    ×4

11. 12
    ×9

12. 98
    ×2

13. 29
    ×9

14. 89
    ×8

15. 75
    ×7

16. 86
    ×7

17. 35
    ×6

18. 65
    ×8

19. 58
    ×4

20. 99
    ×3

COMPUTER CHECK
YOU SHOULD BE ABLE TO FIND EACH ANSWER IN THIS LIST:
65 74 87 90 91 92 108 184 196 210 232 261 297 368 520 525 576 581 602 712

REVIEW 10 Basic division facts

DIVISION DATA BANK

IF YOU KNOW THE MULTIPLICATION FACTS AND REMEMBER THAT MULTIPLICATION AND DIVISION ARE RELATED, YOU SHOULD HAVE LITTLE TROUBLE RECALLING THE DIVISION FACTS.

EXAMPLE:

$$\begin{array}{r} 3 \\ \times 7 \\ \hline 21 \end{array}$$

THIS MULTIPLICATION FACT HAS TWO RELATED DIVISION FACTS.

$$3\overline{)21}^{\,7} \qquad 7\overline{)21}^{\,3}$$

Time yourself to see how quickly you can do the 40 exercises below. Memorize the facts you missed. Repeat the exercises in a day or so to see if you have improved your speed and accuracy.

DIVIDE.

1. $4\overline{)20}$	2. $5\overline{)35}$	3. $6\overline{)18}$	4. $7\overline{)49}$	5. $5\overline{)15}$
6. $8\overline{)32}$	7. $2\overline{)16}$	8. $8\overline{)24}$	9. $3\overline{)27}$	10. $6\overline{)6}$
11. $5\overline{)40}$	12. $4\overline{)16}$	13. $5\overline{)45}$	14. $8\overline{)64}$	15. $2\overline{)14}$
16. $9\overline{)72}$	17. $2\overline{)18}$	18. $5\overline{)0}$	19. $9\overline{)36}$	20. $6\overline{)12}$
21. $4\overline{)28}$	22. $8\overline{)16}$	23. $7\overline{)21}$	24. $8\overline{)48}$	25. $2\overline{)12}$
26. $6\overline{)24}$	27. $9\overline{)81}$	28. $4\overline{)24}$	29. $7\overline{)63}$	30. $3\overline{)12}$
31. $8\overline{)56}$	32. $1\overline{)8}$	33. $3\overline{)18}$	34. $6\overline{)42}$	35. $4\overline{)12}$
36. $9\overline{)54}$	37. $5\overline{)25}$	38. $3\overline{)24}$	39. $6\overline{)36}$	40. $9\overline{)18}$

COMPUTER CHECK

1. 5 2. 7 3. 3 4. 7 5. 3 6. 4 7. 8 8. 3 9. 9 10. 1 11. 8 12. 4 13. 9 14. 8
15. 7 16. 8 17. 9 18. 0 19. 4 20. 2 21. 7 22. 2 23. 3 24. 6 25. 6 26. 4 27. 9 28. 6
29. 9 30. 4 31. 7 32. 8 33. 6 34. 7 35. 3 36. 6 37. 5 38. 8 39. 6 40. 2

12

REVIEW 11 Dividing by a 1-digit number

MEMORY RETRIEVAL— DIVIDING WITH A REMAINDER

	RECALL FACTS.	DIVIDE, THEN MULTIPLY.	SUBTRACT TO GET REMAINDER.

$8\overline{)34}$

$$\begin{array}{ccc} 3 & 4 & 5 \\ \times 8 & \times 8 & \times 8 \\ \hline 24 & 32 & 40 \end{array}$$

TOO BIG

DIVIDE, THEN MULTIPLY.
$$\begin{array}{r} 4 \\ 8\overline{)34} \\ 32 \end{array}$$

SUBTRACT TO GET REMAINDER.
$$\begin{array}{r} 4\ R\ 2 \\ 8\overline{)34} \\ -32 \\ \hline 2 \end{array}$$

DIVIDE.

1. $7\overline{)32}$ 2. $6\overline{)25}$ 3. $7\overline{)53}$ 4. $8\overline{)45}$ 5. $4\overline{)19}$

6. $8\overline{)27}$ 7. $9\overline{)42}$ 8. $6\overline{)41}$ 9. $2\overline{)13}$ 10. $5\overline{)32}$

11. $4\overline{)31}$ 12. $5\overline{)44}$ 13. $9\overline{)70}$ 14. $7\overline{)67}$ 15. $8\overline{)61}$

16. $9\overline{)80}$ 17. $6\overline{)23}$ 18. $2\overline{)11}$ 19. $5\overline{)29}$ 20. $4\overline{)33}$

21. $4\overline{)11}$ 22. $9\overline{)50}$ 23. $6\overline{)53}$ 24. $7\overline{)27}$ 25. $5\overline{)19}$

26. $7\overline{)48}$ 27. $4\overline{)35}$ 28. $5\overline{)23}$ 29. $8\overline{)59}$ 30. $9\overline{)35}$

31. $8\overline{)15}$ 32. $6\overline{)38}$

COMPUTER CHECK
YOU SHOULD BE ABLE TO FIND EACH ANSWER IN THIS LIST:
1 R7   2 R3   3 R3   3 R4   3 R5   3 R6   3 R8   4 R1   4 R3   4 R4   4 R6   5 R1   5 R4   5 R5
6 R1   6 R2   6 R5   6 R6   7 R3   7 R4   7 R5   7 R7   8 R1   8 R3   8 R4   8 R5   8 R8   9 R4

REVIEW 12 Dividing by a 1–digit number

MEMORY RETRIEVAL—DIVIDING IN COLUMNS

REGROUP, THEN
DIVIDE TENS.

DIVIDE ONES.

$6\overline{)246}$

$6\overline{)\overset{4}{246}}$

$6\overline{)\overset{41}{246}}$

DIVIDE.

1. $4\overline{)128}$ 2. $6\overline{)366}$ 3. $9\overline{)270}$ 4. $3\overline{)186}$ 5. $5\overline{)400}$

6. $8\overline{)568}$ 7. $3\overline{)249}$ 8. $2\overline{)108}$ 9. $7\overline{)217}$ 10. $6\overline{)306}$

11. $7\overline{)350}$ 12. $2\overline{)146}$ 13. $5\overline{)205}$ 14. $8\overline{)160}$ 15. $4\overline{)324}$

16. $3\overline{)159}$ 17. $6\overline{)246}$ 18. $9\overline{)819}$ 19. $2\overline{)184}$ 20. $5\overline{)355}$

21. $7\overline{)280}$ 22. $3\overline{)213}$ 23. $8\overline{)648}$ 24. $9\overline{)540}$ 25. $2\overline{)162}$

26. $8\overline{)720}$ 27. $4\overline{)164}$ 28. $6\overline{)480}$ 29. $7\overline{)497}$ 30. $4\overline{)208}$

             31. $5\overline{)300}$ 32. $3\overline{)279}$

COMPUTER CHECK
YOU SHOULD BE ABLE TO FIND EACH ANSWER IN THIS LIST:

14   20   30   31   32   40   41   50   51   52   53   54
       60   61   62   71   73   80   81   83   90   91   92   93

REVIEW 13 Dividing by a 1–digit number

MEMORY RETRIEVAL— DIVIDING WITH REGROUPING

$2\overline{)76}$

DIVIDE TENS.

$$\begin{array}{r} 3 \\ 2\overline{)76} \\ -6 \\ \hline 1 \end{array}$$

REGROUP, THEN DIVIDE ONES.

$$\begin{array}{r} 38 \\ 2\overline{)76} \\ -6 \\ \hline 16 \\ -16 \\ \hline 0 \end{array}$$

DIVIDE.

1. $3\overline{)78}$ 2. $5\overline{)75}$ 3. $7\overline{)84}$ 4. $4\overline{)72}$ 5. $6\overline{)84}$

6. $2\overline{)96}$ 7. $7\overline{)91}$ 8. $3\overline{)87}$ 9. $5\overline{)80}$ 10. $4\overline{)68}$

11. $2\overline{)54}$ 12. $4\overline{)92}$ 13. $5\overline{)95}$ 14. $3\overline{)84}$ 15. $2\overline{)74}$

16. $3\overline{)45}$ 17. $6\overline{)72}$ 18. $5\overline{)60}$ 19. $6\overline{)78}$ 20. $2\overline{)34}$

21. $3\overline{)72}$ 22. $7\overline{)98}$ 23. $3\overline{)57}$ 24. $4\overline{)64}$ 25. $6\overline{)90}$

26. $4\overline{)56}$ 27. $8\overline{)96}$ 28. $5\overline{)65}$ 29. $4\overline{)76}$ 30. $6\overline{)96}$

31. $5\overline{)70}$ 32. $4\overline{)96}$

COMPUTER CHECK
YOU SHOULD BE ABLE TO FIND EACH ANSWER IN THIS LIST:
12   13   14   15   16   17   18   19   23   24   26   27   28   29   37   48

POSTTEST

Clyde generated this posttest based on the 13 reviews of whole number skills. A good score on this test means you are ready to start Chapter 1.

POSTTEST

	1.	2.	3.	4.	5.
A.	46 +12	36 +40	54 +74	82 +63	61 52 +34
B.	36 +17	35 +35	74 +89	78 +28	32 94 +97
C.	84 −36	70 −24	71 −67	73 −36	92 −58
D.	908 −127	437 −282	546 −474	720 −316	893 −547
E.	21 ×4	23 ×3	41 ×6	80 ×4	61 ×7
F.	28 ×3	16 ×6	74 ×8	39 ×6	87 ×7
G.	3)26	8)43	4)37	7)61	5)48
H.	6)126	4)288	5)350	2)146	3)249
I.	8)96	3)81	5)85	6)84	7)98

1 Whole Numbers

Large numbers

You need only the ten digits 0, 1, 2, 3, 4, 5, 6, 7, 8, 9 to write a numeral for any whole number, *no matter how large*. The average number of kilometers between the earth and the sun is shown in this place-value table.

Trillions			Billions			Millions			Thousands			Ones		
hundreds	tens	ones	hundreds	tens	ones	hundreds	tens	ones	hundreds	tens	ones	hundreds	tens	ones
						1	4	8	7	3	1	0	0	0

Standard numeral: **148,731,000**

Starting at the right, each group of three digits (called a **period**) is usually set off with a comma.

Read as: "**one hundred forty-eight million,** seven hundred thirty-one thousand"

To read a large number, first think about the value of each period.

trillions	billions	millions	thousands	ones
4,	372,	053,	007,	203

four trillion, three hundred seventy-two billion, **fifty-three** million, seven thousand, **two hundred three**

EXERCISES
Read aloud.

1. 58,374
2. 195,396
3. 528,030
4. 401,006
5. 7,821,534
6. 9,060,358
7. 923,465
8. 178,025
9. 5,273,456
10. 8,392,051
11. 38,297,438
12. 51,703,004
13. 952,360,000
14. 538,412,073
15. 3,825,506,142
16. 7,020,350,413
17. 79,003,000,580
18. 391,000,000,000
19. 385,700,000,000
20. 521,361,782,534
21. 5,820,000,000,000
22. 48,036,742,100,000
23. 593,120,000,590,000

Here are some number facts about the sun.
Give the standard numeral.

24. Its mass is three hundred thirty-one thousand, nine hundred fifty *times* the mass of the earth.

25. The diameter is one million, three hundred eighty-four thousand kilometers.

26. The temperature at the center is about nineteen million, nine hundred eighty thousand degrees Celsius.

27. It gives the earth about ninety-four trillion kilowatts of energy.

28. The star closest to our solar system is about forty trillion, six hundred eighty-one billion, one hundred forty-seven million kilometers away.

Tens, hundreds, and thousands

Here are some multiples of 10.

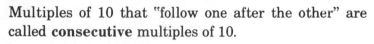

Multiples of 10 that "follow one after the other" are called **consecutive** multiples of 10.

> 90 and 100 are consecutive multiples of 10.
> 430 and 440 are consecutive multiples of 10.

Here are some multiples of 100.

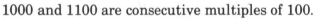

> 1000 and 1100 are consecutive multiples of 100.

Can you give two consecutive multiples of 1000?

EXERCISES

Give the next three multiples of 10.

1. 50	**2.** 70	**3.** 90	**4.** 160	**5.** 380
6. 990	**7.** 1610	**8.** 1900	**9.** 2580	**10.** 3670

Give the next three multiples of 100.

11. 200	**12.** 500	**13.** 900	**14.** 1500	**15.** 2300
16. 3800	**17.** 12,300	**18.** 18,700	**19.** 26,000	**20.** 39,800

Give the next three multiples of 1000.

21. 2000	**22.** 5000	**23.** 7000	**24.** 9000	**25.** 14,000
26. 17,000	**27.** 19,000	**28.** 28,000	**29.** 59,000	**30.** 98,000

Write the two consecutive multiples of 10 that the given number is between.

31. 53 — Answer 50,60

32. 82

33. 95

34. 236

35. 758

36. 996

37. 137

38. 297

39. 599

40. 1235

41. 1364

42. 2375

43. 4991

44. 6998

Write the two consecutive multiples of 100 that the given number is between.

45. 358

46. 526

47. 908

48. 1542

49. 1973

50. 2713

51. 2974

52. 7820

53. 1529

54. 9280

55. 11,248

56. 15,943

57. 23,993

58. 96,421

59. 84,601

Write the two consecutive multiples of 1000 that the given number is between.

60. 2816

61. 5601

62. 9309

63. 12,386

64. 51,742

65. 52,174

66. 68,031

67. 74,395

68. 80,861

69. 99,376

70. 123,452

71. 215,395

72. 109,465

73. 596,645 — 596,000

74. 899,904

Here is how to write a standard numeral as an **expanded numeral**. Notice the multiples that are used.

$$526{,}378 = 500{,}000 + 20{,}000 + 6000 + 300 + 70 + 8$$

| A multiple of: | 100,000 | 10,000 | 1000 | 100 | 10 | 1 |

Give the expanded numeral.

75. 758

76. 2356

77. 4829

78. 6238

79. 39,274

80. 83,261

81. 295,378

82. 563,174

21

Rounding

Sometimes rounded numbers are used instead of exact numbers.

When we use the nearest multiple of 10 as the rounded number, we are **rounding to the nearest 10.**

38 | Round to nearest 10 > 40

51 | Round to nearest 10 > 50

When we use the nearest multiple of 100 as the rounded number, we are **rounding to the nearest 100.**

576 | Round to nearest 100 > 600

621 | Round to nearest 100 > 600

When a number to be rounded is half way between two multiples, round up to the greater multiple.

75 | Round to nearest 10 > 80

850 | Round to nearest 100 > 900

4500 | Round to nearest 1000 > 5000

About 400,000 kg of fish were caught today

EXERCISES

Round to the nearest 10.

1. 71   **2.** 88   **3.** 97   **4.** 155

Round to the nearest 1000.

9. 7586   **10.** 997   **11.** 376,500

Round to the nearest 100.

5. 631   **6.** 641   **7.** 1550   **8.** 3050

Round to the nearest million.

12. 5(432)671   **13.** 5(583)675

22

Here is how I round 67,523 to the nearest 1000.

Step 1. Find the thousands place.

6̲7,523
↑

Step 2. Look 1 place to the right. If the digit is 5 or greater, round "up."

67,523 → 68,000

Use the shortcut to round the following numbers.
Round to the nearest 100.

14. 780   **15.** 923   **16.** 5280   **17.** 650   **18.** 14,350

Round to the nearest 1000.

19. 8500   **20.** 27,499   **21.** 186,501   **22.** 399,846

187,000   400,000

Round to the nearest 100,000.

23. 386,543   **24.** 2,867,321   **25.** 14,977,000   **26.** 16,450,000

The table shows the findings of a recent census.

27. Round each population to the nearest 100,000.

28. Round to the nearest million.

Eight Most Populous States

State	Population
California	19,953,134
New York	18,190,740
Pennsylvania	11,793,909
Texas	11,196,730
Illinois	11,113,976
Ohio	10,652,017
Michigan	8,875,083
New Jersey	7,168,164

Comparing numbers

The first hot-air balloon was built in 1783 by two Frenchmen. Today hot-air ballooning is a sport enjoyed by many.

Hot-air balloonists compete in several events. One event is spot-landing. The balloons must take off and land during a specified time and land near a specified spot. The balloon that lands closest to the spot wins.

Suppose one balloon missed the spot by 1526 m and another missed by 1578 m. To determine which balloon won, the numbers are compared.

Since both have the same number of digits, we start at the left and compare the digits that are in the same place.

```
    ┌─Since 2 < 7─┐
1526        <        1578
        is less than
```

```
    ┌─Since 7 > 2─┐
1578        >        1526
       is greater than
```

EXERCISES

< or >?

1. 864 ● 865
2. 700 ● 699
3. 999 ● 1000
4. 907 ● 970

5. 6493 ● 6385
6. 4863 ● 987
7. 88,235 ● 91,740
8. 64,291 ● 64,289

9. 71,892 ● 53,461
10. 80,007 ● 78,999
11. 354,621 ● 703,945
12. 406,735 ● 406,673

24

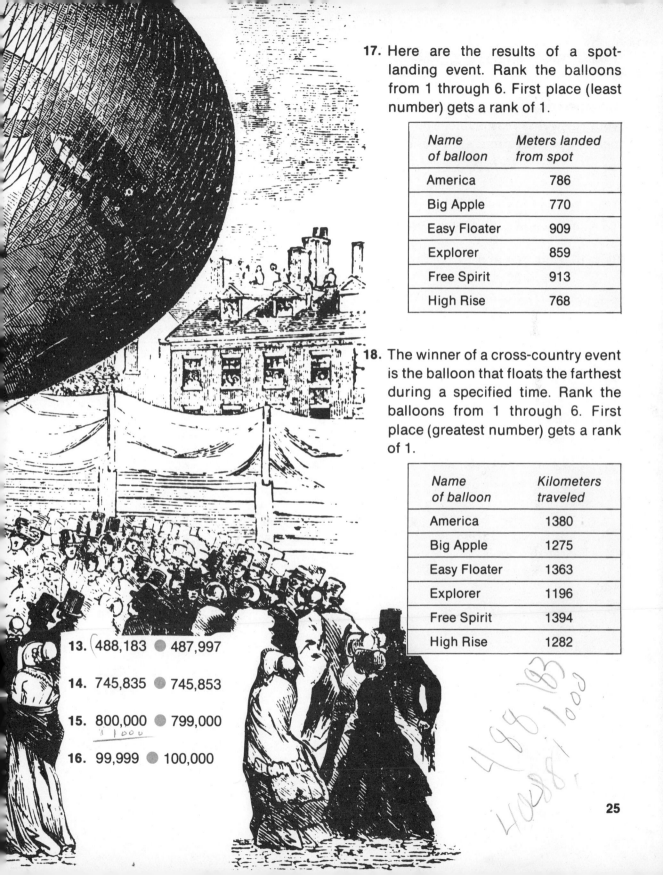

17. Here are the results of a spot-landing event. Rank the balloons from 1 through 6. First place (least number) gets a rank of 1.

Name of balloon	Meters landed from spot
America	786
Big Apple	770
Easy Floater	909
Explorer	859
Free Spirit	913
High Rise	768

18. The winner of a cross-country event is the balloon that floats the farthest during a specified time. Rank the balloons from 1 through 6. First place (greatest number) gets a rank of 1.

Name of balloon	Kilometers traveled
America	1380
Big Apple	1275
Easy Floater	1363
Explorer	1196
Free Spirit	1394
High Rise	1282

13. 488,183 ⬤ 487,997

14. 745,835 ⬤ 745,853

15. 800,000 ⬤ 799,000

16. 99,999 ⬤ 100,000

25

Adding whole numbers

If you estimate a sum before you add, you will know whether your answer is reasonable. You can round each addend to the nearest 100 to estimate the sum.

$$\overset{600}{}\quad \overset{300}{}$$
$$589 + 323$$

The sum is near 900

To find the sum, we add in each column.

Step 1. Add ones and regroup.

$$\begin{array}{r} {}^{1} \\ 589 \\ + 323 \\ \hline 2 \end{array}$$

Step 2. Add tens and regroup.

$$\begin{array}{r} {}^{11} \\ 589 \\ + 323 \\ \hline 12 \end{array}$$

Step 3. Add hundreds.

$$\begin{array}{r} {}^{11} \\ 589 \\ + 323 \\ \hline 912 \end{array}$$

EXERCISES

First estimate the sum. Then add.

1. 373 + 499	2. 287 + 566	3. 675 + 184	4. 858 + 79	5. 467 + 465	6. 897 + 399
7. 742 + 935	8. 868 + 733	9. 879 + 464	10. 656 + 455	11. 363 + 570	12. 367 + 678

Add.

13. $8.26 + 1.37	14. $6.85 + 2.37	15. $8.31 + 5.46	16. $9.76 + 3.85	17. $6.74 + 3.21
18. 6482 + 7358	19. 5761 + 3897	20. 9473 + 6745	21. 4235 + 3849	22. 2058 + 3979
23. 56248 + 39746	24. 51742 + 39165	25. 80375 + 29654	26. 503498 + 128745	27. 736429 + 167893

Add.

28.	952	29.	521	30.	521	31.	623
	163		630		835		507
	+ 798		+ 708		+ 477		+ 31

32.	703	33.	591	34.	124	35.	218
	259		538		202		162
	384		322		419		907
	+ 801		+ 960		+ 716		+ 669

36.	5258	37.	5366	38.	7436	39.	5234
	3940		2170		2918		7183
	7132		8422		3756		6129
	+ 8679		+ 7359		+ 2943		+ 7438

Match. Find the sums by estimating.

40. 1536 + 294   a. 1185

41. 399 + 582   b. 1422

42. 908 + 695   c. 1297

43. 911 + 386   d. 1830

44. 620 + 314 + 488   e. 2080

45. 375 + 529 + 281   f. 981

46. 692 + 575 + 813   g. 1603

Find the missing digits.

47.	38 ▉ 9	48.	▉ 9 8 ▉	49.	563 ▉ 25
	+ 4 ▉ 6 ▉		+ 6 ▉ 7 ▉ 9		+ 3 ▉ 796 ▉
	8094		141131		▉ 1 ▉ 7 ▉ 1

Round to the nearest 100.

1. 496

2. 739

3. 850

4. 967

5. 1421

6. 1530

7. 2674

8. 5382

9. 6250

10. 9950

11. 37,825

12. 59,500

Subtracting whole numbers

You can estimate a difference by rounding each number to the nearest 100.

823 – 294

The difference is near 500.

To find the difference, we subtract in each column.

Step 1. Not enough ones.
Regroup 1 ten for 10 ones.

$$\begin{array}{r} 8\ \overset{1}{\cancel{2}}\ 3 \\ -2\ 9\ 4 \end{array}$$

Step 2. Subtract ones.

$$\begin{array}{r} 8\ \overset{1}{\cancel{2}}\ 3 \\ -2\ 9\ 4 \\ \hline 9 \end{array}$$

Step 3. Not enough tens.
Regroup 1 hundred for 10 tens.

$$\begin{array}{r} \overset{7}{\cancel{8}}\ \overset{11}{\cancel{2}}\ 3 \\ -2\ 9\ 4 \\ \hline 9 \end{array}$$

Step 4. Subtract tens.

$$\begin{array}{r} \overset{7}{\cancel{8}}\ \overset{11}{\cancel{2}}\ 3 \\ -2\ 9\ 4 \\ \hline 2\ 9 \end{array}$$

Step 5. Subtract hundreds.

$$\begin{array}{r} \overset{7}{\cancel{8}}\ \overset{11}{\cancel{2}}\ 3 \\ -2\ 9\ 4 \\ \hline 5\ 2\ 9 \end{array}$$

EXERCISES
**First estimate the difference.
Then subtract.**

1.	385 − 162	**2.**	531 − 283
3.	617 − 356	**4.**	420 − 274
5.	569 − 372	**6.**	913 − 187
7.	$4.42 − 3.65	**8.**	$12.86 − 7.53
9.	$46.32 − 22.78	**10.**	$58.10 − 47.64
11.	$42.22 − 16.79	**12.**	$34.23 − 7.78
13.	8263 − 3288	**14.**	5082 − 2659
15.	7938 − 3814	**16.**	8842 − 7966
17.	5934 − 359	**18.**	2686 − 1347

Sometimes you have to regroup more than once before you can subtract.

Step 1. Not enough ones. No tens. Regroup 1 hundred for 10 tens.

$$\begin{array}{r} \overset{5}{\cancel{6}}\!^{1}0\,2 \\ -357 \\ \hline \end{array}$$

Step 2. Regroup 1 ten for 10 ones.

$$\begin{array}{r} \overset{5\,9}{\cancel{6}}\!\overset{1}{\cancel{0}}\,2 \\ -357 \\ \hline \end{array}$$

Step 3. Subtract.

$$\begin{array}{r} \overset{5\;9}{\cancel{6}}\!\overset{1}{\cancel{0}}\!^{1}2 \\ -357 \\ \hline 245 \end{array}$$

Subtract.

19.	20.	21.	22.	23.	24.
503 − 265	702 − 384	804 − 796	200 − 35	400 − 138	800 − 463

25.	26.	27.	28.	29.	30.
7021 − 1673	8003 − 5236	8013 − 5278	3107 − 1288	8000 − 2134	4000 − 3906

31.	32.	33.	34.	35.	36.
5821 − 2774	5963 − 4877	5062 − 3748	3051 − 1773	6000 − 4193	2800 − 766

To find a difference like this, I decrease each number by 1. The difference is the same and there is no regrouping.

$$\begin{array}{r} 9000 \longrightarrow 8999 \\ -4763 \longrightarrow -4762 \end{array}$$

Use the shortcut to find the differences.

37.	38.	39.	40.	41.
800 − 274	7000 − 2975	10000 − 7358	23000 − 18654	36000 − 17368

What is the sum of the first two odd numbers? $1 + 3 = ?$

What is the sum of the first three odd numbers? $1 + 3 + 5 = ?$

What is the sum of the first four odd numbers? $1 + 3 + 5 + 7 = ?$

Guess: What is the sum of the first hundred odd numbers?

Check your guess.

Practice exercises

Add.

1.	529 + 788	**2.**	356 + 429	**3.**	752 + 386	**4.**	714 + 299	**5.**	637 + 540

Remember that you can add numbers in any order. Look for sums of 10.

6.	38 9 72 + 41	**7.**	52 96 44 18 + 53	**8.**	328 252 767 + 833	**9.**	5937 2615 7875 + 1483

Subtract.

10.	758 − 294	**11.**	936 − 314	**12.**	529 − 286	**13.**	415 − 379	**14.**	603 − 258

15.	502 − 359	**16.**	700 − 675	**17.**	3002 − 1758	**18.**	9000 − 2654	**19.**	18132 − 7964

20.	32109 − 14836	**21.**	52374 − 35695	**22.**	81034 − 7526	**23.**	493000 − 158271	**24.**	638002 − 59708

Compute. Remember to work inside the grouping symbols first.

25. (78 + 52) − 29

26. 78 + (52 − 29)

27. (358 − 156) − 78

28. 358 − (156 − 78)

29. (900 − 532) + 53

30. 900 − (532 + 53)

31. (98 + 36) − (70 + 19)

32. (163 − 129) + (800 − 593)

33. (6381 − 592) + (753 + 96)

34. (3974 + 2831) − (3000 − 714)

35. (4983 + 627) − (40 − 8)

36. (295 + 6041) − (985 − 26)

37. (2539 − 109) + (863 − 92)

38. (4409 − 1283) + (62 − 19)

39. (7513 − 4998) − (253 + 1097)

40. (610 + 5347) − (1983 − 625)

Mathematics and world geography

Great Britain

1. The United Kingdom includes Great Britain (England, Wales, Scotland) and Northern Ireland.

   a. What is the population of Great Britain?

   b. What is the land area of Great Britain?

   c. How much larger in area is England than Scotland?

   d. How many fewer people live in Wales than in Scotland?

2. Oxford University is the oldest university in England. Records show that lectures were given at Oxford as early as 1117. How many years was that before Columbus came to America?

3. The largest cathedral of the Church of England is St. Paul's Cathedral in London. It was built between the years 1675 and 1710. How long did it take to build?

Country	Land area (square kilometers)	Population (recent census)
England	130,357	45,870,000
Wales	20,761	2,724,000
Scotland	78,761	5,217,000
Northern Ireland	14,118	1,534,000

Multiplying by a 1-digit number

This skier is practicing for a downhill race. During practice one day she skied a 783-meter run 8 times. To find how many meters she skied that day, we can multiply.

Step 1. Multiply ones and regroup.

$$\begin{array}{r} \overset{2}{783} \\ \times\ 8 \\ \hline 4 \end{array}$$

Step 2. Multiply tens and add. Then regroup.

$$\begin{array}{r} \overset{62}{783} \\ \times\ 8 \\ \hline 64 \end{array}$$

Step 3. Multiply hundreds and add.

$$\begin{array}{r} \overset{62}{783} \\ \times\ 8 \\ \hline 6264 \end{array}$$

The answer is reasonable because 783×8 is about 800×8, or 6400.

EXERCISES

First estimate the product. Then multiply.

1. 78
   × 4

2. 59
   × 6

3. 73
   × 8

4. 85
   × 5

5. 94
   × 7

6. 292
   × 5

7. 311
   × 7

8. 529
   × 9

9. 614
   × 8

10. 673
    × 6

Multiply.

11. $5.96
    × 4

12. $7.84
    × 3

13. $9.21
    × 8

14. $7.56
    × 6

15. $7.92
    × 7

16. 3821
    × 5

17. 7456
    × 3

18. 9378
    × 6

19. 2916
    × 4

20. 5304
    × 2

21. 82771
    × 8

22. 65382
    × 7

23. 59307
    × 6

24. 68259
    × 9

25. 73006
    × 5

26. 563 × 3

27. 958 × 6

28. 1814 × 7

29. 3254 × 5

30. 61078 × 4

31. 93865 × 9

Solve.

32. A one-day chair lift ticket costs $12.75. How much would it cost for 3 days?

33. There are two downhill runs. One is 783 meters and the other is 1002 meters. How much longer is the second run?

34. One day Beth skied the longer downhill run (see exercise 33) 6 times. How many meters was that?

Excursion ■□■□■□■□■□■□■□■□■□

You can use your fingers to multiply by 9. Here is how to find 8 × 9.

Hold your hands in front of you with your fingers extended. Since you are multiplying by 8, fold down the 8th finger from the left. The picture shows how you can see the product, 72.

Try this with 3 × 9, 7 × 9, etc.

Multiplying by multiples of 10, 100, and 1000

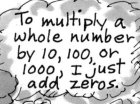

To multiply a whole number by 10, 100, or 1000, I just add zeros.

$$42 \times 10 = 420$$
$$58 \times 100 = 5800$$
$$136 \times 1000 = 136000$$

Remember that the associative property of multiplication tells us that:

$$46 \times 30 = 46 \times (3 \times 10) = (46 \times 3) \times 10$$

So to multiply by 30 we can multiply by 3 and then by 10.

I first write a 0 in the ones place and then multiply by 3.

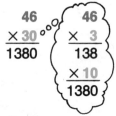

```
  46          46
× 30        ×  3
————        ————
1380         138
            × 10
            ————
            1380
```

```
  46
× 30
————
1380
```

EXERCISES
Give each product.

1. 37×10
2. 37×100
3. 37×1000

4. 562×10
5. 562×100
6. 562×1000

7. 7563×10
8. 7563×100
9. 7563×1000

10. 80×10
11. 80×100
12. 80×1000

13. 700×10
14. 700×100
15. 700×1000

16. 1000×10
17. 1000×100
18. 1000×1000

Multiply.

19. $\begin{array}{r} 57 \\ \times\ 20 \\ \hline \end{array}$	20. $\begin{array}{r} 57 \\ \times\ 200 \\ \hline \end{array}$	21. $\begin{array}{r} 57 \\ \times\ 2000 \\ \hline \end{array}$	22. $\begin{array}{r} 570 \\ \times\ 200 \\ \hline \end{array}$
23. $\begin{array}{r} 638 \\ \times\ 30 \\ \hline \end{array}$	24. $\begin{array}{r} 638 \\ \times\ 300 \\ \hline \end{array}$	25. $\begin{array}{r} 638 \\ \times\ 3000 \\ \hline \end{array}$	26. $\begin{array}{r} 63800 \\ \times\ 30 \\ \hline \end{array}$
27. $\begin{array}{r} 598 \\ \times\ 80 \\ \hline \end{array}$	28. $\begin{array}{r} 473 \\ \times\ 50 \\ \hline \end{array}$	29. $\begin{array}{r} 675 \\ \times\ 60 \\ \hline \end{array}$	30. $\begin{array}{r} 341 \\ \times\ 90 \\ \hline \end{array}$
31. $\begin{array}{r} 462 \\ \times\ 300 \\ \hline \end{array}$	32. $\begin{array}{r} 296 \\ \times\ 500 \\ \hline \end{array}$	33. $\begin{array}{r} 800 \\ \times\ 400 \\ \hline \end{array}$	34. $\begin{array}{r} 300 \\ \times\ 700 \\ \hline \end{array}$
35. $\begin{array}{r} 5673 \\ \times\ 3000 \\ \hline \end{array}$	36. $\begin{array}{r} 9846 \\ \times\ 700 \\ \hline \end{array}$	37. $\begin{array}{r} 5034 \\ \times\ 8000 \\ \hline \end{array}$	38. $\begin{array}{r} 7735 \\ \times\ 9000 \\ \hline \end{array}$

Complete the table.

39.

Minutes	15	38	75	120	135	212
Seconds						

Solve.

40. A marathon (a foot race of just over 42 kilometers) has been run in 2 hours and 9 minutes. How many minutes is that?

41. The speed of sound in air at sea level at 0°C is about 332 meters per second. How far will sound travel in 30 seconds?

42. The speed of light is about 299,793 kilometers per second. How far does light travel in a minute?

Add.

1. $\begin{array}{r} 78 \\ +\ 29 \\ \hline \end{array}$

2. $\begin{array}{r} 356 \\ +\ 75 \\ \hline \end{array}$

3. $\begin{array}{r} 298 \\ +\ 574 \\ \hline \end{array}$

4. $\begin{array}{r} 893 \\ +\ 277 \\ \hline \end{array}$

5. $\begin{array}{r} 3654 \\ +\ 2985 \\ \hline \end{array}$

6. $\begin{array}{r} 4736 \\ +\ 999 \\ \hline \end{array}$

7. $\begin{array}{r} 26 \\ 35 \\ 44 \\ +\ 29 \\ \hline \end{array}$
8. $\begin{array}{r} 529 \\ 638 \\ 466 \\ +\ 583 \\ \hline \end{array}$

Multiplying by a 2-digit number

In a 24-hour race a car averaged 184 kilometers per hour for the first 12 hours. We can multiply 184×12 to find how many kilometers the car traveled in 12 hours.

Remember that the distributive property tells us that:

$$184 \times 12 = 184 \times (2 + 10) = (184 \times 2) + (184 \times 10)$$

So to multiply by 12 we can multiply by 2, multiply by 10, and add.

Step 1. Multiply 184 by 2 to find how far the car traveled in 2 hours.

$$
\begin{array}{r}
184 \\
\times\ 1\textbf{2} \\
\hline
368 \leftarrow 184 \times 2
\end{array}
$$

Step 2. Multiply 184 by 10 to find how far the car traveled in 10 hours.

$$
\begin{array}{r}
184 \\
\times\ \textbf{1}2 \\
\hline
368 \\
1840 \leftarrow 184 \times 10
\end{array}
$$

Step 3. Add to find how many kilometers the car traveled in 12 hours.

$$
\begin{array}{r}
184 \\
\times\ 12 \\
\hline
368 \\
184 \\
\hline
2208 \leftarrow 184 \times 12
\end{array}
$$

EXERCISES
Multiply.

1.	58	2.	65	3.	74	4.	92	5.	89
	×12		×46		×33		×69		×52

6.	156	7.	474	8.	238	9.	506	10.	821
	×54		×53		×75		×24		×86

11.	734	12.	593	13.	658	14.	291	15.	756
	×49		×77		×92		×37		×54

16.	3214	17.	5978	18.	6359	19.	4618	20.	3921
	×68		×86		×75		×34		×93

21.	53826	22.	75346	23.	93580	24.	296374	25.	729108
	×38		×46		×68		×89		×27

Solve.

26. The winning car in the 24-hour race averaged 197 kilometers per hour. How far did the car go?

27. One car averaged 192 kilometers per hour during the first 18 hours and 186 kilometers per hour during the last 6 hours. How far did the car go in the race?

28. During the first half of the 24-hour race a car traveled 2172 kilometers. During the second half it averaged 178 kilometers per hour. How far did it travel?

29. The car that came in last traveled 4399 kilometers. How much farther did the winning car travel? (See exercise 26.)

Excursion ■O■O■O■O■O■O■O■O■O■O■O

Finger Multiplication

You can use your fingers to find the product of 9 and a two-digit number *if* the tens digit of the two-digit number is less than the ones digit.

Example. 9 × 27

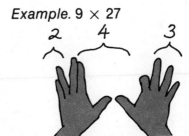

Make a space after the second finger from the left. Put down the seventh finger from the left. Read the answer: 243. Try this method with other problems. Check.

Multiplying by a 3-digit number

Study these shortcuts for multiplying by a 3-digit number.

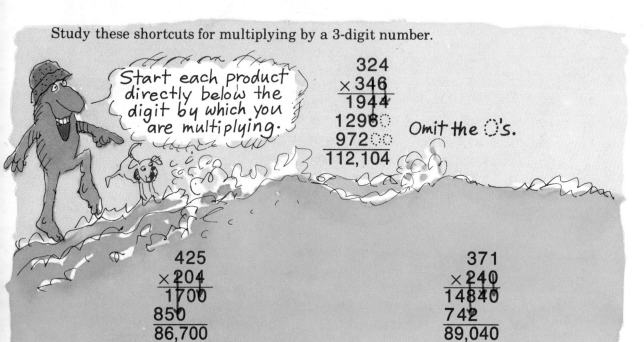

```
      324
    × 346
     1944
    1296○
   972○○
  112,104
```

Omit the ○'s.

```
      425
    × 204
     1700
    850
   86,700
```

```
      371
    × 240
    14840
    742
   89,040
```

If you always write each product directly below the digit by
which you are multiplying, you will make few mistakes.

EXERCISES
Multiply.

1.	753 × 162	**2.**	821 × 143	**3.**	742 × 234	**4.**	658 × 255	**5.**	291 × 368
6.	362 × 248	**7.**	455 × 937	**8.**	258 × 342	**9.**	615 × 839	**10.**	727 × 189
11.	1538 × 429	**12.**	1965 × 364	**13.**	2742 × 295	**14.**	3953 × 338	**15.**	5829 × 426

Multiply.

16. 523
× 306
3138
1569

17. 421
× 603

18. 592
× 402

19. 603
× 501

20. 304
× 606

21. 571
× 630

22. 473
× 220

23. 217
× 300

24. 546
× 207

25. 3614
× 403

26. 2983
× 258

27. 7521
× 560

28. 6438
× 352

29. 2059
× 803

30. 5246
× 293

31. 3958
× 405

32. 7042
× 200

33. 5063
× 540

34. 9384
× 398

Solve.

35. There were five hundred twelve tickets sold for a city baseball tournament. Each ticket sold for $1.25. What was the total in ticket sales?

36. The food committee for a club picnic bought 7 kilograms of hot dogs for $1.89 a kilogram and 10 dozen buns for $.59 a dozen. How much were these two items?

37. Marcia bought 12 golf balls for 75¢ each. She gave the clerk a ten-dollar bill. How much change should she have received?

38. In Campbell Junior High there are 27 more girls than boys. What is the total enrollment, if there are 342 girls?

Find the end number.

39.

40.

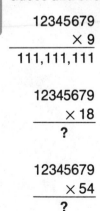

Guess and check!

12345679
× 9
111,111,111

12345679
× 18
?

12345679
× 54
?

39

Dividing by a 1-digit number

Carol, Joan, and Susan were given a box containing 113 records for working at a neighbor's garage sale. To find how many records each should get we can divide:

$$113 \div 3$$

Step 1. Not enough hundreds. Think about regrouping 1 hundred for 10 tens.

$$3\overline{)113}$$

Step 2. Divide tens. Subtract.

$$\begin{array}{r} 3 \\ 3\overline{)113} \\ -9 \\ \hline 2 \end{array}$$

Step 3. Regroup and divide ones.

$$\begin{array}{r} 37\ \textbf{R2} \\ 3\overline{)113} \\ -9 \\ \hline 23 \\ -21 \\ \hline 2 \end{array}$$

The remainder is 2.

Each girl would get 37 records. They would have to decide who would get the remaining 2 records.

EXERCISES
Divide.

1. $2\overline{)246}$ 2. $2\overline{)137}$ 3. $3\overline{)58}$ 4. $4\overline{)64}$ 5. $5\overline{)95}$

6. $8\overline{)345}$ 7. $4\overline{)826}$ 8. $7\overline{)367}$ 9. $9\overline{)875}$ 10. $9\overline{)146}$

11. $6\overline{)935}$ 12. $2\overline{)134}$ 13. $7\overline{)534}$ 14. $5\overline{)947}$ 15. $3\overline{)816}$

16. $8\overline{)\$5.68}$ 17. $7\overline{)\$3.85}$ 18. $6\overline{)\$9.54}$ 19. $9\overline{)\$2.07}$ 20. $4\overline{)\$5.84}$

21. $2\overline{)3946}$ 22. $5\overline{)5108}$ 23. $3\overline{)3742}$ 24. $2\overline{)5965}$ 25. $7\overline{)3782}$

26. $3\overline{)3914}$ 27. $4\overline{)5678}$ 28. $6\overline{)4071}$ 29. $4\overline{)3049}$ 30. $8\overline{)9246}$

31. $7\overline{)7003}$ 32. $4\overline{)5208}$ 33. $3\overline{)4631}$ 34. $9\overline{)2403}$ 35. $6\overline{)1149}$

36. $5\overline{)31604}$ 37. $2\overline{)78251}$ 38. $5\overline{)39283}$ 39. $8\overline{)75691}$ 40. $8\overline{)64238}$

41. $6\overline{)90177}$ 42. $7\overline{)72104}$ 43. $7\overline{)63029}$ 44. $4\overline{)98106}$ 45. $3\overline{)75236}$

46. $2\overline{)129634}$ 47. $5\overline{)792381}$ 48. $9\overline{)691085}$ 49. $6\overline{)397615}$ 50. $9\overline{)263842}$

Solve.

51. 25 comic books in each box
13 boxes
How many comic books?

52. Sold a radio for $7.50
Was given $20
How much change?

53. 3-day garage sale
Took in $382.11
What was the daily average?

54. Sold 2 bicycles for $12 each
Sold 3 bicycles for $19 each
What was the average price?

 Use all of these digits to make an 8-digit number.

1, 2, 3, 4, 5, 6, 7, 8

Divide your number by 9.
Did you get a whole-number quotient?
Rearrange the digits in as many ways as you can.
Divide each number by 9. Do you ever get a remainder?

$72,538,146 \div 9$

41

Dividing by a 2-digit number

Dividing by a two-digit number is usually more difficult than dividing by a one-digit number because we have not memorized the multiplication facts for most two-digit numbers. This means that we have to estimate the digits in the quotient. Study this example.

Step 1. No thousands or hundreds in the quotient. The first digit will be in the tens place.

$$\begin{array}{r} XX \\ 57\overline{)2056} \end{array}$$

Step 2. 57 is near 60. Since we know the multiplication facts for 60, we think about dividing by 60.

$$\begin{array}{r} 3 \\ 57\overline{)2056} \end{array}$$

Step 3. The guess is 3. Multiply 57 by 3.

$$\begin{array}{r} 3 \\ 57\overline{)2056} \\ -171 \\ \hline 34 \end{array}$$ It works!

Step 4. Guess the next digit.

$$\begin{array}{r} 35 \\ 57\overline{)2056} \\ -171 \\ \hline 346 \end{array}$$

Step 5. The guess is 5. Multiply 57 by 5.

$$\begin{array}{r} 35 \\ 57\overline{)2056} \\ -171 \\ \hline 346 \\ -285 \\ \hline 61 \end{array}$$ Too big!

Step 6. Since 5 is too small, try 6.

$$\begin{array}{r} 36 \text{ R}4 \\ 57\overline{)2056} \\ -171 \\ \hline 346 \\ -342 \\ \hline 4 \end{array}$$ It works!

EXERCISES
Divide.

1. 18)593
2. 24)842
3. 31)900

4. 25)675
5. 32)942
6. 48)876

7. 38)965
8. 11)527
9. 41)993

10. 52)1404
11. 68)2584
12. 72)2088

13. 41)3157
14. 77)2464
15. 92)4324

16. 79)6080
17. 28)4044
18. 81)4536

19. 49)1773
20. 52)3860
21. 51)1836

22. 74)1998
23. 89)4162
24. 35)1113

25. 22)9460
26. 45)1281
27. 36)1492

28. 71)365986
29. 82)274164
30. 39)500813

Solve.

31. Four backpackers agreed to divide 68 kilograms of supplies evenly. How much should each backpacker carry?

32. If a large pizza costs $4.75 and a pitcher of root beer costs $1.25, how much do 3 pizzas and 2 pitchers of root beer cost?

33. Karl earned $4.95, $5.74, and $3.88 on the three days he worked. He needs $20 to buy a football. How much more does he need to earn?

Keeping Skills Sharp

Subtract.

1. 275
   − 188

2. 352
   − 167

3. 4203
   − 1735

4. 6000
   − 2044

5. 6523
   − 1741

6. 3998
   − 1689

7. 40305
   − 16758

8. 703004
   − 216558

9. 80000
   − 17735

Dividing by a 3-digit number

328)89356

Step 1. Divide and subtract.

```
          2
328 )89356
    - 656
      237
```

Since 8 divided by 3 is about 2, I try 2!

Step 2. Regroup.

```
          2
328 )89356
    - 656
     2375
```

Step 3. Divide and subtract.

```
         27
328 )89356
    - 656
     2375
   - 2296
       79
```

Since 23 divided by 3 is about 7, I try 7!

Step 4. Regroup.

```
         27
328 )89356
    - 656
     2375
   - 2296
      796
```

Step 5. Divide and subtract.

```
        272 R140
328 )89356
    - 656
     2375
   - 2296
      796
    - 656
      140
```

Since 7 divided by 3 is about 2, I try 2.

EXERCISES

Divide.

1. 112)35274

2. 208)69782

3. 115)59386

4. 234)74261

5. 326)37821

6. 402)59784

7. 453)60715

8. 526)52830

9. 704)42065

10. 628)32978

11. 750)74216

12. 378)93852

13. 288)756031

14. 813)258921

15. 529)653184

16. 478)953165

17. 937)742167

18. 653)406314

19. 892)556395

20. 960)814638

Solve.

21. 74 weeks
How many days?

22. 595 days
How many weeks?

23. 38 days
How many hours?

24. 888 eggs
How many dozen?

25. 768 months
How many years?

26. 2700 minutes
How many hours?

27. 11,680 days
How many years?
[Use 365 days
for 1 year.]

28. 15 years
How many days?

Properties of addition and multiplication

In this lesson we will review some properties of addition and multiplication. Remembering the properties can sometimes help with computing.

ADDITION	MULTIPLICATION
The Adding 0 Property	**The Multiplying by 1 Property**
The sum of any number and 0 is the number.	The product of any number and 1 is the number.
$358 + 0 = 358$	$594 \times 1 = 594$
The Commutative Property of Addition	**The Commutative Property of Multiplication**
Changing the order of the addends does not change the sum.	Changing the order of the factors does not change the product.
$267 + 139 = 139 + 267$	$68 \times 57 = 57 \times 68$
The Associative Property of Addition	**The Associative Property of Multiplication**
Changing the grouping of the addends does not change the sum.	Changing the grouping of the factors does not change the product.
$(18 + 37) + 13 = 18 + (37 + 13)$	$(28 \times 4) \times 25 = 28 \times (4 \times 25)$

The Distributive Property

$$19 \times (8 + 2) = (19 \times 8) + (19 \times 2)$$

EXERCISES

See if you can compute each answer in your head by using one of the properties above.

128 + (75 + 25)

23 × (4 × 25)

1. $(128 + 75) + 25$

2. $(225 + 185) + 15$

3. $(23 \times 4) \times 25$

4. $(627 + 45) + 55$

5. $(47 \times 5) \times 20$

6. $(245 \times 250) \times 4$

7. $(13 \times 6) + (13 \times 4)$

8. $(23 \times 3) + (23 \times 7)$

9. $(52 \times 60) + (52 \times 40)$

Mathematics in careers

Oceanographers are scientists who study the ocean. They study the physical and chemical properties of the ocean, as well as all forms of life in the ocean.

1. **a.** Which ocean is the largest?
   b. Which ocean is the smallest?
   c. How much larger is the Pacific Ocean than the Atlantic Ocean?
   d. What is the total area of the oceans?
   e. The total area of the earth's surface is 509,917,870 square kilometers. How much of the earth's surface area is not ocean?

2. The deepest known spot in the Pacific Ocean is Challenger Deep. It is 11,033 meters below the surface. The deepest known spot in the Atlantic Ocean is in the Puerto Rico Trench, 8648 meters below the surface. How much deeper is Challenger Deep?

3. The highest mountain in the world is Mount Everest, which is 8848 meters high. If Mount Everest were put into Challenger Deep, how far below the surface of the water would the top of Mount Everest be?

Areas of Oceans	
Ocean	Area (in square kilometers)
Pacific	165,200,000
Atlantic	81,662,000
Indian	73,441,700
Antarctic	13,000,000
Arctic	14,090,000

Problem solving

These steps can help you solve word problems.

1. Read the problem carefully.
2. Picture in your mind what is happening.
3. What information is given?
4. What is the question?
5. What arithmetic should be used?
6. Estimate the answer.
7. Do the arithmetic and check your answer with your estimate.

Many birds migrate long distances. The most well-traveled bird is the Arctic tern. It migrates from the North Pole to the South Pole and back. It flies about 40,000 kilometers a year.

Golden plover

Robin

Lesser yellowlegs

Blue-wing teal

Blackpolled warbler

Gray-cheeked thrush

1. A blue-wing teal that was banded (a ring put around its leg) in northern Alberta, Canada, was seen in Venezuela exactly 30 days later. If this distance is about 6100 kilometers, how many kilometers per day were averaged?

2. A lesser yellowlegs flew from Cape Cod, Massachusetts, to the French West Indies in 6 days. It averaged 509 kilometers per day. How far did it fly?

3. The gray-cheeked thrush flies from northern Florida to northwest Alaska, a distance of 6500 kilometers. It averages about 210 kilometers per day. How long does it take to migrate the 6500 kilometers?

4. Robins have been known to fly from Iowa to Alaska, a distance of about 4800 kilometers, in 78 days. How many kilometers do they average each day?

5. Golden plovers hold the nonstop record. They fly from northeast Canada to South America nonstop, a distance of 3800 kilometers. If they fly 190 kilometers per day, how many days do they fly without stopping?

6. The blackpolled warbler migrates from Florida to western Alaska in the spring. It averages 56 kilometers per day for the first 29 days and then 320 kilometers per day for the next 15 days. How far is that?

CHAPTER CHECKUP

Read aloud. [pages 18–19]

1. 5,265,328
2. 7,007,007,007
3. 81,081,273,006

Write the standard numeral. [pages 18–19]

4. seventeen million
5. two hundred billion

6. eight trillion, eighteen billion, eighty thousand

Round. [pages 22–23]

7. 7583 to the nearest hundred.
8. 23,488 to the nearest thousand.

9. 47,500 to the nearest thousand.
10. 8,754,321 to the nearest hundred thousand.

Add. [pages 26–27]

11.	578	12.	9835	13.	293	14.	36748
	+ 466		+ 2768		476		867
					+ 351		+ 9988

Subtract. [pages 28–29]

15.	8321	16.	702	17.	5000	18.	603508
	− 5673		− 427		− 2354		− 168739

434768

Multiply. [pages 32–39]

19.	2783	20.	53	21.	482	22.	568
	× 6		× 26		× 321		× 306

Divide. [pages 40–45]

23. 9)4763
24. 8)6449
25. 38)58361
26. 405)19360

Solve. [pages 48–49]

27. Eighteen busloads of 56 students each went to see their football team play in the championship game. Two hundred seventy-four students did not go. How many students in all?

28. Joan bought 3 shirts for $7 each and a sweater for $9.95. How much change did she get from $40?

Project

1. Find out how many minutes a day each of your classmates listens to the radio. (These data could be listed on the chalkboard.)

2. Compute the average number of minutes listened. Give your answer to the nearest whole number.

3. How many classmates listen

   a. more than the average?
   b. less than the average?
   c. twice as much as the average?
   d. half as much as the average?

4. Make a bar graph like the one shown here.

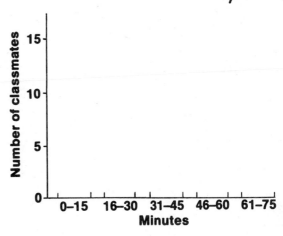

Time spent listening to radio each day

CHAPTER REVIEW

Round to the nearest thousand.

thousands place
↓
$63,672 \Rightarrow 64,000$
↑
This digit is
5 or greater.

$$\begin{array}{r} 1\,1 \\ 358 \\ +267 \\ \hline 625 \end{array}$$

$$\begin{array}{r} 29 \\ \cancel{302} \\ -177 \\ \hline 125 \end{array}$$

$$\begin{array}{r} 321 \\ \times 34 \\ \hline 1284 \leftarrow 4 \times 321 \\ 9630 \leftarrow 30 \times 321 \\ \hline 10,914 \end{array}$$

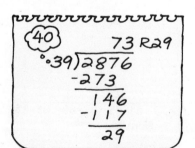

$$\begin{array}{r} (40) \qquad 73 \text{ R}29 \\ 39\overline{)2876} \\ -273 \\ \hline 146 \\ -117 \\ \hline 29 \end{array}$$

Round to the nearest hundred.

1. 673
2. 650
3. 89,341

Round to the nearest thousand.

4. 7388
5. 2500
6. 67,832

Add.

7. $\begin{array}{r} 563 \\ +288 \end{array}$
8. $\begin{array}{r} 463 \\ +297 \end{array}$
9. $\begin{array}{r} 5864 \\ +2995 \end{array}$
10. $\begin{array}{r} 87351 \\ +25489 \end{array}$

11. $\begin{array}{r} 29 \\ 37 \\ +56 \end{array}$
12. $\begin{array}{r} 463 \\ 297 \\ +341 \end{array}$
13. $\begin{array}{r} 589 \\ 678 \\ +838 \end{array}$
14. $\begin{array}{r} 2975 \\ 467 \\ 5986 \\ +321 \end{array}$

Subtract.

15. $\begin{array}{r} 526 \\ -238 \end{array}$
16. $\begin{array}{r} 732 \\ -581 \end{array}$
17. $\begin{array}{r} 6731 \\ -2951 \end{array}$
18. $\begin{array}{r} 56342 \\ -8756 \end{array}$

19. $\begin{array}{r} 904 \\ -656 \end{array}$
20. $\begin{array}{r} 5000 \\ -276 \end{array}$
21. $\begin{array}{r} 65002 \\ -14975 \end{array}$
22. $\begin{array}{r} 30204 \\ -16578 \end{array}$

Multiply.

23. $\begin{array}{r} 475 \\ \times 8 \end{array}$
24. $\begin{array}{r} 36 \\ \times 43 \end{array}$
25. $\begin{array}{r} 57 \\ \times 65 \end{array}$

26. $\begin{array}{r} 394 \\ \times 62 \end{array}$
27. $\begin{array}{r} 592 \\ \times 326 \end{array}$
28. $\begin{array}{r} 548 \\ \times 602 \end{array}$

Divide.

29. $8\overline{)5287}$
30. $7\overline{)4921}$
31. $23\overline{)5261}$

32. $53\overline{)16165}$
33. $148\overline{)16673}$
34. $321\overline{)26543}$

52

Our place-value system for writing numerals is based on the number 10. We can, if we wish, use other whole numbers as bases for place-value systems. Here is the way to use 5 as a base.

Group single blocks into groups of five blocks.

Put the bars of 5 into groups of 5 bars.

There are 124₅ blocks. (Read as "one two four base five.")

How many blocks in all? Write a base 5 numeral.

1. 2. 3. 4.

Copy and complete this table.

	5.	6.	7.	8.	9.	10.	11.	12.	13.
Base 10	3	5	7	10	15	19	24	25	23	57
Base 5	3₅	?	?	?	?	?	?	?	?	?

Use a base five numeral to give

14. the number of people in your family.

15. your age in years.

16. the number of students in your class.

17. the number of states in the United States.

Form W

a b c d   a b c d   a b c d   a b c d   a b c
14   34   14   4   30
a b c d   a b c d   c d   a b c
15   31
a b c   a b c

MAJOR CHECKUP
Standardized Format

Choose the correct letter.

1. The standard numeral for four billion, twenty five thousand is

    a. 4,025,000
    b. 4,000,025,000
    c. 4,000,000,025,000
    d. none of these

2. Write in words.
7,000,000,000,000

    a. seven million
    b. seven quintillion
    c. seven billion
    d. none of these

3. Round 48,377 to the nearest thousand.

    a. 48,000
    b. 50,000
    c. 49,000
    d. none of these

4. Round 29,950 to the nearest hundred.

    a. 29,900
    b. 29,800
    c. 30,000
    d. none of these

5. Add.

$$5673 + 4899$$

10572

    a. 1572
    b. 10,562
    c. 10,572
    d. none of these

6. Add.

$$632 + 577 + 298$$

1507

    a. 1507
    b. 1497
    c. 1407
    d. none of these

7. Subtract.

$$5297 - 3898$$

1399

    a. 2399
    b. 1399
    c. 1409
    d. none of these

8. Subtract.

$$6000 - 3956$$

2044

    a. 3044
    b. 3043
    c. 2044
    d. none of these

9. Multiply.

$$37 \times 26$$

222
74
962

    a. 962
    b. 296
    c. 926
    d. none of these

10. Multiply.

$$372 \times 305$$

1860
00
1116
113460

    a. 13,020
    b. 2976
    c. 113,460
    d. none of these

11. Divide.

$$25\overline{)4036}$$

    a. 161 R11
    b. 160 R36
    c. 275
    d. none of these

12. Divide.

$$37\overline{)7548}$$

    a. 240
    b. 24
    c. 204
    d. none of these

54

2
Decimals— Addition and Subtraction

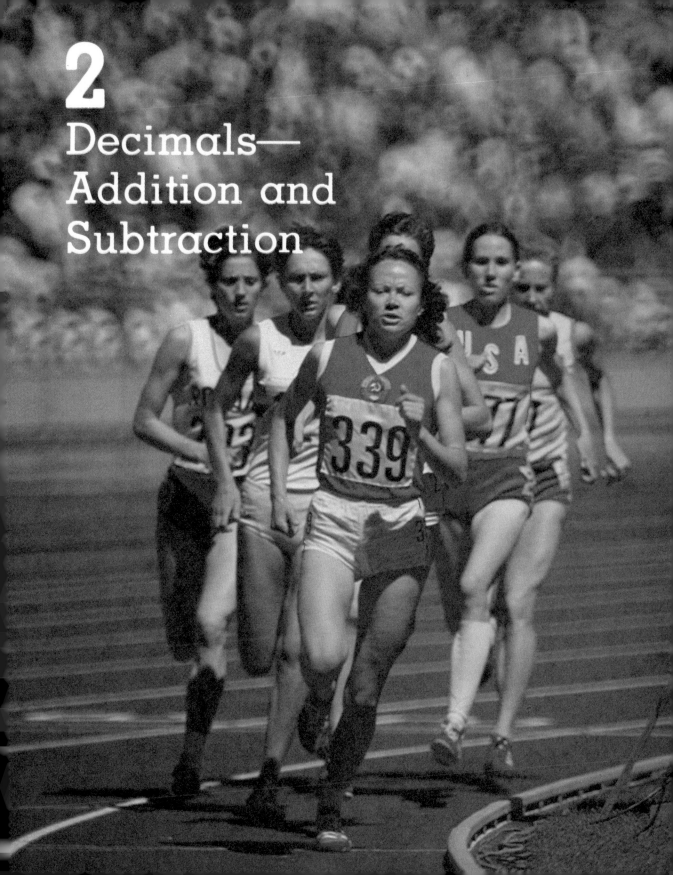

Tenths and hundredths

Decimal fractions (or just **decimals**) are written using our place-value system. In this system the value of each place is one tenth the value of the place to its left. To write decimals we extend the place-value system to the right of the ones place. The digits in this table show how many unit squares are shaded.

The standard numeral is written like this:

1.7

It is read as "one and seven tenths."

A decimal point separates the ones place and the tenths place.

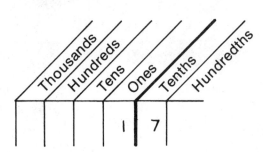

Study this example.

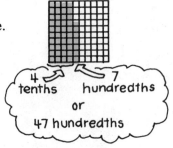

4 tenths 7 hundredths
or
47 hundredths

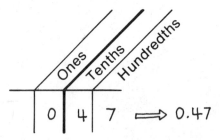

$0 \quad 4 \quad 7 \implies 0.47$

Read as "forty-seven hundredths."

Read aloud.

1. 0.3   2. 0.03   3. 0.9   4. 0.09   5. 0.27   6. 0.58   7. 0.30

8. 2.6   9. 3.06   10. 5.36   11. 4.67   12. 24.35   13. 67.08   14. 235.43

Give the standard numeral.

15. eight tenths

16. eight hundredths

17. eight hundred

18. two and three tenths

19. six and five hundredths

20. fourteen and fourteen hundredths

21. two hundred three

22. two hundred and three tenths

23. five and six hundredths

24. five hundred six

25. ten and three tenths

26. one hundred and three tenths

How many unit squares are shaded?

27.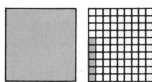

28.

29.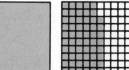

30.

31.

32.

33.

Copy the numeral and place a decimal so that the statement makes sense.

34.

In a bicycle race I averaged 2675 kilometers per hour.

35.

It is 258° Celsius today.

36. I weigh 4825 kilograms.

37. For lunch I ate 25 hamburgers.

57

More about decimals

The place value system can be extended as far as needed in both directions.

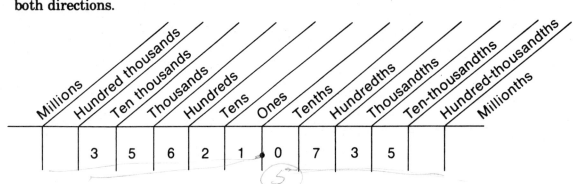

Millions	Hundred thousands	Ten thousands	Thousands	Hundreds	Tens	Ones	Tenths	Hundredths	Thousandths	Ten-thousandths	Hundred-thousandths	Millionths
	3	5	6	2	1	0	7	3	5			

Here is how to read a decimal.

1. Read the whole-number part. ——————→ thirty-five thousand six hundred twenty-one

2. Say "and" for the decimal point. ——→ and

3. Read the fraction part as if it were a ——→ seven hundred thirty-five ten-whole number. Then say the name thousandths of the place of the last digit.

EXAMPLES.

47.00005   forty-seven and five hundred-thousandths

200.376   two hundred and three hundred seventy-six thousandths

I just say two hundred point three seven six.

EXERCISES
Read aloud in two ways.

1. 0.008	2. 0.0008	3. 0.00008	4. 0.000008	5. 0.035
6. 0.0035	7. 0.0352	8. 0.165	9. 0.2734	10. 0.00231
11. 6.007	12. 0.603	13. 600.003	14. 0.827	15. 800.027
16. 627.0627	17. 43.1675	18. 5000.0005	19. 67.359	20. 45.0036

Write the standard numerals.

21. eight thousand
22. eight thousandths
23. nine hundredths
24. nine hundred
25. twenty-four thousandths
26. twenty-four hundredths
27. eighty-seven ten-thousandths
28. nine hundred twenty-six millionths
29. six hundred three thousandths
30. six hundred and three thousandths
31. five hundred forty thousandths
32. five hundred and forty thousandths
33. eight point six five four
34. two hundred point zero zero three

Look for a pattern.
Give the next three numbers.

35. 0.4, 0.5, 0.6, . .
36. 1.2, 1.3, 1.4, . . .
37. 7.8, 7.9, 8.0, . . .
38. 5.6, 5.7, 5.8, . . .
39. 0.02, 0.03, 0.04, . . .
40. 0.27, 0.28, 0.29, . . .
41. 0.003, 0.004, 0.005, . . .
42. 0.057, 0.058, 0.059, . . .
43. 4.143, 4.144, . . .
44. 6.056, 6.057, . . .

Give a number that is between the two numbers.

45. 59.8, 60.0
46. 0.32, 0.34
47. 5.6, 5.7
48. 7.53, 7.54
49. 9.00, 9.01
50. 0.305, 0.306
51. 2, 2.1
52. 3.99, 4

Keeping Skills Sharp

Multiply.

1. 92×13

2. 46×25

3. 87×52

4. 126×12

5. 628×16

6. 521×28

7. 468×50

8. 906×49

9. 3718×74

10. 4926×38

Practice exercises

> 1 decimeter (dm) = 0.1 meter (m)
>
> 1 centimeter (cm) = 0.01 m
>
> 1 millimeter (mm) = 0.001 m

Complete.

1. 2 dm = ___?___ m
2. 2 cm = ___?___ m
3. 2 mm = ___?___ m
4. 8 dm = ___?___ m
5. 8 cm = ___?___ m
6. 8 mm = ___?___ m
7. 10 dm = ___?___ m
8. 10 cm = ___?___ m
9. 10 mm = ___?___ m
10. 27 dm = ___?___ m
11. 27 cm = ___?___ m
12. 27 mm = ___?___ m
13. 100 dm = ___?___ m
14. 100 cm = ___?___ m
15. 100 mm = ___?___ m
16. 375 dm = ___?___ m
17. 57 cm = ___?___ m
18. 148 mm = ___?___ m

millions
↓

6,800,000

6.8 million

This number is between 6 and 7 million. It can be written like this.

How many millions?

19. 8,200,000
20. 5,700,000
21. 12,800,000
22. 45,600,000
23. 68,750,000

2,400,000,000

Change to standard numerals.

24.

PUEBLO SUN

WORLD POPULATION REACHES 2.4 BILLION! POWER BLACKOUTS BLAMED BY CHIATRIST

25.

PHILLY TRUMPET

VOYAGER II IS 4.5 TRILLION KILOMETERS FROM EARTH

Mathematics and science

Read these facts about the earth.

1. Some geologists estimate that the earth is about 4.5 billion years old.

2. **a.** The earth spins like a top, causing night and day. A point on the equator spins at a rate of about 1600 kilometers per hour.

   b. The earth also revolves around the sun, causing years. It revolves once around the sun in 365 days, 6 hours 9 minutes and 9.54 seconds. It travels around the sun at an average rate of about 107,200 kilometers per hour.

3. **a.** About 148,225,000 square kilometers of the earth's surface is land.

   b. About 361,847,000 square kilometers of the earth's surface is water.

4. The distance around the earth at the equator is about 40,076 kilometers.

5. The mass of the earth is about 5.52 times as much as the mass of the same volume of water.

6. About 0.67 of the earth is made up of silicon dioxide (SiO_2).

7. The earth is 0.00000037 times as far from the sun as it is from the next nearest star.

Comparing and ordering decimals

Some National League Batting Champs			
Year	Player	Team	Ave.
1970	Rico Carty	Atlanta	.366
1971	Joe Torre	St. Louis	.363
1972	Billy Williams	Chicago	.333
1973	Pete Rose	Cincinnati	.338
1974	Ralph Garr	Atlanta	.353
1975	Bill Madlock	Chicago	.354

To compare the batting averages of Rico Carty and Joe Torre, we compare decimals. We can compare these decimals by comparing the digits that are in the same places.

Rico Carty   .366 > .363   Joe Torre

Rico Carty had a greater batting average.

Another example.

52.08 > 6.74

Since I know 52 is greater than 6, I don't have to compare digits in this example.

62

< or >?

1. 0.2 ● 0.3

2. 0.06 ● 0.05

3. 0.009 ● 0.008

4. 0.2 ● 0.02

5. 0.004 ● 0.03

6. 0.1 ● 0.08

7. 0.006 ● 0.2

8. 0.3 ● 0.004

9. 0.82 ● 0.85

10. 0.74 ● 0.71

11. 5.38 ● 5.83

12. 6.75 ● 6.57

13. 38.21 ● 38.54

14. 71.69 ● 71.7

15. 5.936 ● 59.36

16. 782.76 ● 780.99

17. 83.5 ● 8.76

18. 0.759 ● 1

19. 2 ● 1.899

20. 7.564 ● 7.099

21. 8.63 ● 16.58

22. 47.02 ● 9.385

23. 7.216 ● 72.16

24. 53.06 ● 5.899

25. Arrange the six batting averages given on page 62 in order from highest to lowest.

26. In one World Series, Lou Brock's batting average was .414 and pitcher Bob Gibson's batting average was .091. Who had the higher average?

Team Pitching	Earned-run Averages
Boston	3.37
New York	3.23
Kansas City	3.69
Chicago	2.45
California	3.19
Minnesota	3.15
Detroit	3.31
Washington	3.40
Cleveland	3.24
Baltimore	3.32

27. Which team had the lowest earned-run average?

28. Which team had the highest earned-run average?

29. Which had the lower earned-run average, Detroit or Baltimore?

30. List the teams in order from lowest to highest earned-run average.

Rounding

Round decimals just as you would round whole numbers. You can think about the number line. For example, suppose that you want to round 12.73 to the nearest whole number. Think about where 12.73 is located on the number line.

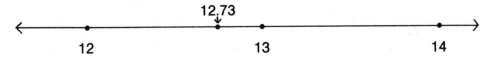
12.73

12   13   14

It is nearer 13. So, 12.73 rounded to the nearest whole number (or nearest one) is 13.

Here is a rounding shortcut.

Round to the nearest one.

ones
place
↓
12.73 ——→ 13

Since the next digit to the right is 5 or greater, I round to 13.

Round to the nearest hundredth.

hundredths
place
↓
7.2043 ——→ 7.20

Since the next digit to the right is less than 5, I round to 7.20.

EXERCISES
Round to the nearest one.

1. 3.4   2. 3.7   3. 15.1   4. 15.9   5. 2.26   6. 2.96

7. $13.48   8. $27.51   9. $124.50

Round to the nearest tenth.

10. 0.73   11. 0.77   12. 8.94   13. 8.96   14. 12.411   15. 27.501

16. $7.38   17. $19.41   18. $142.67

Round to the nearest hundredth.

19. 4.673   **20.** 21.987   **21.** 5.635   **22.** 4.8133   **23.** 2.7758   **24.** 16.296

25. 0.078   **26.** 0.0977   **27.** 19.999

Round to the nearest thousandth.

28. 2.8359   **29.** 5.7461   **30.** 8.4965   **31.** 0.8295   **32.** 3.6182   **33.** 14.7293

34. 6.0996   **35.** 7.7598   **36.** 4.2996

The speed record for a bicycle is 204.734 kilometers per hour. (A lead car had a mounted wind shield to break the wind.) Round the number to the nearest

37. hundredth

38. whole number

39. tenth

A world speed record for a skateboard was 86.886 kilometers per hour. Round to the nearest

40. tenth

41. hundredth

42. whole number

Excursion ▪●▪●▪●▪●▪●▪●▪●▪●▪●▪●▪●▪●▪●▪●
Look up the winning speed records for the Indianapolis 500. In what way have the speeds changed? Make a line graph to show what you found.

Adding decimals

To add decimals, we line up the decimal points and add in the same way that we add whole numbers.

Step 1. Add.

```
  5.62
+ 4.97
─────
     9
```

Step 2. Add and regroup.

```
  1
  5.62
+ 4.97
─────
   .59
```

Step 3. Add.

```
   1
  5.62
+ 4.97
─────
 10.59
```

EXERCISES
Add.

1. 4.73 + 2.13	**2.** 15.9 + 23.5	**3.** 0.735 + 0.187	**4.** 27.56 + 38.28	**5.** 16.05 + 38.57
6. 5.37 + 2.9	**7.** 90.6 + 53.4	**8.** 0.425 + 0.295	**9.** 6.711 + 0.32	**10.** 34.47 + 96.36
11. $7.84 + 2.67	**12.** $7.56 + 8.17	**13.** $18.90 + 3.59	**14.** $29.76 + 31.90	**15.** $762.82 + 375.74
16. 3.658 + 9.825	**17.** 76.7 + 38.57	**18.** 79.46 + 8.98	**19.** 56.37 + 6.57	**20.** 70.69 + 27.39
21. 6543.2 + 38.2	**22.** 781.06 + 74.68	**23.** 9.2305 + 9.1753	**24.** 0.72961 + 0.29683	**25.** 834.75 + 42.8

Add.

26. 0.02 + 31.4

27. 3.6 + 0.94

28. 48 + 5.06

29. 25.8 + 3.79

30. 226.4 + 15.84

31. 119.6 + 289

32. 39.54 + 7.621

33. 4.328 + 0.7493

34. 0.593 + 16.48

35. 0.00295 + 0.0088

36. 3.526 + 48.79

37. 5483 + 23.77

Solve.

38. To practice for the cross-country team, Carol ran 4.5 km each morning and 6.8 km each evening. How far did she run each day?

39. At the beginning of the sixth grade, Bill weighed 38 kg. During the next year he gained 3.9 kg. How much did he weigh then?

40. The four sections of a bike trail measure 8.9 km, 7.8 km, 9.0 km, and 8.7 km. What is the total distance?

Excursion ▣◈▣◈▣◈▣◈▣
In a magic square, the sum of the numbers in each row, column, and diagonal is the same. Copy and complete this magic square.

5.8		
	5.5	
5.4		5.2

Divide.

1. 15)945

2. 23)966

3. 35)2874

4. 52)1930

5. 47)3555

6. 68)9180

7. 92)18960

8. 70)19618

9. 83)35279

10. 66)25028

Subtracting decimals

Average Monthly Precipitation
(in centimeters)

City	Jan.	Feb.	Mar.	Apr.	May	June	July	Aug.	Sept.	Oct.	Nov.	Dec.
Birmingham, Ala.	12.7	13.5	15.3	11.4	8.6	10.2	13.2	12.4	8.5	7.6	8.9	12.7
Chicago, Ill.	4.8	4.1	6.9	7.6	9.4	10.4	8.6	8.1	6.9	7.1	5.6	4.8
Honolulu, Ha.	9.7	8.4	7.4	3.3	2.5	0.8	1.0	2.3	2.5	4.6	5.6	7.6
Little Rock, Ark.	13.2	10.9	12.2	12.4	13.5	9.1	8.4	7.1	8.1	7.4	10.4	10.4
Miami, Fla.	5.1	4.8	5.8	9.9	16.3	18.8	17.3	17.8	24.1	20.8	7.1	4.3
New York, N.Y.	8.4	7.1	10.2	8.6	9.4	8.4	9.4	11.2	9.9	7.8	8.6	8.4

The average yearly precipitation in Birmingham is 135 centimeters and in Honolulu it is 55.7 centimeters. We subtract to find the difference.

Step 1. Line up the decimal points.
Since 135 = 135.0, write a zero in the tenths place.

$$
\begin{array}{r}
135.0 \\
-\ 55.7 \\
\hline
\end{array}
$$

Step 2. Regroup.

$$
\begin{array}{r}
135.0 \\
-\ 55.7 \\
\hline
\end{array}
$$

Step 3. Subtract.

$$
\begin{array}{r}
135.0 \\
-\ 55.7 \\
\hline
79.3
\end{array}
$$

The average precipitation is 79.3 centimeters more in Birmingham.

Here are some other examples of subtracting decimals.

$$
\begin{array}{r}
5.231 \\
-1.584 \\
\hline
3.647
\end{array}
\qquad
\begin{array}{r}
9.830 \\
-2.586 \\
\hline
7.244
\end{array}
$$

EXERCISES
Subtract.

1.   59.6
    − 13.5
	2. 8.42
	    − 0.26
		3. 72.6
		    − 7.8
			4. 9.68
			    − 3.14
				5. 85.3
				    − 28.9

6.   0.314
    − 0.109
	7. 60.2
	    − 28.9
		8. 5.19
		    − 3.74
			9. 0.302
			    − 0.195
				10. 9.64
				    − 3.98

11.   5.918
    − 0.265
	12. 72.95
	    − 3.98
		13. 0.7426
		    − 0.4285
			14. 86.52
			    − 32.97
				15. 646.4
				    − 289.6

16.   61.83
    − 59.34
	17. 6.882
	    − 2.817
		18. 6.752
		    − 0.395
			19. 93.71
			    − 0.78
				20. 87.25
				    − 3.95

21. 70.2 − 26.14

      70.2
     − 26.14

22. 581.68 − 59.38

23. 74.729 − 27.351

24. 723.16 − 56.87

25. 95.305 − 4.26

26. 16.3 − 5.491

27. 28.9 − 16.03

28. 90.06 − 5.178

29. 263.3 − 59.648

30. 520.4 − 9.871

Solve. Use the chart on the previous page.

31. What is the yearly precipitation in Chicago?

32. Which city gets more precipitation in a year, Chicago or Honolulu?

33. How much precipitation does New York get during the first half of the year? During the second half? How much more during the second half?

34. Which city gets more precipitation in a year, Little Rock or Miami? How much more?

Estimating sums and differences

If you estimate first, you will know whether your answer is reasonable.

$$\begin{array}{r} 6.1 \\ +4.96 \\ \hline 11.06 \end{array}$$

$$\begin{array}{r} 15.40 \\ -9.27 \\ \hline 6.13 \end{array}$$

EXERCISES

First estimate each sum. Then add.

1. 3.55
    + 2.5

2. 72.6
    + 39.4

3. 0.23
    + 4.583

4. 5.41
    + 23.8

5. 18.917
    + 9.6

6. 9.66
    + 3.15

7. 81.4
    + 0.56

8. 4.307
    + 0.853

9. 9.85
    + 15

10. 6.73
    + 2.496

First estimate each difference. Then subtract.

11. 5.37
    − 3.85

12. 29.4
    − 0.6

13. 2.18
    − 1.4

14. 3.92
    − 2.18

15. 62.5
    − 36.974

16. 7.21
    − 2.943

17. 74
    − 6.951

18. 5.84
    − 0.39

19. 3.43
    − 2.583

20. 6.89
    − 2.948

First estimate. Then compute.

21. 5.9 + 38.74

22. 63.5 − 29

23. 85 − 3.645

24. (2.8 + 3) − 1.64

25. (5.84 − 2.6) + 0.59

26. (7.4 − 2.34) − 2

27. (9.6 + 7.8) − 6.4

28. 9.6 + (7.8 − 6.4)

29. (15.2 − 9.48) − 4.6

30. 15.2 − (9.48 − 4.6)

31. (47.6 − 3.82) + 15.79

32. 47.6 − (3.82 + 15.79)

1. (48.3 − 16.7) − 8.3

2. 48.3 − (16.7 − 8.3)

3. (9.6 − 3.25) + (8.72 − 3.96)

4 (18.2 + 4.6) − (9.21 + 8.55)

Skill Game

Tell which is closer to the target number, 50.

1. **a.** $\boxed{5}\boxed{2}$ + $\boxed{7}\boxed{6}$ – $\boxed{8}\boxed{4}$ → 50
   b. $\boxed{7}\boxed{8}$ + $\boxed{4}\boxed{5}$ – $\boxed{5}\boxed{6}$ → 50

2. **c.** $\boxed{9}\boxed{3}$ + $\boxed{4}\boxed{0}$ – $\boxed{6}\boxed{8}$ → 50
   d. $\boxed{7}\boxed{8}$ + $\boxed{6}\boxed{9}$ – $\boxed{4}\boxed{0}$ → 50

Play the game.

1. Make a table like this.

   $\boxed{}\boxed{}$ + $\boxed{}\boxed{}$ – $\boxed{}\boxed{}$ → 50

2. A game leader will mix up these digit cards. The leader draws a card, replaces it, and continues until 6 cards have been drawn.

   $\boxed{0}$ $\boxed{1}$ $\boxed{2}$ $\boxed{3}$ $\boxed{4}$ $\boxed{5}$ $\boxed{6}$ $\boxed{7}$ $\boxed{8}$ $\boxed{9}$

3. As each card is drawn write the digit somewhere in your table.

4. Place a decimal point any place you wish in each pair of digits.
   For example:

   John's table:

   $\boxed{6}\boxed{0}$ + $\boxed{4}\boxed{7}$ – $\boxed{6}\boxed{3}$ → 50

   Karen's table:

   $\boxed{4}\boxed{6}$ + $\boxed{3}\boxed{6}$ – $\boxed{0}\boxed{7}$ → 50

5. The player closest to the target number, 50, wins the game. Who came closer, John or Karen?

Mathematics in careers

Many businesses have employees known as *payroll clerks*, who compute and pay the salary of each employee. After computing an employee's salary, the payroll clerk deducts some money for federal income tax and social security. (Some employees may choose to have more money deducted from their salary for such things as savings bonds, group medical insurance, group life insurance, etc.)

The following tables show the amounts to be deducted for federal income tax and social security.

Federal Income Tax Withholding (Weekly Payroll)

Not Married				Married						
Weekly salary		Number of exemptions		Weekly salary		Number of exemptions				
At least	But less than	0	1	At least	But less than	0	1	2	3	4
$200	$210	$33.10	$29.60	$200	$210	$24.70	$22.10	$19.50	$16.90	$14.30
210	220	35.50	32.00	210	220	26.50	23.90	21.30	18.70	16.10
220	230	38.10	34.40	220	230	28.40	25.70	23.10	20.50	17.90
230	240	40.90	36.80	230	240	30.60	27.50	24.90	22.30	19.70
240	250	43.70	39.60	240	250	32.80	29.60	26.70	24.10	21.50
250	260	46.50	42.40	250	260	35.00	31.80	28.60	25.90	23.30
260	270	49.30	45.20	260	270	37.20	34.00	30.80	27.70	25.10
270	280	52.10	48.00	270	280	39.40	36.20	33.00	29.80	26.90
280	290	54.90	50.80	280	290	41.80	38.40	35.20	32.00	28.90
290	300	57.70	53.60	290	300	44.30	40.70	37.40	34.20	31.10

Social Security Tax Withholding (Weekly Payroll)

At least	But less than	Tax withheld	At least	But less than	Tax withheld	At least	But less than	Tax withheld
$199.50	$201.50	$11.73	$233.50	$235.50	$13.72	$267.50	$269.50	$15.71
201.50	203.50	11.85	235.50	237.50	13.84	269.50	271.50	15.82
203.50	205.50	11.96	237.50	239.50	13.95	271.50	273.50	15.94
205.50	207.50	12.08	239.50	241.50	14.07	273.50	275.50	16.06
207.50	209.50	12.20	241.50	243.50	14.19	275.50	277.50	16.18
209.50	211.50	12.31	243.50	245.50	14.30	277.50	279.50	16.29
211.50	213.50	12.43	245.50	247.50	14.42	279.50	281.50	16.41
213.50	215.50	12.55	247.50	249.50	14.54	281.50	283.50	16.53
215.50	217.50	12.67	249.50	251.50	14.65	283.50	285.50	16.64
217.50	219.50	12.78	251.50	253.50	14.77	285.50	287.50	16.76
219.50	221.50	12.90	253.50	255.50	14.89	287.50	289.50	16.88
221.50	223.50	13.02	255.50	257.50	15.01	289.50	291.50	16.99
223.50	225.50	13.13	257.50	259.50	15.12	291.50	293.50	17.11
225.50	227.50	13.25	259.50	261.50	15.24	293.50	295.50	17.23
227.50	229.50	13.37	261.50	263.50	15.36	295.50	297.50	17.35
229.50	231.50	13.48	263.50	265.50	15.47	297.50	299.50	17.46
231.50	233.50	13.60	265.50	267.50	15.59	299.50	301.50	17.58

EXERCISES

Copy and complete this table.

Employee	Number of exemptions	Weekly salary	Payroll deductions Income tax	Social security	Total	Take-home pay
*Chaney, A.	1	$222	$34.40	$13.02	$47.42	$174.58
Dyer, M.	3	261				
Felker, R.	0	224				
Klick, J.	2	253				
*Lingol, P.	1	280				
Murphy, P.	3	272				
*Skoczen, L.	1	218				
Ward, F.	4	295				

*Single employee

73

Problem solving

Drag racing began in the early 1950's. The car that travels 400 meters in the shortest time wins the race.

Generally two decimals are used to show how a dragster performed. They are written like this:

8.72/261.58

The first number tells the number of seconds that it took to travel the distance. It is sometimes called the *elapsed time*. The second number tells the speed (in kilometers per hour) of the dragster when the car reached the finish line. This speed is sometimes called the *terminal speed*.

Here are the results of a certain class of racers.

Car	Driver	Time/Speed
Comet	Pride	8.71/264.54
Early Finish	Brent	8.68/267.04
Good Bye	Goza	8.64/273.72
Lightning II	Evans	8.67/269.45
Power Plus	Jennings	8.73/258.17
Smokie	Murphy	8.72/260.02

1. How many cars finished the race in less than 8.70 seconds?

2. How many cars had a terminal speed that was more than 269.5 kilometers per hour?

3. Which car won the class?

4. What was the terminal speed of the winning car?

5. What was the elapsed time of the car that placed last?

6. Find the difference of the elapsed times of the first- and last-place cars.

7. What was the difference of the terminal speeds of the first- and second-place cars?

8. What was the difference of the terminal speeds of the second- and third-place cars?

EXCURSION ▰▰▰▰▰▰▰▰▰▰▰▰▰▰▰
A frog fell to the bottom of a well that was 3 meters deep. During the first hour, the frog climbed up 17 centimeters and then slid back 10 centimeters. At this rate, how long did it take the frog to climb out of the well?

CHAPTER CHECKUP

Read. [pages 56–59]

1. 0.3 2. 0.03 3. 0.003 4. 7.6 5. 93.17 6. 8.1358

Give the standard numeral. [pages 56–59]

7. two and six tenths
8. six and three hundredths
9. forty-two thousandths
10. two hundred six thousandths
11. two hundred and six thousandths
12. five hundred four ten thousandths

< or >? [pages 62–63]

13. 0.03 ● 0.004 14. 73.2 ● 73.4 15. 2.999 ● 3 16. 5.7346 ● 5.3382

Round 15.6599 to the nearest [pages 64–65]

17. tenth 18. one 19. hundredth 20. thousandth

Add. [pages 66–67, 70–71]

21. $\begin{array}{r} 5.7 \\ +3.8 \\ \hline \end{array}$ 22. $\begin{array}{r} 3.98 \\ +0.47 \\ \hline \end{array}$ 23. $\begin{array}{r} 2.08 \\ +5.26 \\ \hline \end{array}$

24. 3.48 + 1.962

25. 25.37 + 0.4876

Subtract. [pages 68–71]

26. $\begin{array}{r} 7.4 \\ -3.8 \\ \hline \end{array}$ 27. $\begin{array}{r} 5.93 \\ -2.86 \\ \hline \end{array}$ 28. $\begin{array}{r} 30.2 \\ -19.5 \\ \hline \end{array}$

29. 4.32 − 1.837

30. 25 − 2.68

Solve. [pages 74–75]

31. 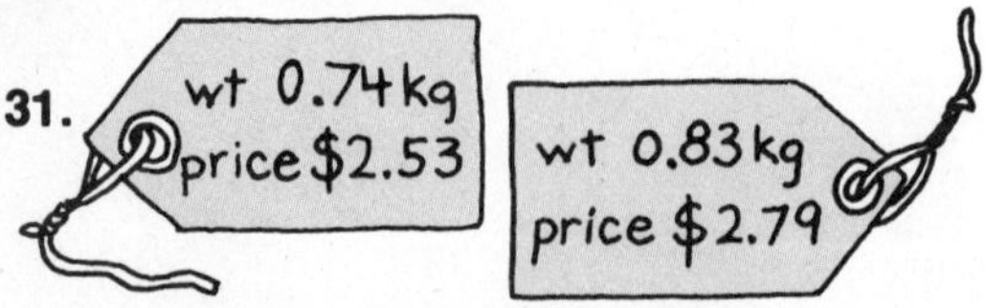
wt 0.74kg
price $2.53
wt 0.83kg
price $2.79

a. What is the total cost?
b. What is the total weight?

32. 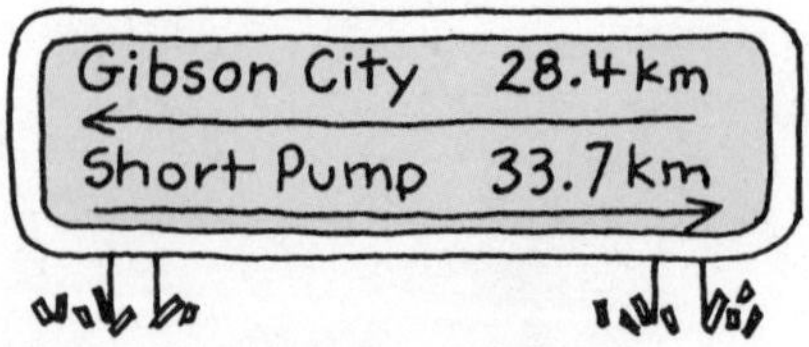
Gibson City 28.4km
Short Pump 33.7km

How far apart are the two towns?

Project

Think about standing under a basketball net and jumping straight up as high as you can. The distance that you could jump beyond your normal reach is your vertical jump. First guess what it would be. Then follow these steps to measure it.

1. Blacken the end of a middle finger with a pencil. While standing *flat-footed*, mark as high as you can reach on a paper strip that is taped to the wall. Measure the height of your mark to the nearest centimeter. Convert the height to meters.

2. From a standing position, jump to see how high you can mark on the same paper. Measure the distance to the nearest centimeter and convert it to meters.

3. Subtract to find your vertical jump in meters.

4. **a.** When all your classmates have measured their vertical jumps, list them on the chalkboard. Show the results on a graph like this:

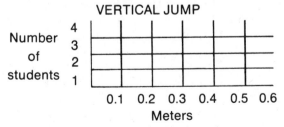

VERTICAL JUMP

Number of students

   b. List some facts shown by your graph.

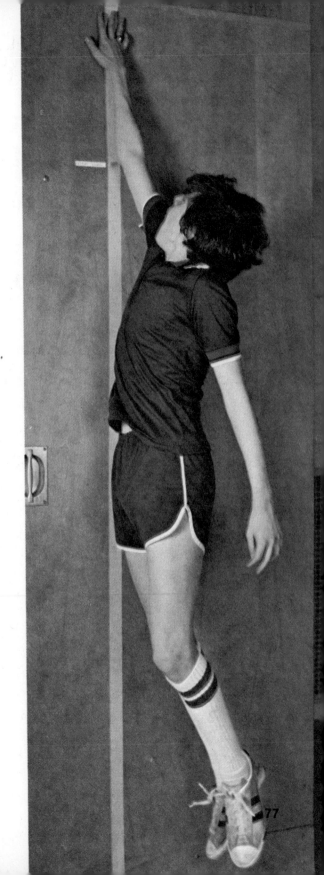

77

CHAPTER REVIEW

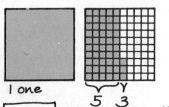

1 one | 5 tenths 3 hundredths

1.53

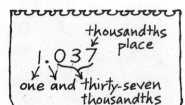

thousandths place

1.037

one and thirty-seven thousandths

Round to the nearest 1.

ones place

43.6

5 or greater

44

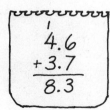

1
4.6
+3.7
8.3

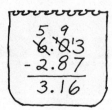

5 9
6.0¹3
-2.87
3.16

How many unit squares are shaded?

1. 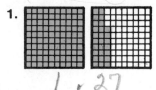 1.27

2.   .78

3.   .91

Read.

4. 0.6   5. 0.08   6. 7.124

7. 6.057   8. 38.64   9. 29.4321

Round to the nearest 1.

10. 26.3 26   11. 38.9 39   12. 47.5 48

13. 6.09   14. 12.499   15. 117.511 118

Round to the nearest 0.1.

16. 0.67   17. 0.61   18. 0.65

19. 13.341   20. 28.784 28.8 21. 31.976 32.0

Add.

22.   5.9   23.   6.57   24. 5.25 + 0.776
    + 8.7   + 3.88
                               25. 0.843 + 27.9

Subtract.

26.   8.77   27.   0.608   28. 36.05 - 2.166
    - 3.98   - 0.419
                               29. 14.035 - 6.27

78

CHAPTER CHALLENGE

Code

A	C	E	I	L	N	P	S	T	W	Y
6.7	3.8	0.42	1.67	3.24	0.087	0.001	5.2	0.33	6.23	4.51

Where does a 200-kilogram gorilla sleep?

six and seven tenths ☐

eighty-seven thousandths ☐

four and fifty-one hundredths ☐

0.94 + 5.8 − 5.07 ☐

9.03 − 5.7 − 3 ☐

100 − 99.999 ☐

0.25 + 2.99 ☐

10 − (3.9 − 0.6) ☐

12.5 − (5.9 + 2.8) ☐

0.12 + 0.3 ☐

0.5 greater than 5.73 ☐

95.47 − 1.8 − 86.97 ☐

15 − (12.3 + 2.613) ☐

9.2 − (10 − 1.13) ☐

0.083 less than 5.283 ☐

MAJOR CHECKUP
Standardized Format

Choose the correct letter.

1. The standard numeral for three hundred million forty-two is

   a. 342,000,000
   b. 300,000,042
   c. 3,000,042
   d. none of these

2. Round 783,499 to the nearest thousand.

   a. 783,000
   b. 784,000
   c. 780,000
   d. none of these

3. Add.

   2965
  +4763

   a. 6628
   b. 7628
   c. 7728
   d. none of these

4. Subtract.

   6003
  −4297

   a. 1706
   b. 2706
   c. 2816
   d. none of these

5. Multiply.

   6703
   ×5

   a. 45,515
   b. 33,515
   c. 3365
   d. none of these

6. Multiply.

   47
  ×28

   a. 1216
   b. 470
   c. 1316
   d. none of these

7. Divide.

   6)3716

   a. 619 R2
   b. 620 R6
   c. 618
   d. none of these

8. The standard numeral for two hundred and nine thousandths is

   a. 200.009
   b. 0.209
   c. 0.0209
   d. none of these

9. Round 67.751 to the nearest one.

   a. 67
   b. 67.8
   c. 68
   d. none of these

10. Add.

   4.37
  +2.69

   a. 6.06
   b. 0.0706
   c. 7.06
   d. none of these

11. Add.

   3.98 + 42.7

   a. 46.68
   b. 82.5
   c. 8.25
   d. none of these

12. Subtract.

   5.007
  −0.389

   a. 5.718
   b. 5.382
   c. 4.618
   d. none of these

3
Decimals—Multiplication and Division

$1.75
× 3.2 lb
$5.60

Multiplying decimals

The go-cart averaged 19.5 kilometers per hour for 3.5 hours. We can multiply to find out how far the go-cart went. To estimate the product, we round each number to the nearest whole number and multiply.

$$
\begin{array}{r}
19.5 \\
\times\, 3.5 \\
\end{array}
\qquad
\begin{array}{r}
20 \\
\times\, 4 \\
\hline
80 \\
\end{array}
$$

The product should be about 80.

Here is how to find the product of two decimals.

Step 1. Multiply the numbers as whole numbers.

$$
\begin{array}{r}
19.5 \\
\times\, 3.5 \\
\hline
97\ 5 \\
585 \\
\hline
682\ 5 \\
\end{array}
$$

Step 2. Count the digits to the right of the decimal points.

$$
\begin{array}{r}
19.\underline{5} \quad \text{1 digit} \\
\times\, 3.\underline{5} \quad +\text{1 digit} \\
\hline
97\ 5 \\
585 \\
\hline
682\ 5 \quad \text{2 digits} \\
\end{array}
$$

Step 3. Count off the same number of digits to place the decimal point in the product.

$$
\begin{array}{r}
19.5 \\
\times\, 3.5 \\
\hline
97\ 5 \\
585 \\
\hline
68.2\ 5 \\
\end{array}
$$

The go-cart went 68.25 km.

EXERCISES
First estimate the product. Then multiply.

1. $\begin{array}{r} 3.9 \\ \times\, 6.8 \\ \end{array}$
2. $\begin{array}{r} 5.7 \\ \times\, 2.1 \\ \end{array}$
3. $\begin{array}{r} 6.3 \\ \times\, 3.9 \\ \end{array}$
4. $\begin{array}{r} 7.8 \\ \times\, 1.8 \\ \end{array}$
5. $\begin{array}{r} 7.2 \\ \times\, 5.2 \\ \end{array}$
6. $\begin{array}{r} 9.1 \\ \times\, 7.6 \\ \end{array}$

7. $\begin{array}{r} 5.26 \\ \times\, 4.2 \\ \end{array}$
8. $\begin{array}{r} 3.28 \\ \times\, 3.5 \\ \end{array}$
9. $\begin{array}{r} 7.42 \\ \times\, 6.1 \\ \end{array}$
10. $\begin{array}{r} 9.06 \\ \times\, 7.4 \\ \end{array}$
11. $\begin{array}{r} 7.52 \\ \times\, 8.9 \\ \end{array}$
12. $\begin{array}{r} 3.91 \\ \times\, 5.3 \\ \end{array}$

Multiply.

13. 6.7 × 0.42	14. 0.57 × 3.5	15. 0.29 × 0.64	16. 79 × 6.3	17. 8.2 × 0.51	18. 65 × 0.39
19. 368 × 2.7	**20.** 5.04 × 32	**21.** 67.3 × 4.1	**22.** 5.82 × 0.73	**23.** 6.42 × 8.1	**24.** 75.9 × 0.36
25. 7.52 × 1.24	**26.** 9.38 × 1.03	**27.** 26.1 × 2.41	**28.** 5.18 × 72.5	**29.** 93.6 × 29.3	**30.** 8.53 × 6.78

Solve.

31. A can of oil contains 0.96 liters of oil. How much oil do 5 cans contain?

32. One lap around a certain go-cart track is 1.2 kilometers. How far is 2.5 laps around the track?

33. The winning cart averaged 37.5 kilometers per hour. It took 1.6 hours to complete the race. How many kilometers long was the race?

34. In a 48.5-kilometer race, the winning cart averaged 32.4 kilometers per hour for the first 1.25 hours. Then it made a pit stop. How many kilometers did it have to go after the pit stop?

Excursion ■●■●■●■●■●■●■●■●■●■●■●■●■●■●

$(1 \times 9) + 2 = ?$ Guess first.
$(12 \times 9) + 3 = ?$ $(1234 \times 9) + 5 = ?$
$(123 \times 9) + 4 = ?$ $(12345 \times 9) + 6 = ?$

Zeros in multiplication

Sometimes when you multiply decimals you must write extra zeros in the product in order to get the decimal point in the correct place. Study these examples.

$$\begin{array}{r} 0.06 \\ \times\,0.5 \\ \hline .030 \end{array}\Big\}3$$

One zero had to be written in the product so that there are three digits to the right of the decimal point.

$$\begin{array}{r} 0.32 \\ \times\,0.03 \\ \hline .0096 \end{array}\Big\}4$$

Two zeros had to be written in the product.

EXERCISES
Multiply.

1. $\begin{array}{r}0.02\\ \times\,0.3\\ \hline\end{array}$	2. $\begin{array}{r}0.11\\ \times\,0.5\\ \hline\end{array}$	3. $\begin{array}{r}2.1\\ \times\,0.04\\ \hline\end{array}$	4. $\begin{array}{r}3.1\\ \times\,0.12\\ \hline\end{array}$	5. $\begin{array}{r}0.67\\ \times\,0.03\\ \hline\end{array}$	6. $\begin{array}{r}0.05\\ \times\,0.4\\ \hline\end{array}$
7. $\begin{array}{r}0.35\\ \times\,3.6\\ \hline\end{array}$	8. $\begin{array}{r}0.35\\ \times\,0.6\\ \hline\end{array}$	9. $\begin{array}{r}0.79\\ \times\,0.08\\ \hline\end{array}$	10. $\begin{array}{r}0.35\\ \times\,0.006\\ \hline\end{array}$	11. $\begin{array}{r}55.7\\ \times\,0.38\\ \hline\end{array}$	12. $\begin{array}{r}5.76\\ \times\,5.4\\ \hline\end{array}$
13. $\begin{array}{r}55.7\\ \times\,2.31\\ \hline\end{array}$	14. $\begin{array}{r}5.7\\ \times\,0.008\\ \hline\end{array}$	15. $\begin{array}{r}0.002\\ \times\,0.13\\ \hline\end{array}$	16. $\begin{array}{r}0.006\\ \times\,0.05\\ \hline\end{array}$	17. $\begin{array}{r}0.538\\ \times\,12.7\\ \hline\end{array}$	18. $\begin{array}{r}58.9\\ \times\,3.56\\ \hline\end{array}$
19. $\begin{array}{r}38.9\\ \times\,2.84\\ \hline\end{array}$	20. $\begin{array}{r}7.56\\ \times\,3.06\\ \hline\end{array}$	21. $\begin{array}{r}9.21\\ \times\,71.4\\ \hline\end{array}$	22. $\begin{array}{r}0.704\\ \times\,55.6\\ \hline\end{array}$	23. $\begin{array}{r}36.5\\ \times\,1.83\\ \hline\end{array}$	24. $\begin{array}{r}0.825\\ \times\,26.5\\ \hline\end{array}$
25. $\begin{array}{r}3.78\\ \times\,1.52\\ \hline\end{array}$	26. $\begin{array}{r}0.942\\ \times\,3.75\\ \hline\end{array}$	27. $\begin{array}{r}68.3\\ \times\,2.91\\ \hline\end{array}$	28. $\begin{array}{r}0.754\\ \times\,0.169\\ \hline\end{array}$	29. $\begin{array}{r}3.82\\ \times\,61.5\\ \hline\end{array}$	30. $\begin{array}{r}3.82\\ \times\,19.6\\ \hline\end{array}$

$1 \times 1 = ?$	Guess first.	$9 \times 9 = ?$	Guess first.
$11 \times 11 = ?$	$1111 \times 1111 = ?$	$99 \times 99 = ?$	$9999 \times 9999 = ?$
$111 \times 111 = ?$	$11111 \times 11111 = ?$	$999 \times 999 = ?$	$99999 \times 99999 = ?$

Mathematics and world geography

Australia

1. Australia was first settled by Europeans in 1788. How many years ago was that?

2. In the 15 years that followed World War II, more than 1,700,000 people emigrated to Australia. What was the yearly average? Round your answer to the nearest whole number.

3. Anthropologists believe that the first people to inhabit Australia (the Australian aborigines) came from Southeast Asia about 18,000 years ago. When Australia was first settled by Europeans, there were about 300,000 Australian aborigines. Today there are only about 40,000 pure-blooded aborigines. How much has their population decreased?

4. a. What is the total area of Australia?
   b. What is the total population of Australia?

Australia States and Territories	Area (square kilometers)	Population
New South Wales	801,428	4,589,600
Victoria	227,619	3,496,200
Queensland	1,727,522	1,823,400
South Australia	984,377	1,172,800
Western Australia	2,527,621	1,027,400
Tasmania	68,332	389,900
Australian Capital Territory	2,432	143,800
Northern Territory	1,347,519	85,500

Some multiplication shortcuts

When you multiply by 10, 100, or 1000, you get a product that is greater than the number you multiplied.

Multiplying by 10	2.783
	× 10
	27.830

$2.783 \times 10 = 27.83$

Multiplying by 100

$2.783 \times 100 = 278.3$

Multiplying by 1000

$2.783 \times 1000 = 2783.$

To multiply by 10, I move the decimal point 1 place to the right.

I move the decimal point to the right as many places as there are zeros.

When you multiply by 0.1, 0.01, or 0.001, you get a product that is less than the number you multiplied.

Multiplying by 0.1	13.7
	× 0.1
	1.37

$13.7 \times 0.1 = 1.37$

Multiplying by 0.01

$13.7 \times 0.01 = 0.137$

Multiplying by 0.001

$13.7 \times 0.001 = 0.0137$

To multiply by 0.1, I move the decimal point 1 place to the left.

EXERCISES

Give each product.

1. 4.3×1
2. 4.3×10
3. 4.3×100
4. 4.3×1000
5. 4.3×0.1
6. 4.3×0.01
7. 4.3×0.001
8. 4.3×0.0001

9. 28×1
10. 28×0.1
11. 28×0.01
12. 28×0.001
13. 28×10
14. 28×100
15. 28×1000
16. 28×10000

17. 23.751×1
18. 23.751×10
19. 23.751×100
20. 23.751×1000
21. 23.751×0.1
22. 23.751×0.01
23. 23.751×0.001
24. 23.751×0.0001

Give each product.   4,753

25. 475.3 × 0.01   **26.** 621.5 × 10   **27.** 53.87 × 100

28. 6.28 × 0.01   **29.** 0.5836 × 1000   **30.** 4725.6 × 0.001

31. 6.7 × 0.001   **32.** 6.7 × 1000   **33.** 0.906 × 1000

Complete.

34. 6.3 × __?__ = 63   **35.** 6.3 × __?__ = 0.63

36. 7.25 × __?__ = 72.5   **37.** 7.25 × __?__ = 0.725

38. 526.3 × __?__ = 52.63   **39.** 526.3 × __?__ = 5.263

40. 0.84 × __?__ = 0.0084   **41.** 0.673 × __?__ = 67.3

42. 5683 × __?__ = 5.683   **43.** __?__ × 100 = 93.4

44. __?__ × 10 = 86.72   **45.** __?__ × 0.01 = 87.53

Solve.

46. 1 meter = 100 centimeters

Longest moustache
2.59 meters
How many centimeters?

47. 1 centimeter = 0.01 meter

Longest beard
533.4 centimeters
How many meters?

87

Problem solving

Scientists believe that there are about 100,000 different kinds of butterflies. Since there are so many kinds, some different types are hard to tell apart. For example, the Monarch and the Viceroy look so much alike that birds can't tell them apart. As soon as a young bird learns that Monarchs taste bad, he refuses to dine on either Monarchs or Viceroys.

Notice that the pictures do not show actual size. You will need a centimeter ruler for exercises 1 through 6. (If you need to, trace the ruler on page 134.)

Monarch
For actual size, multiply measurement by 1.2.

Viceroy
For actual size, multiply measurement by 1.2.

Measure to the nearest 0.1 centimeter and compute the wing-span of each butterfly. Round each wingspan to the nearest 0.1 cm.

1. Monarch

2. Viceroy

3. Tiger Swallowtail

4. Buckeye

5. Mourning Cloak

6. American Copper

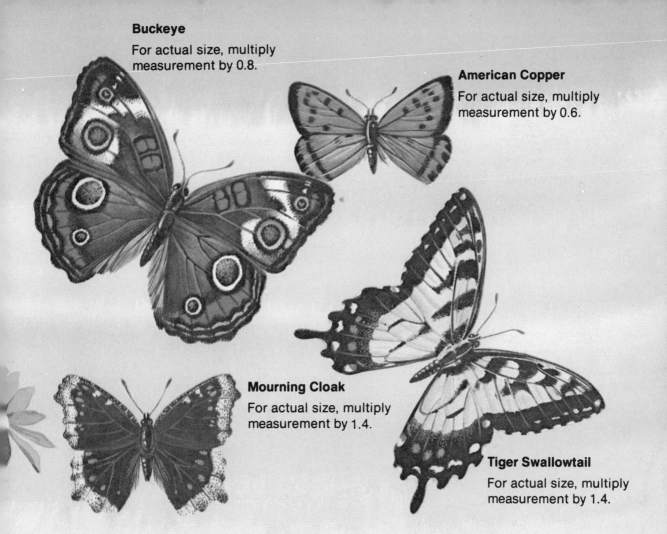

Buckeye
For actual size, multiply measurement by 0.8.

American Copper
For actual size, multiply measurement by 0.6.

Mourning Cloak
For actual size, multiply measurement by 1.4.

Tiger Swallowtail
For actual size, multiply measurement by 1.4.

7. How much greater is the wingspan of the Tiger Swallowtail than the wingspan of the Mourning Cloak? *Hint:* Use your answers to exercises 3 and 5.

8. The smallest butterfly known is the Western Pygmy Blue. It has a wingspan of 1.4 cm. How much greater is the wingspan of the American Copper?

9. The largest butterfly found in North America is the Giant Swallowtail. Its wingspan is 9.3 times as much as the Western Pygmy Blue. (See exercise 8.) What is the wingspan of the Giant Swallowtail?

10. Which butterfly pictures are larger than full scale? How much greater are the wingspans in the picture than the actual wingspans?

Dividing a decimal by a whole number

Dividing a decimal by a whole number is like dividing a whole number by a whole number.

If you first estimate the quotient, you will know whether your answer is reasonable. Estimate the quotient by rounding to the nearest whole number.

Study these examples.

EXAMPLE 1.

$$2\overline{)10}$$

$$2\overline{)9.78}$$

Step 1.
Divide ones.

$$\begin{array}{r} 4 \\ 2\overline{)9.78} \\ -8 \\ \hline 1 \end{array}$$

Step 2.
Regroup.

$$\begin{array}{r} 4 \\ 2\overline{)9.78} \\ -8 \\ \hline 1\,7 \end{array}$$

Step 3.
Divide tenths.
Be sure to place the decimal point in the quotient.

$$\begin{array}{r} 4.8 \\ 2\overline{)9.78} \\ -8 \\ \hline 1\,7 \\ -1\,6 \\ \hline 1 \end{array}$$

Step 4.
Regroup.

$$\begin{array}{r} 4.8 \\ 2\overline{)9.78} \\ -8 \\ \hline 1\,7 \\ -1\,6 \\ \hline 18 \end{array}$$

Step 5.
Divide hundredths.

$$\begin{array}{r} 4.89 \\ 2\overline{)9.78} \\ -8 \\ \hline 1\,7 \\ -1\,6 \\ \hline 18 \\ -18 \\ \hline 0 \end{array}$$

Is the quotient near 5?

EXAMPLE 2.

$$\begin{array}{r} 1.48 \\ 53\overline{)78.44} \\ -53 \\ \hline 25\,4 \\ -21\,2 \\ \hline 4\,24 \\ -4\,24 \\ \hline 0 \end{array}$$

EXAMPLE 3.

$$\begin{array}{r} 0.75 \\ 4\overline{)3.00} \\ -2\,8 \\ \hline 20 \\ -20 \\ \hline 0 \end{array}$$

EXERCISES

Divide.

1. $5\overline{)8}$
2. $8\overline{)1}$
3. $4\overline{)1}$
4. $5\overline{)3}$
5. $4\overline{)30}$

6. $4\overline{)0.3}$
7. $8\overline{)30}$
8. $8\overline{)0.3}$
9. $5\overline{)0.07}$
10. $2\overline{)0.5}$

11. $6\overline{)3.12}$
12. $3\overline{)0.72}$
13. $4\overline{)26.3}$
14. $9\overline{)0.459}$
15. $7\overline{)2.954}$

16. $8\overline{)4.368}$
17. $5\overline{)39.65}$
18. $9\overline{)4.815}$
19. $7\overline{)34.23}$
20. $6\overline{)537.6}$

21. $12\overline{)44.4}$
22. $18\overline{)651.6}$
23. $24\overline{)85.92}$
24. $37\overline{)239.39}$
25. $64\overline{)128.64}$

26. $47\overline{)143.82}$
27. $83\overline{)42.33}$
28. $91\overline{)278.46}$
29. $75\overline{)243}$
30. $86\overline{)3225}$

31. $123\overline{)801.96}$
32. $204\overline{)73.032}$
33. $418\overline{)685.52}$
34. $528\overline{)331.848}$

Solve.

35. Four mountain climbers have to carry a total of 58.2 kilograms of supplies. How much should each climber carry if they divide the supplies evenly?

36. The climbers began at an elevation of 1858.5 meters above sea level. Twelve hours later, they were at an elevation of 3172.5 meters.

    a. How many meters did they climb?
    b. How many meters did they average each hour?

Divide 2 by 3.
Does your calculator round or just drop extra digits?

More about division

Before dividing, we will use a shortcut for estimating the quotient.

$$39\overline{)9265.1}$$

Step 1. Round the divisor to the nearest ten.

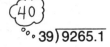

$$39\overline{)9265.1}$$

Step 2. Find the first digit of the quotient.

$$\overset{2}{39\overline{)9265.1}}$$

Step 3. Since the 2 is in the hundreds place, fill in two zeros.

$$\overset{200}{39\overline{)9265.1}}$$

Notice that the division will never come out evenly. In such cases we usually round the quotient.

$$\overset{237.566}{39\overline{)9265.100}}$$
$$-\underline{78}$$
$$146$$
$$-\underline{117}$$
$$295$$
$$-\underline{273}$$
$$22\ 1$$
$$-\underline{19\ 5}$$
$$2\ 60$$
$$-\underline{2\ 34}$$
$$260$$
$$-\underline{234}$$
$$26$$

Rounded to the nearest hundredth ▷ 237.57

The quotient is between 200 and 300.

Is the quotient between 200 and 300?

EXERCISES
Choose the quotient by estimating.

1. $38\overline{)2002.6}$
   a. 0.527
   b. 5.27
   c. 52.7
   d. 527

2. $42\overline{)153.3}$
   a. 0.365
   b. 3.65
   c. 36.5
   d. 365

3. $59\overline{)270.81}$
   a. 0.459
   b. 4.59
   c. 45.9
   d. 459

4. $96\overline{)195.84}$
   a. 0.204
   b. 2.04
   c. 20.4
   d. 204

5. $26\overline{)9.36}$ **6.** $42\overline{)2.184}$ **7.** $53\overline{)397.5}$

a. 0.36   **a.** 0.052   **a.** 0.75
b. 3.6   **b.** 0.52   **b.** 7.5
c. 36   **c.** 5.2   **c.** 75
d. 360   **d.** 52   **d.** 750

Divide. Round each quotient to the nearest hundredth.

8. $8\overline{)1}$ **9.** $6\overline{)1}$ **10.** $9\overline{)6}$

11. $6\overline{)5.97}$ **12.** $2\overline{)0.3956}$ **13.** $7\overline{)1.5931}$

14. $12\overline{)39.7}$ **15.** $16\overline{)5.63}$ **16.** $32\overline{)8.1}$

17. $17\overline{)0.264}$ **18.** $25\overline{)4.234}$ **19.** $83\overline{)97.76}$

20. $215\overline{)765.38}$ **21.** $308\overline{)96.748}$ **22.** $492\overline{)100.563}$

Give each sum.

1. 3.8 + 9.6
2. 15.8 + 28.3
3. 29.9 + 37.4
4. 16 + 3.8
5. 2.9 + 4.05
6. 3.68 + 29.8

Give each difference.

7. 15.7 − 2.3
8. 18 − 6.5
9. 23.4 − 7.8
10. 52.6 − 3.74
11. 83 − 2.97
12. 75 − 3.75

Multiply across and multiply down.

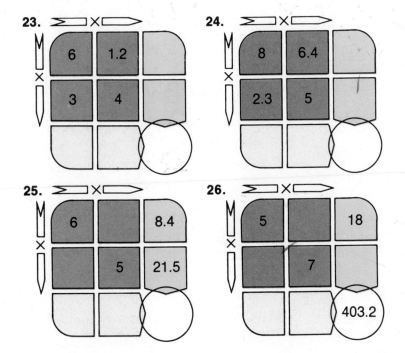

23.

6	1.2	
3	4	

24.

8	6.4	
2.3	5	

25.

6		8.4
	5	21.5

26.

5		18
	7	
		403.2

93

Problem solving

To find the average number of points that Beal scored during the first four games, we add the four numbers and divide by 4.

$$3 + 4 + 3 + 5 = 15$$

```
      3.75
  4)15.00
   -12
     3 0
    -2 8
      20
     -20
       0
```

Rounded to the nearest tenth, her scoring average for the first four games was 3.8.

Player	Height in cm	Weight in kg	Game 1	Game 2	Game 3	Game 4	Game 5	Game 6
Beal	160	48	3	4	3	5	9	7
Davis	150	41.5	8	5	7	8	7	6
Franklin	162	49.5	5	7	8	3	4	3
Lopez	155	45.5	2	5	0	4	5	4
Manning	153	44	4	6	7	6	0	8
Porter	147	39.5	6	4	2	5	3	6
Rogers	157	46.5	0	3	4	4	3	5
Wilson	158	48.5	8	5	6	8	6	7

EXERCISES
Round each decimal answer to the nearest tenth.

1. How many points did the team score in their first game?

2. How many more points did the team score in their sixth game than in their first game?

3. What is the average height of the team members?

4. What is the average weight of the team members?

5. How many points did Davis average during the first five games?

6. In which games did Franklin score below her average?

7. The player who holds the school scoring record (not a member of the present team) averaged 9.5 points per game for 12 games. How many points did she score?

8. Who had the greater scoring average, Wilson or Lopez? How much greater?

9. What was the team's average score for the first three games?

10. What was the team's average score for the first six games?

Dividing by a decimal

To divide by a decimal, we can first divide as if the divisor were a whole number. Then we can estimate to place the decimal in the quotient.

EXAMPLE. $1.2\overline{)74.76}$

Step 1. Divide 7476 by 12.

```
      6 23
1.2)74.76
   -72
    27
   -24
     36
    -36
      0
```

Step 2. Estimate the quotient. The quotient will be "near" 70.

$1.2\overline{)74.76}$

```
    70
 1)74.76
```

Step 3. Place the decimal point in the quotient.

```
     62.3
1.2)74.76
   -72
    27
   -24
     36
    -36
      0
```

If we multiply *both* the divisor and the dividend by the same nonzero number, the quotient remains the same.

```
   4    Multiply      4
3)12     by 10.    30)120
```

```
   17    Multiply        17
2)34      by 100.   200)3400
```

This fact gives us a shortcut for dividing by a decimal.

Step 1. Move both decimal points 1 place to the right. (Multiply by 10.)

$1.2\overline{)74.7.6}$

Now we can divide by the whole number, 12.

Step 2. Divide.

```
       62.3
1.2)74.7.6
   -72
    27
   -24
     36
    -36
      0
```

96

EXERCISES
Divide.

Need to supply a zero

1. $0.5\overline{)36.5}$ 2. $0.5\overline{)365}$ 3. $0.3\overline{)927}$ 4. $0.02\overline{)0.642}$ 5. $0.07\overline{)0.91}$

6. $0.04\overline{)13.20}$ 7. $0.003\overline{)0.1701}$ 8. $0.9\overline{)1.287}$ 9. $0.08\overline{)56}$ 10. $0.005\overline{)7.5}$

11. $3.5\overline{)1.05}$ 12. $5.2\overline{)19.24}$ 13. $6.3\overline{)3.654}$ 14. $0.28\overline{)20.16}$ 15. $0.31\overline{)0.0961}$

16. $5.3\overline{)14.151}$ 17. $1.28\overline{)59.776}$ 18. $0.235\overline{)5.1324}$ 19. $46.2\overline{)1186.878}$

Divide. Round each quotient to the nearest tenth.

20. $0.8\overline{)29.7}$ 21. $0.06\overline{)368}$ 22. $0.14\overline{)5.297}$ 23. $2.6\overline{)7.438}$

24. $7.5\overline{)62.91}$ 25. $3.9\overline{)7.503}$ 26. $0.78\overline{)68.2}$ 27. $1.23\overline{)49.37}$

28. $4.56\overline{)68.214}$ 29. $0.387\overline{)5.2837}$ 30. $1.06\overline{)0.3577}$ 31. $98.7\overline{)62.357}$

Solve.

32. How much will 2.4 kilograms of hamburger cost if 1 kilogram of hamburger is $1.80?

33. How many 0.25 kilogram servings can you get from 5.75 kilograms of hamburger?

34. How many 0.3-meter pieces can be cut from a 2.7-meter roll of ribbon?

35. If ribbon costs 78¢ a meter, how much will 3.8 meters of ribbon cost? Round your answer to the nearest cent.

36. On a trip, Ms. Miers bought 28 liters of gasoline for 19.9¢ per liter and 23.4 liters of gasoline for 18.9¢ per liter. How much did she spend for gasoline? Round each purchase to the nearest cent.

37. A customer bought a liter of oil for $.95. He gave the attendant a $10 bill. If gasoline sold for 17.9¢ a liter, how many liters of gasoline could he buy with the change? Round to the nearest tenth of a liter.

Practice exercises

Multiply.

1. 3.84	**2.** 56.5	**3.** 81.3	**4.** 7.02	**5.** 51.8
$\times 1.9$	$\times 5.3$	$\times 0.27$	$\times 5.8$	$\times 6.4$

6. 5.36	**7.** 38.5	**8.** 4.93	**9.** 6.35	**10.** 71.5
$\times 4.02$	$\times 5.63$	$\times 2.81$	$\times 34.6$	$\times 11.5$

Divide. Round each quotient to the nearest hundredth.

11. $5.7\overline{)0.548}$ **12.** $0.68\overline{)4.82}$ **13.** $2.6\overline{)2.964}$ **14.** $0.53\overline{)0.8349}$ **15.** $4.8\overline{)0.7529}$

16. $0.26\overline{)75}$ **17.** $3.12\overline{)3.906}$ **18.** $4.08\overline{)52.831}$ **19.** $0.225\overline{)729.84}$ **20.** $0.826\overline{)3.0715}$

Compute. [You should be able to do these problems without pencil and paper.]

21. $(58.7 + 3.9) - 3.9$

22. $(358.62 - 16.94) + 16.94$

23. $(8.6 \times 5.3) \div 5.3$

24. $(2.25 \div 0.15) \times 0.15$

25. $(24.6 \times 7.8) \div 24.6$

26. $(5.76 \div 0.18) \times 0.18$

27. $(9.283 + 4.295) - 9.283$

28. $(3.719 \times 1.065) \div 3.719$

Find each end number.

29.

30.

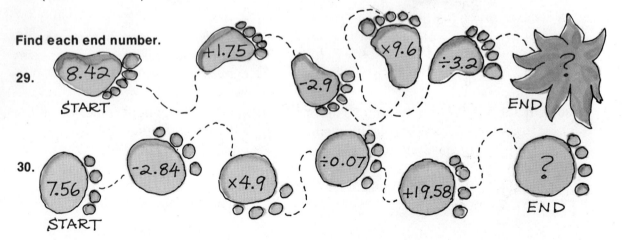

98

$(\boxed{3}\boxed{0}\boxed{6} \times \boxed{3}\boxed{4}\boxed{1}) - \boxed{8}\boxed{6}\boxed{5} \rightarrow 100$

$$\begin{array}{r} 30.6 \\ \times 3.41 \\ \hline 306 \\ 1224 \\ 918 \\ \hline 104.346 \end{array}$$

$$\begin{array}{r} 104.346 \\ -\ 8.65 \\ \hline 95.696 \end{array} \qquad \begin{array}{r} 100.000 \\ -95.696 \\ \hline 4.304 \end{array}$$

How close did these players come to the target number? Round each quotient to the nearest hundredth.

1. $(\boxed{6}\boxed{4}\boxed{1} \div \boxed{3}\boxed{0}\boxed{8}) \times \boxed{3}\boxed{5}\boxed{6} \rightarrow 100$

2. $(\boxed{8}\boxed{6}\boxed{3} \times \boxed{1}\boxed{6}\boxed{0}) - \boxed{4}\boxed{5}\boxed{3} \rightarrow 100$

3. $(\boxed{1}\boxed{3}\boxed{6} \times \boxed{5}\boxed{0}\boxed{3}) \div \boxed{8}\boxed{4}\boxed{6} \rightarrow 100$

4. $(\boxed{5}\boxed{3}\boxed{6} + \boxed{1}\boxed{3}\boxed{0}) - \boxed{6}\boxed{8}\boxed{4} \rightarrow 100$

Play the game.

1. Choose a game leader. Make two cards for each of the digits 0 through 9.

2. Draw a table like this on your paper.

   $(\square\square\square \quad \square\square\square) \quad \square\square\square \rightarrow 100$

3. The game leader displays nine digit cards.

4. Each player has five minutes to fill in the digits in his or her table, write in any two operation signs ($+$, $-$, $\times$, $\div$), and place three decimal points.

5. The player getting closest to the target number, 100, wins the game.

CHAPTER CHECKUP

Multiply. [pages 82–84, 98–99]

1.	3.9 × 0.5	2.	4.2 × 2.7	3.	13.8 × 3.8	4.	50.7 × 0.21	5.	40.3 × 31.4	6.	8.07 × 1.04

Multiply. [pages 86–87]

7. 5.8×10

8. 4.3×100

9. 0.5671×100

10. 3.2×0.1

11. 5.6×0.01

12. 3214.6×0.001

Divide. [pages 90–93]

13. $3\overline{)13.68}$

14. $5\overline{)3.9}$

15. $9\overline{)3.483}$

16. $10\overline{)67.34}$

17. $21\overline{)37.8}$

18. $82\overline{)323.08}$

19. $134\overline{)3457.2}$

20. $503\overline{)3274.53}$

Divide. Round each quotient to the nearest hundredth.
[pages 96–97]

21. $6\overline{)5.8}$

22. $0.07\overline{)39.7}$

23. $0.009\overline{)6.73}$

24. $3.2\overline{)67.65}$

25. $0.12\overline{)1.397}$

26. $0.62\overline{)4.18}$

27. $12.4\overline{)58.369}$

28. $2.79\overline{)493.752}$

Solve. [pages 88–89, 94–95]

29. To buy a stereo set, Mark has been saving $3.75 a week for the last 12 weeks. How much money has he saved during the 12 weeks?

30. The stereo that Mark wants costs $176.25. Mark now has $45. If he can save $3.75 a week, how much longer does he have to save to buy the stereo set?

Project

$$\begin{array}{r} 321\,4.6 \\ -.001 \\ \hline 32146 \end{array}$$

For these projects, you may wish to work with a classmate.

1. See how many pieces of notebook paper there are in a stack that is 1 centimeter thick. Divide to find the thickness of 1 sheet. Round your answer to the nearest thousandth of a centimeter.

2. Use a balance to determine the weight of 1 paper clip. Round your answer to the nearest hundredth of a gram. *Hint:* First see how many paper clips it takes to make a gram.

3. Can you find out how far apart the grooves are on a record?

Multiply.

1. 2.7
   × 8

2. 3.9
   × 0.6

3. 0.57
   × 9

4. 0.35
   × 0.7

5. 0.02
   × 0.3

6. 6.7
   × 3.4

7. 9.28
   × 3.6

8. 5.47
   × 6.24

Give each product.

9. 6.5×10

10. 1.23×10

11. 3.8×0.1

12. 623.4×0.01

13. 37.611×100

14. 0.48×1000

Divide.

15. $5\overline{)23.25}$

16. $3\overline{)1.44}$

17. $9\overline{)321.3}$

18. $6\overline{)0.426}$

19. $5\overline{)3.1}$

20. $8\overline{)0.0584}$

21. $12\overline{)2.76}$

22. $25\overline{)3.2}$

23. $40\overline{)0.72}$

Divide. Round each quotient to the nearest hundredth.

24. $0.9\overline{)5.762}$

25. $0.8\overline{)93.58}$

26. $0.05\overline{)3.711}$

27. $2.5\overline{)7.12}$

28. $0.19\overline{)46}$

29. $8.1\overline{)0.731}$

Compute the average.
Round to the nearest tenth.

30. 8, 8, 9, 5, 6, 3

31. 28, 31, 26, 25, 38

32. 126, 143, 182, 135

Sidebar worked examples:

$$6.3 \times 0.21 \quad \text{3 places}$$
$$63$$
$$126$$
$$1.323 \quad \text{3 places}$$

$$3.75 \times 10 = 37.5$$
$$6.21 \times 0.01 = .0621$$

$$8.81$$
$$3\overline{)26.43}$$
$$-24$$
$$24$$
$$-24$$
$$3$$
$$-3$$
$$0$$

$$6.055$$
$$0.32\overline{)1.9376}$$
$$-192$$
$$176$$
$$-160$$
$$160$$
$$-160$$
$$0$$

$$6, 4, 3, 8$$
$$5.25 \to 5.3$$
$$4\overline{)21.00}$$
$$-20$$
$$10$$
$$-8$$
$$20$$
$$-20$$
$$0$$
$$6$$
$$4$$
$$3$$
$$+8 \quad 4 \text{ numbers}$$
$$21$$

CHAPTER CHALLENGE

Complete.

1.

+	
4.6		12.4
5.9	4.9	

2.

+	
6.8	9.7	
	5.8	
3.4		

3.

−	
0.77		0.39
0.52		0.25

4.

×	
2.4		8.64
	4.5	
12.84		

5.

×	
12.4	0.2	
3.1	0.5	

6.

×	
6.8		27.2
3.4	5	

13 a b c d
33 a b c d
13 a b c d
3 a b c d
29 a b c d
14 a b c d
34 a b c d
14 a b c d
4 c d
30 a b c d
15
31
a b c
a b c
a b c

MAJOR CHECKUP

Standardized Format

Choose the correct letter.

1. The standard numeral for six million sixty thousand six is

a. 6,066,000
b. 6,060,006
c. 6,000,066
d. none of these

2. 67,480,000 rounded to the nearest million is

a. 60,000,000
b. 67,000,000
c. 68,000,000
d. none of these

3. Give the sum.

$$56 + 381 + 9$$

a. 446
b. 447
c. 456
d. none of these

4. Give the difference.

$$5002 - 1327$$

a. 4775
b. 4785
c. 3675
d. none of these

5. Multiply.

$$\begin{array}{r} 324 \\ \times\,602 \\ \hline \end{array}$$

a. 195,048
b. 20,088
c. 196,148
d. none of these

6. Divide.

$$38\overline{)7752}$$

a. 204
b. 240
c. 24
d. none of these

7. The standard numeral for 3.7 million is

a. 37,000,000
b. 3,000,000.7
c. 3,700,000
d. none of these

8. 4.2031 rounded to the nearest hundredth is

a. 4.21
b. 4.20
c. 4.203
d. none of these

9. Add

$$3.71 + 28.6$$

a. 7.57
b. 75.7
c. 31.31
d. none of these

10. Subtract.

$$70.03 - 2.56$$

a. 78.47
b. 78.57
c. 67.47
d. none of these

11. Multiply.

$$\begin{array}{r} 0.32 \\ \times\,2.4 \\ \hline \end{array}$$

a. 0.768
b. 7.68
c. 76.8
d. none of these

12. Divide.

$$0.08\overline{)1.72}$$

a. 0.215
b. 2.15
c. 21.5
d. none of these

4
Number
Theory

The whole numbers

In this chapter you will first work with the set of whole numbers.

$$\{0, 1, 2, 3, \ldots\}$$

The 3 dots tell me that the numbers go on forever in the same manner.

The study of the whole numbers dates back to about 500 B.C. At that time, the ancient Greeks began to explore and to classify the whole numbers. In this lesson you will be asked to take some of the same whole-number "journeys."

EXERCISES
Here are the first four triangular numbers.

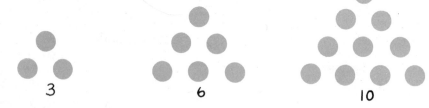

1   3   6   10

1. What is the fifth triangular number? The sixth triangular number? The seventh?

2. Notice that each triangular number can be written as a sum.

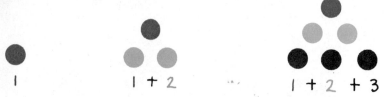

1   1 + 2   1 + 2 + 3

   Express the fourth triangular number as a sum.

3. Find the tenth triangular number by addition. Find the twentieth triangular number.

Here are the first four square numbers.

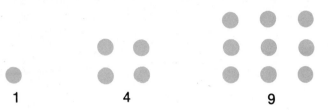 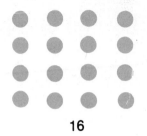

1   4   9   16

4. Give the next three square numbers.

**Square numbers can also be written as a sum of odd numbers.
The set of odd numbers: {1, 3, 5, 7, 9, 11, . . .}**

  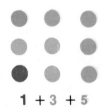

1   1 + 3   1 + 3 + 5

5. Write the next square number as a sum of odd numbers.

6. Find the eighth square number by addition.

7. Find the tenth square number by addition.

**Here are the first four rectangular numbers. Notice that each
figure is one dot wider than it is high.**

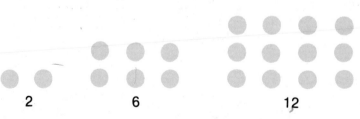 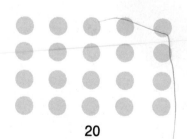

2   6   12   20

8. Find the next three rectangular numbers.

9. See if you can find a pattern for expressing the rectangular
numbers as sums.
Find the tenth rectangular number by addition.

Sets of whole numbers

Below are two sets of whole numbers. The elements of set W are the first 10 whole numbers. The elements of set O are the first 5 odd numbers.

$$W = \{0, 1, 2, 3, 4, 5, 6, 7, 8, 9\}$$

$$O = \{1, 3, 5, 7, 9\}$$

Since every element of set O is also an element of W, O is a **subset** of W. It is easy to see that O is a subset of W if we list the elements of each set inside loops like this:

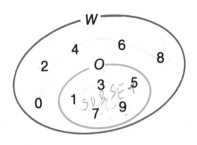

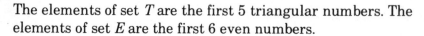

The elements of set T are the first 5 triangular numbers. The elements of set E are the first 6 even numbers.

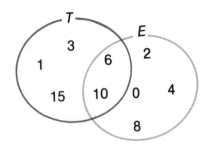

The **intersection** of sets T and E is the set of elements that are in both T and E.

We write: $T \cap E = \{6, 10\}$

We read: T intersection E equals the set containing 6 and 10.

The **union** of sets T and E is the set of elements that are in T or in E, or in both.

We write: $T \cup E = \{0, 1, 2, 3, 4, 6, 8, 10, 15\}$

We read: T union E equals the set containing 0, 1, 2, 3, 4, 6, 8, 10, and 15.

EXERCISES

True or false?

1. The even numbers are a subset of the whole numbers.

2. The whole numbers are a subset of the even numbers.

3. The odd numbers are a subset of the even numbers.

4. The triangular numbers are a subset of the odd numbers.

Give the intersection and union.

5.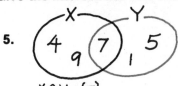

$X \cap Y = \{7\}$
$X \cup Y = \{1,4,5,7,9\}$

6.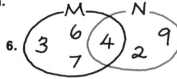

7.

8.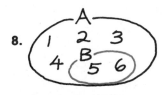

9. D = {0,2,4,5,8,10,12}
   E = {0,3,6,9,12}

10. R = {0,5,10,15,20}
    S = {0,4,8,12,16,20}

11. P = {1,2,3,4,5,6}
    Q = {1,3,6,10,15}

12. Y = {0,2,4,6,8,10}
    Z = {1,3,5,7,9}

Hint: The empty set has no elements.
   We write: ∅
   We read: The empty set.

13. Try to find a quick way to find the sum of the first 50 odd numbers.

$$1 = 1$$
$$1 + 3 = 4$$
$$1 + 3 + 5 = 9$$
$$1 + 3 + 5 + 7 = 16$$

Hint: What kind of number is each sum?

Keeping Skills Sharp

Round 793.576 to the nearest

1. hundred
2. tenth
3. hundredth
4. ten
5. one

Round 56,95960 to the nearest

6. one
7. hundredth
8. thousandth
9. ten-thousandth
10. ten

109

Factors

Both 2 and 4 are **factors**, or **divisors**, of 8. 3 is not a factor of 8 because there is no whole number that you can multiply by 3 to get 8.

The set of all factors of 8:

$X = \{1, 2, 4, 8\}$

The set of all factors of 12:

$Y = \{1, 2, 3, 4, 6, 12\}$

Notice that 1, 2, and 4 are in both sets of factors. They are **common factors** of 8 and 12.

The intersection of X and Y is the set of common factors of 8 and 12.

$X \cap Y = \{1, 2, 4\}$

The **greatest common factor** (GCF) of 8 and 12 is 4.

EXERCISES

Give the set of factors for each number.

1. 2　　　　**2.** 9　　　　**3.** 21　　　　**4.** 36　　　　**5.** 48　　　　**6.** 50

Give the set of all common factors for each pair of numbers.

7. 6, 9　　　**8.** 12, 18　　　**9.** 15, 21　　　**10.** 36, 48　　　**11.** 8, 9　　　**12.** 24, 48

13. Give the GCF of each pair of numbers in exercises 7–12.

14. Is it possible for two numbers to have no factors in common?

Who am I?

15. I am a factor of every number.

16. I am a common factor of every pair of numbers.

17. Copy and complete. (You may wish to extend the table.)

Number	1	2	3	4	5	6	7	8	9	10
Factors	1	1, 2	1, 3	1, 2, 4						
Number of factors	1	2	2	3						

Whole numbers with exactly 2 factors are called **prime numbers.**

Whole numbers (other than 0) having more than 2 factors are called **composite numbers.**

18. Look at your completed table and give the first 4 prime numbers.

19. Give the first 12 prime numbers.

20. Give the first 12 composite numbers.

21. What is the smallest number that has exactly 3 factors?

22. What is the smallest number that has exactly 4 factors?

23. Give the greatest prime number that is less than 50.

24. Give the smallest composite number.

25. How many composite numbers are less than 50?

Is 2311 a prime number?

Prime factorization

Every composite number can be factored into a product of prime numbers. Notice that the numbers in the bottom row of each **factor tree** are prime numbers.

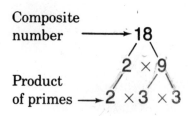

Composite
number $\longrightarrow$ 18

2×9

Product
of primes $\longrightarrow 2 \times 3 \times 3$

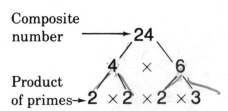

Composite
number $\longrightarrow$ 24

4×6

Product
of primes $\rightarrow 2 \times 2 \times 2 \times 3$

To express a composite number as a product of prime numbers is to give the **prime factorization** of the composite number.

prime factorization

$18 = 2 \times 3 \times 3$

prime factorization

$24 = 2 \times 2 \times 2 \times 3$

112

EXERCISES
Copy and complete these factor trees.

1.
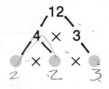
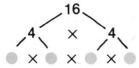
2   2   3

2.
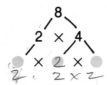
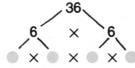
2   2 × 2

3.
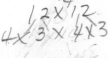

4.

Give the prime factorization.

5. 6	**6.** 15	**7.** 21	**8.** 28
9. 32	**10.** 38	**11.** 42	**12.** 48
13. 50	**14.** 56	**15.** 64	**16.** 72
17. 80	**18.** 84	**19.** 96	**20.** 100
21. 112	**22.** 128	**23.** 132	**24.** 144

EXCURSION ⬤❂⬤❂⬤❂⬤❂⬤❂⬤❂⬤❂⬤❂⬤❂⬤❂⬤

Any even number greater than 2 can be expressed as a sum of two primes. (This was first proposed by a mathematician called Goldbach.)

$$4 = 2 + 2$$
$$6 = 3 + 3$$
$$8 = 3 + 5$$

Express other even numbers as the sum of two primes.

Give each sum or difference.

1. 3.86 + 2.59
2. 7.09 − 3.14
3. 2.678 + 3.259
4. 9.1783 − 2.9999
5. 15.86 + 123.4
6. 32.785 − 2.96
7. 252 − 1.96
8. 58.03 + 26.529
9. 741.03 + 26.975
10. 28.1 − 6.942

Multiples

If you multiply the whole numbers by 3, you get the numbers shown in red. They are called **multiples** of 3.

Multiples of 3	0	1	2	3	4	5	6	7	8	9	10	11	12	13

Multiples of 4	0	1	2	3	4	5	6	7	8	9	10	11	12	13

The set of multiples of 3:

$A = \{0, 3, 6, 9, \ldots\}$

The set of multiples of 4:

$B = \{0, 4, 8, 12, \ldots\}$

The intersection of set A and set B is the set of **common multiples** of 3 and 4.

$A \cap B = \{0, 12, 24, \ldots\}$

The smallest common multiple, other than 0, is called the **least common multiple** (LCM). The least common multiple of 3 and 4 is 12.

EXERCISES

Give four multiples of each number.

1. 2   2. 3   3. 5   4. 7   5. 9   6. 12

Give two common multiples for each pair of numbers.

7. 2, 3   8. 3, 4   9. 2, 4   10. 5, 7   11. 10, 6   12. 3, 6

13. Give the LCM for each pair of numbers in exercises 7–12.

True or false?

14. Every number is a multiple of itself.   15. Every number is a factor of itself.

16. 1 is a multiple of every number.   17. 1 is a factor of every number.

18. Every number is a multiple of 1.

19. Every number is a factor of 1.

20. 2 is a factor of 6.

21. 6 is a multiple of 2.

22. 5 is a factor of 10.

23. 10 is a multiple of 5.

24. 6 is a factor of 9.

25. 9 is a multiple of 6.

26. If a first number is a factor of a second number, then the second number is a multiple of the first number.

Copy and complete.

27.
GCF

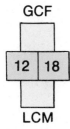

| 6 | 8 |

LCM

28.
GCF

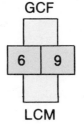

| 6 | 9 |

LCM

29.
GCF

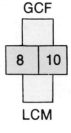

| 8 | 10 |

LCM

30.
GCF

| 12 | 18 |

LCM

31.
GCF

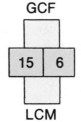

| 15 | 6 |

LCM

32.
GCF

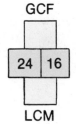

| 24 | 16 |

LCM

33. In exercises 27–32, compare the product of the "green" numbers with the product of the "yellow" numbers. What did you find?

34. Multiples of 2 are called **even numbers**. What can you say about the digit in the ones place of any even number?

35. Whole numbers that are not even numbers are called **odd numbers**. What can you say about the digit in the ones place of any odd number?

Divisibility

Since there is no remainder, we say that 225 is divisible by 3.

In this lesson you will learn some shortcuts for telling whether or not a whole number is divisible by 2, 3, 4, or 5.

A whole number is divisible by 2 if its last digit is divisible by 2. These numbers are divisible by 2:

753**8**   296**0**

A whole number is divisible by 3 if the sum of its digits is divisible by 3. These numbers are divisible by 3:

{1 + 3 + 2 + 6} {1 + 7 + 4 + 2 + 1}

1 3 2 6   1 7,4 2 1

A whole number is divisible by 4 if its last two digits are divisible by 4. These numbers are divisible by 4:

57**28**   36,5**36**

A whole number is divisible by 5 if its last digit is divisible by 5. These numbers are divisible by 5:

721**0**   374**5**

EXERCISES

Which of these numbers are divisible by 2? By 3? By 4? By 5?

1. 595
2. 780
3. 315
4. 724
5. 3684
6. 2917
7. 5634
8. 8216
9. 72,930
10. 52,654
11. 38,955
12. 72,610
13. 81,220
14. 39,464
15. 57,282
16. 34,060
17. 38,121
18. 26,305
19. 74,152
20. 60,372

21. See if you can find a rule for divisibility by 9. *Hint:* It is similar to the rule for divisibility by 3.

22. Can you find a rule for divisibility by 6?

Mathematics in careers

EXERCISES

1. In one city a taxi ride costs 25¢ for the first 0.1 kilometer and 10¢ for each additional 0.1 kilometer.

    a. How much is a 1-kilometer fare?
    b. How much is a 3.5-kilometer fare?
    c. How much is a 7-kilometer fare?

2. In another city a taxi ride costs 95¢ for the first 0.5 kilometer and 10¢ for each additional 0.1 kilometer. Compute the fare for

    a. 2.4 kilometers.
    b. 1.9 kilometers.
    c. 6.3 kilometers.

3. Suppose that a taxi ride costs 95¢ for the first 0.5 kilometer and 10¢ for each additional 0.1 kilometer. How far could a passenger ride for $4.25?

Variables

The letter m in the expression is a **variable**.

If we **substitute** a 5 for m, we get the expression shown. After we substitute we can **simplify** the expression. To simplify the expression is to write the simplest numeral for the number. When we simplify we get 12.

Study this example.

First, substitute for the variables. Then, simplify the expression.

A	a	n
5	2	4

$(A + a) - n$

Substitute: $(5 + 2) - 4$
Simplify: 3

EXERCISES
Substitute and simplify.

b	B	C	g	r
2	0	6	7	3

1. $5 + C$ **2.** $8 \times g$ **3.** $C \times 4$ **4.** $C \div 2$ **5.** $B \times 10$

6. $B + r$ **7.** $C + g$ **8.** $g + C$ **9.** $r + g + C$ **10.** $(C + g) - b$

Substitute and simplify.

a	b	D	d	S	T
9	6	7	8	5	4

11. $a \times b$ 12. $D \times d$ 13. $3 \times S$ 14. $5 \times T$ 15. $b \times d$

16. $d \times b$ 17. $a \times d$ 18. $D + d$ 19. $d + S$ 20. $13 - a$

21. $17 - D$ 22. $12 - d$ 23. $b \times D$ 24. $2 \times S \times a$ 25. $(D + d) - a$

26. Substitute your age in years for n and simplify.
   a. In 5 years I will be $n + 5$ years
   b. 6 years ago I was $n - 6$ years old.

27. Substitute your weight in kilograms for w and simplify.
   a. If I lose 4 kilograms, I will weigh $w - 4$ kilograms.
   b. If I gain 3 kilograms, I will weigh $w + 3$ kilograms.

Let h be your height in centimeters. Write an expression for a height that is

28. 5 centimeters less.

29. 8 centimeters more.

30. 2 times as much.

Write an expression for

31. 4 more than a number n.

32. 6 more than a number x.

33. 7 less than a number y.

34. 12 less than a number y.

35. a number x increased by 3.

36. a number y increased by 5.

37. a number r decreased by 1.

38. a number z decreased by 3.

39. 5 times a number b.

40. 6 times a number x.

41. the sum of a number m and 9.

42. the product of 5 and a number y.

43. 7 subtracted from a number c.

44. a number a divided by 2.

45. 6 divided by a number d.

★46. 3 less than 6 times a number m.

Solving addition and subtraction equations

If we let n be the number of marbles in the box that is closed we get the equation

$$n + 3 = 11$$

$$n + 3 = 11$$

To **solve** the equation is to find the number that we can substitute for n to make the equation true.

To solve the equation we can subtract 3 from *both sides* and then simplify both sides.

$$n + 3 - 3 = 11 - 3$$
$$n = 8$$

To check the solution we substitute 8 for n in the first equation. Since the equation is true, it checks!

Check: $8 + 3 = 11$

To solve this equation we can add 6 to *both sides* and then simplify both sides.

$$m - 6 = 17$$
$$m - 6 + 6 = 17 + 6$$
$$m = 23$$

Check: $23 - 6 = 17$

120

EXERCISES
Solve and check.

1. $n + 6 = 23$
   Hint: Subtract 6 from both sides.

2. $8 + n = 37$
   Hint: Subtract 8 from both sides.

3. $x + 7 = 19$

4. $11 + n = 27$

5. $10 + h = 38$

6. $z + 19 = 29$

7. $y + 18 = 46$

8. $15 + t = 31$

9. $17 + y = 35$

10. $s + 23 = 29$

11. $r + 37 = 43$

12. $27 + w = 52$

13. $42 + n = 73$

14. $38 + k = 95$

15. $14 + x = 29$

16. $43 + y = 102$

17. $n - 28 = 35$
    Hint: Add 28 to both sides.

18. $k - 42 = 39$
    Hint: Add 42 to both sides.

19. $a - 18 = 19$

20. $h - 23 = 16$

21. $e - 27 = 23$

22. $r - 15 = 25$

23. $k - 32 = 28$

24. $b - 35 = 73$

25. $d - 42 = 32$

26. $g - 33 = 26$

27. $x - 30 = 53$

28. $s - 39 = 61$

29. $f - 28 = 45$

30. $c - 46 = 58$

31. $y - 47 = 40$

32. $j - 52 = 27$

33. $x + 17 = 32$

34. $a - 62 = 41$

35. $n - 58 = 19$

36. $x - 72 = 53$

37. $a - 8 = 35$

38. $r - 15 = 69$

★ 39. $14 - a = 9$

★ 40. $65 - x = 27$

Keeping Skills Sharp

Multiply.

1. $\begin{array}{r} 3.8 \\ \times\,1.6 \\ \hline \end{array}$

2. $\begin{array}{r} 27 \\ \times\,2.3 \\ \hline \end{array}$

3. $\begin{array}{r} 38.2 \\ \times\,3.8 \\ \hline \end{array}$

4. $\begin{array}{r} 6.75 \\ \times\,0.14 \\ \hline \end{array}$

5. $\begin{array}{r} 396 \\ \times\,0.25 \\ \hline \end{array}$

6. $\begin{array}{r} 7.53 \\ \times\,3.8 \\ \hline \end{array}$

7. $\begin{array}{r} 0.8354 \\ \times\,6.14 \\ \hline \end{array}$

8. $\begin{array}{r} 25.35 \\ \times\,1.05 \\ \hline \end{array}$

9. $\begin{array}{r} 7.493 \\ \times\,3.07 \\ \hline \end{array}$

10. $\begin{array}{r} 0.0395 \\ \times\,0.101 \\ \hline \end{array}$

Equations in problem solving

The pony express carried mail from St. Joseph, Missouri, to Sacramento, California, a distance of 1966 miles. In 1860 this ad appeared in a newspaper:

> WANTED - Young, skinny, wiry fellows not over 18. Must be expert riders willing to risk death.

To solve each problem:

1. Write an equation.
2. Solve the equation.
3. Check the solution in the problem.

1. Two of the most famous men who worked for the pony express were James B. "Wild Bill" Hickok and William F. Cody, "Buffalo Bill." When they were hired, Wild Bill Hickok was 23 years old. He was 8 years older than Buffalo Bill. How old was Buffalo Bill?

$$\text{Hint: } n + 8 = 23$$

Buffalo Bill's age → n Wild Bill's age → 23

2. The pony express had a weight limit of 125 pounds for their riders. Wild Bill Hickok weighed about 33 pounds more than the limit. How much did he weigh?

3. At one time a total of 477 men worked for the pony express. Of these, 79 were riders and the rest worked at the relay stations. How many worked at the relay stations?

4. By Overland Mail, a letter from St. Joseph, Missouri, to Sacramento took 21 days. This was 9 days longer than by pony express. How many days did it take by pony express?

5. The distance between relay stations was about 11 miles. After a rider reached the first relay station, he still had about 64 miles left to ride. About how far did each rider ride?

6. The record time of 185 hours was set when the pony express carried Lincoln's inaugural address. It took 55 hours less than the first trip. How long did it take to make the first trip?

BEADLE'S

Dime

New York Library

COPYRIGHTED IN 1888, BY BEADLE & ADAMS.

ENTERED AT THE POST OFFICE AT NEW YORK, N. Y., AT SECOND CLASS MAIL RATES.

Vol. XL.
Published Every Wednesday.

M. J. IVERS & CO., PUBLISHERS,
(James Sullivan, Proprietor),
379 Pearl Street, New York, September 19, 1888.

Ten Cents a Copy.
$5.00 a Year.

No. 517

BUFFALO BILL'S FIRST TRAIL,

OR

WILL CODY

THE

PONY EXPRESS RIDER

BY

NED BUNTLINE

Solving multiplication equations

Each box contains the same number of marbles. If we let n be the number of marbles in each box, we get the equation

This is a short way to write $3 \times n$.

$$3n = 12$$

To solve the equation, we *divide* both sides by 3 and then simplify both sides.

$$\frac{3n}{3} = \frac{12}{3}$$

$$n = 4$$

Remember that we can use a bar to show division.

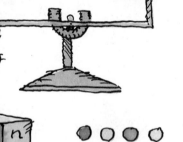

The solution is 4. To check the solution, we substitute 4 for n in the first equation. We get a true equation, so the solution checks.

Study these examples.

$$5n = 45 \qquad\qquad 8n = 23$$

$$\frac{5n}{5} = \frac{45}{5} \qquad\qquad \frac{8n}{8} = \frac{23}{8}$$

$$n = 9 \qquad\qquad n = 2.875$$

Check: $5 \times 9 = 45$ Check: $8 \times 2.875 = 23$

```
     2.875
 8 )23.000
   -16
     7 0
    -6 4
      60
     -56
      40
     -40
       0
```

124

EXERCISES

Solve and check.

1. $4n = 24$
2. $5n = 30$
3. $6n = 42$
4. $3y = 21$
5. $2n = 12$
6. $8k = 88$
7. $5z = 50$
8. $7n = 70$
9. $4x = 28$
10. $8w = 120$
11. $4j = 48$
12. $9y = 108$
13. $2n = 18$
14. $6n = 72$
15. $7n = 91$
16. $3n = 51$
17. $3x = 45$
18. $6n = 120$

Solve and check. Give the solution as a decimal.

19. $2j = 19$
20. $8w = 20$
21. $10c = 43$
22. $8x = 44$
23. $2k = 57$
24. $4m = 49$
25. $8t = 7$
26. $4y = 9$
27. $10r = 58$
28. $20v = 58$
29. $12s = 75$
30. $25z = 140$
31. $4n = 33$
32. $8x = 3$
33. $4w = 23$

Find the number by writing and solving an equation.
Check the solution in the problem.

I AM THINKING OF A NUMBER

34. If I multiply it by 3, I get 42.
35. If I multiply it by 4, I get 39.
36. If I add 19 to it, I get 57.
37. If I subtract 37 from it, I get 74.

Divide.

1. $2.1\overline{)20.223}$
2. $1.1\overline{)3.916}$
3. $0.30\overline{)16.110}$
4. $3.2\overline{)2.1312}$
5. $50\overline{)458.50}$
6. $6.3\overline{)505.89}$
7. $78.4\overline{)337.12}$
8. $9.21\overline{)66.312}$
9. $0.803\overline{)39.347}$
10. $6.25\overline{)331.25}$

Exponents

Notice that the factor 2 occurs 5 times.

$2 \times 2 \times 2 \times 2 \times 2$

2^5

Read "2^5" as "two to the fifth power."

Here is a short way to write the expression.

The 5 is called an **exponent**.
The exponent tells the number of times
the base, 2, is used as a factor.

Other examples. $5 \times 5 = 5^2$ $6 \times 6 \times 6 = 6^3$

"five to the second power"   "six to the third power"
or "five squared"   or "six cubed"

EXERCISES
Write, using an exponent.

1. $2 \times 2 \times 2$ 2. 3×3 3. $4 \times 4 \times 4 \times 4 \times 4$ 4. $5 \times 5 \times 5$

5. 6×6 6. $7 \times 7 \times 7$ 7. 10 8. 10×10

9. $10 \times 10 \times 10$ 10. $10 \times 10 \times 10 \times 10$ 11. $10 \times 10 \times 10 \times 10 \times 10$

Give the standard numeral.

12. 2^4 13. 4^2 14. 3^2 15. 2^3 16. 5^4 17. 4^5

Complete.

				18.	19.	20.
Power of 10	10^1	10^2	10^3	10^4	10^5	10^6
Standard numeral	10	100	1000	?	?	?
Number of 0s in standard numeral	1	2	3	?	?	?

21. In your complete table, compare the exponent of 10
    with the number of 0s in the standard numeral. Are
    they the same?

$$1^3 = ?$$ *Guess first.*

$$1^3 + 2^3 = ?$$ $$1^3 + 2^3 + 3^3 + 4^3 = ?$$

$$1^3 + 2^3 + 3^3 = ?$$ $$1^3 + 2^3 + 3^3 + 4^3 + 5^3 = ?$$

Mathematics and science

Scientists often write numbers in **scientific notation**. For example, the diameter of the sun, written in scientific notation, is

$$1.38 \times 10^6 \text{ kilometers}$$

A number in scientific notation is the product of a number between 1 and 10 and a power of 10. Here are some more examples of numbers written in scientific notation:

3.2×10^1 $\qquad$ 4.56×10^2 $\qquad$ 8×10^3 $\qquad$ 2.03×10^4

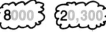

$3.2 \times 10 = 32$ $\quad$ $4.56 \times 100 = 456$ $\quad$ 8000 $\quad$ $20,300$

Notice that a whole-number exponent tells the number of places to the right the decimal point must be moved to express the number as a standard numeral.

EXERCISES

Give the standard numeral.

1. 3×10^3 $\qquad$ **2.** 5.3×10^4 $\qquad$ **3.** 6.04×10^5 $\qquad$ **4.** 2.753×10^6

Express each of the following numbers in scientific notation.

5. 2600 $\qquad$ **6.** 384,000 $\qquad$ **7.** 5,930,000 $\qquad$ **8.** 369,000,000,000

9. The sun is about 150,000,000 kilometers from the earth.

10. The sun is thought to be about 6,000,000,000 years old.

11. The mass of the sun is about 332,000 times greater than the mass of the earth.

12. The temperature at the center of the sun is about 20,000,000 degrees Celsius.

CHAPTER CHECKUP

True or false? [pages 106–109]

1. The whole numbers are a subset of the even numbers.

2. The square numbers are a subset of the even numbers.

3. A is a subset of B.

4. $B = \{6, 7, 8, 9, 10\}$

5. $A \cap B = \{4, 5\}$

6. $A \cup B = \{1, 2, 3, 4, 5, 6, 7, 8, 9, 10\}$

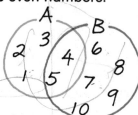

Give the greatest common factor of the two numbers.
[pages 110–111]

7. 12, 18   8. 8, 10   9. 6, 12   10. 14, 15

Give the prime factorization of each number. [pages 112-113]

11. 6   12. 18   13. 36   14. 42   15. 72   16. 156

Give the least common multiple of the two numbers.
[pages 114–115]

17. 3, 5   18. 4, 6   19. 5, 10   20. 8, 9

a	c	r	y
3	2	7	9

Substitute and simplify. [pages 118–119]

21. $a + 5$ 22. $9 - c$ 23. $15 - y$ 24. $r + 18$

25. $r + c$ 26. $y - r$ 27. $20 - (a + y)$ 28. $5 \times (y - a)$

Solve each equation. [pages 120–125]

29. $n + 18 = 21$ 30. $n - 6 = 19$ 31. $14 + n = 42$

32. $3n = 21$ 33. $5n = 65$ 34. $13n = 78$

Give the standard numeral. [pages 126–127]

35. 2^4 36. 4^2 37. 10^3 38. 3^5 39. 10^4 40. 1^6

128

1. Make a dot diagram like the one shown above.

2. Find a way to use your dot diagram to find all factors of 6. Of 12.

3. How can you use your dot diagram to find the GCF of 6 and 12?

4. Use your diagram to find the first four multiples of 4. Of 6.

5. How can you use your dot diagram to find the LCM of 4 and 6?

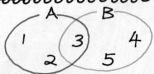

CHAPTER REVIEW

A B
1 3 4
2 5

Intersection: A ∩ B = {3}
Union: A ∪ B = {1, 2, 3, 4, 5}

---

8 {1, 2, 4, 8} Set of all factors of 8
12 {1, 2, 3, 4, 6, 12} Set of all factors of 12
The greatest common factor is 4.

Whole numbers with exactly 2 factors are called prime numbers.

{1, 7}
7 is a prime number

---

6 {0, 6, 12, 18...} Set of all multiples of 6
9 {0, 9, 18, 27...} Set of all multiples of 9
The least common multiple (other than 0) is 18.

$n + 11 = 17$ $5n = 15$
$n + 11 - 11 = 17 - 11$ $\dfrac{5n}{5} = \dfrac{15}{5}$
$n = 6$ $n = 3$
Check: $6 + 11 = 17$ Check: $5 \times 3 = 15$

---

2 × 2 × 2
$2^3 = 8$

Give the intersection and the union.

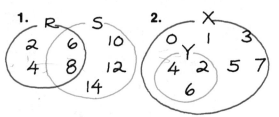

1. R   S
    2   6   10
    4   8   12
          14

2.   X
    O   1   3
      Y
    4   2   5   7
        6

Give the greatest common factor (GCF).

3. 6   4. 12   5. 18   6. 27
   9   16   24   45

Which of these numbers are prime numbers?

7. 9   8. 11   9. 19   10. 27

11. 39   12. 43   13. 49   14. 51

Give the least common multiple (LCM).

15. 5   16. 8   17. 12   18. 15
    6   12   16   20

Solve and check.

19. $n + 13 = 23$ 20. $n - 18 = 30$

21. $9n = 27$ 22. $15n = 165$

Give the standard numeral.

23. 3^2 24. 2^4 25. 10^2 26. 10^3

CHAPTER CHALLENGE

In this lesson you will work with an arithmetic that uses only the 12 numbers on a clock face. Since only 12 numbers are used, it is called a modulo 12 (mod 12) arithmetic.

Here is how to add 7 and 8.

Start at 7.   Move the hand 8 units *clockwise*.

$$7 + 8 = 3 \text{ (mod 12)}$$

Here is how to subtract 8 from 7.

Start at 7.   Move the hand 8 units *counterclockwise*.

$$7 - 8 = 11 \text{ (mod 12)}$$

EXERCISES

Add or subtract in mod 12. (*Hint:* Think about a clock as shown above.)

1. $6 + 6$ 2. $6 + 7$ 3. $9 + 5$ 4. $10 + 10$ 5. $11 + 9$

6. $3 + 2$ 7. $11 + 10$ 8. $11 + 1$ 9. $3 + 12$ 10. $7 + 12$

11. $9 + 12$ 12. $11 + 12$ 13. $3 - 5$ 14. $4 - 6$ 15. $7 - 9$

16. $11 - 12$ 17. $8 - 3$ 18. $6 - 6$ 19. $10 - 10$ 20. $9 - 12$

21. What number on the 12-hour clock acts just as 0 does in regular arithmetic?

To multiply in mod 12, we can think about adding in mod 12.

$$5 + 5 + 5 = 3 \text{ (mod 12)}$$

$$3 \times 5 = 3 \text{ (mod 12)}$$

Multiply in mod 12.

22. 2×6 23. 2×8 24. 2×3

25. 2×5 26. 3×4 27. 3×6

28. 4×3 29. 4×4 30. 5×3

Form W X

13 a b c d   33 a b c d   13 a b c d   3 a b c d   29 a b c d
14 a b c d   34 a b c d   14 a b c d   4 c d   30 a b c d
15 a b c   a b c   a b c   b c   31 a b c d

MAJOR CHECKUP
Standardized Format

Choose the correct letter.

1. 56,752 rounded to the nearest hundred is

    a. 56,700
    b. 56,800
    c. 57,000
    d. none of these

2. Add.

$$624$$
$$38$$
$$+577$$

    a. 1238
    b. 1139
    c. 1239
    d. none of these

3. Subtract.

$$6025$$
$$-1773$$

    a. 4252
    b. 5252
    c. 5752
    d. none of these

4. Multiply.

$$248$$
$$\times\ 72$$

    a. 18,836
    b. 17,836
    c. 18,856
    d. none of these

5. Divide.

$$43\overline{)8944}$$

    a. 208
    b. 280
    c. 28
    d. none of these

6. The standard numeral for five hundred and six thousandths is

    a. 0.506
    b. 600.006
    c. 506,000
    d. none of these

7. Give the sum.

$$6.7 + 0.488$$

    a. 0.555
    b. 7.188
    c. 55.5
    d. none of these

8. Give the difference.

$$9.6 - 0.38$$

    a. 9.22
    b. 5.8
    c. .58
    d. none of these

9. Multiply.

$$0.13$$
$$\times 0.04$$

    a. 0.52
    b. 0.052
    c. 0.0052
    d. none of these

10. Divide.

$$0.9\overline{)3.771}$$

    a. 4.19
    b. 41.9
    c. 0.419
    d. none of these

11. The least common multiple of 4 and 6 is

    a. 12
    b. 24
    c. 2
    d. none of these

12. The greatest common factor of 8 and 12 is

    a. 24
    b. 4
    c. 1
    d. none of these

5
Measurement

Measuring length

The basic unit for measuring length in the metric system is the **meter (m)**. The dog is about 1 meter long. These units of length are used in the metric system:

1 kilometer (km) = 1000 meters	1 decimeter (dm)*= 0.1 meter
1 hectometer (hm)*= 100 meters	1 centimeter (cm) = 0.01 meter
1 dekameter (dam)*= 10 meters	1 millimeter (mm) = 0.001 meter
1 meter (m) = 1 meter	

Notice that our metric system, like our place-value system, is based on the number 10. Because of this, decimals are used in writing metric measurements.

```
centimeters  1  2  3  4  5  6  7  8  9  10  11  12  13  14
```

The length of the segment is 1 dm + 2 cm + 5 mm, or 12.5 cm.
What is the length of the segment in mm?

*These units are seldom used, but it is sometimes useful to know about them.

EXERCISES

Measure to the nearest centimeter.

1. your height   2. your waist measure

3. your arm span   4. your foot length

5. the width of your desk top

6. the length of a chalk eraser

7. the width of a book

8. the height of a table

9. Measure the width of a chalkboard to the nearest decimeter.

10. Measure the length of your classroom to the nearest meter.

11. Measure the width of a door to the nearest centimeter.

12. Measure the length of a straight pin to the nearest millimeter.

Get a ruler marked off in millimeters. Draw segments having these lengths.

13. 1 mm   14. 1 cm   15. 1 dm   16. 15 mm   17. 5.1 cm

18. 2.5 cm   19. 3.6 cm   20. 128 mm   21. 12.8 cm   22. 1.28 dm

23. Draw a segment that is 21 cm long.
    a. How many mm long is it?
    b. How many dm long is it?

24. On the chalkboard, draw a segment that is 1.23 m long.
    a. How many dm long is it?
    b. How many cm long is it?
    c. How many mm long is it?

25. On the chalkboard, draw a segment that is 425 mm long.
    a. How many cm long is it?
    b. How many dm long is it?
    c. How many m long is it?

135

Changing units in the metric system

One advantage of the metric system is that we can change easily from one unit to another.

EXAMPLE 1.   Change 4.372 m to cm.
There are 100 cm in a meter, so multiply by 100.
Notice that when you change to a smaller unit, you have a larger number.

$$4.372 \times 100 = 437.2$$

$$4.372 \text{ m} = 437.2 \text{ cm}$$

EXAMPLE 2.   Change 392 m to km.
There is 0.001 km in a meter, so multiply by 0.001.
Notice that when you change to a larger unit, you have a smaller number.

$$392 \times 0.001 = 0.392$$

$$392 \text{ m} = 0.392 \text{ km}$$

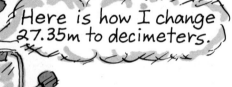

Step 1.   I think about the metric units matched with the digits. The unit used in the measurement (m) is matched to the digit in the ones place.

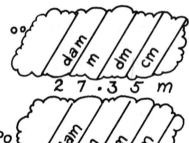

Step 2.   Next I move the decimal point so that the new unit (dm) is in the ones place.

Step 3.   Then I write the new unit, dm.

Here are two more examples.

Change 528.3 cm to meters.

Change 32.56 m to kilometers.

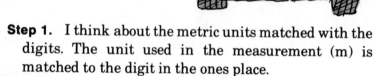
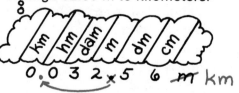

136

EXERCISES

Copy and complete.

	mm	cm	dm	m	dam	hm	km
1.				100			
2.							8
3.			400				
4.	5348						

Complete.

5. 2 m = __?__ dm

6. 4 m = __?__ cm

7. 5 m = __?__ mm

8. 1245 m = __?__ km

9. 1500 m = __?__ km

10. 354 m = __?__ km

11. 6.7 m = __?__ cm

12. 59.2 m = __?__ dm

13. 63.5 m = __?__ km

14. 83 cm = __?__ m

15. 57.2 cm = __?__ mm

16. 63.8 cm = __?__ dm

17. 63 km = __?__ m

18. 58.9 dm = __?__ mm

19. 173 mm = __?__ cm

20. 173 mm = __?__ dm

21. 173 mm = __?__ m

22. 675.41 mm = __?__ m

23. 52.3 km = __?__ m

24. 52.3 mm = __?__ cm

25. 42.77 m = __?__ cm

26. 42.77 cm = __?__ m

27. 56.761 m = __?__ km

28. 35.92 km = __?__ m

29. In the Olympic Games, one race is 10,000 m long. How many kilometers is that?

30. One Olympic swimming race is 1.5 km long. How many meters is that?

31. At one time the world high-jump record was 2.27 m. How many centimeters is that?

32. At one time the world shot-put record was 21.60 m. How many millimeters is that?

Perimeter and circumference

The **perimeter** of a figure is the distance around the figure. Here are some examples.

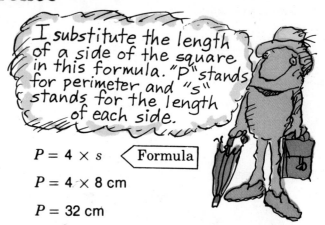

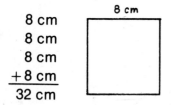

8 cm
8 cm
8 cm
+8 cm
————
32 cm

$P = 4 \times s$ ◁ Formula

$P = 4 \times 8$ cm

$P = 32$ cm

The perimeter is 32 cm.

5 m
3 m
5 m
+3 m
————
16 m

$P = 2 \times l + 2 \times w$ ◁ Formula

$P = 2 \times 5\text{ m} + 2 \times 3\text{ m}$

$P = 10\text{ m} + 6\text{ m}$

$P = 16\text{ m}$

The perimeter is 16 m.

The distance around a circle is called the **circumference**. The circumference of a circle (C) is equal to π (pi—a number slightly greater than 3) times the diameter (d). We'll use 3.14 as a decimal approximation for π.

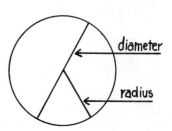

diameter

radius

EXAMPLE.

2 dm

$C = \pi \times d$ ◁ Formula

$C \approx 3.14 \times 2$ dm

$C \approx 6.28$ dm

$\approx$ is read "is approximately equal to."

138

EXERCISES

Give the perimeter of each figure.

1.

3 m, 2 m

2.
4.3 cm

3.
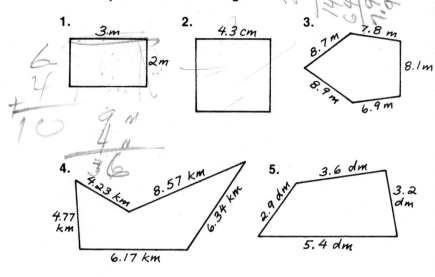
8.7 m, 7.8 m, 8.1 m, 6.9 m, 8.9 m

4.

4.23 km, 8.57 km, 6.34 km, 4.77 km, 6.17 km

5.

3.6 dm, 2.9 dm, 3.2 dm, 5.4 dm

Give the circumference of each circle.

6. 4.7 cm

7. 5.8 cm

8. 6.4 cm

Solve.

9. Ceiling molding is needed for a rectangular room that measures 4.46 meters by 6.25 meters.

   a. How many meters of molding will be needed? Round your answer up to the nearest 0.5 meter.
   b. If molding is 37¢ a meter, how much will the molding for the ceiling cost?

10. The diameter of a certain bicycle wheel is 65 centimeters.

    a. How far does the bicycle travel when the wheel turns 1 revolution?
    b. How many revolutions does the wheel make in a kilometer?

Give each sum.

1. 5.94 + 2.87

2. 3.056 + 2.785

3. 0.39 + 0.28 + 0.64

4. 5.6 + 7.9 + 3.8

5. 2.6 + 7.4 + 7.4

6. 9.8 + 3.62

7. 19 + 2.7

8. 3.8 + 0.24 + 0.9

9. 7.5 + 0.54 + 2

10. 4.8 + 0.006 + 2.53

Area

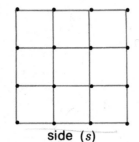

The area of a region is the number of square units that it takes to cover the region.

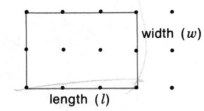

side (s)

width (w)

length (l)

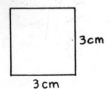

height (h)

base (b)

SQUARE

Formula	$A = s^2$

$A = 3 \text{ cm} \times 3 \text{ cm}$

$A = 9 \text{ cm}^2$

RECTANGLE

Formula	$A = l \times w$

$A = 3 \text{ cm} \times 2 \text{ cm}$

$A = 6 \text{ cm}^2$

PARALLELOGRAM

Formula	$A = b \times h$

$A = 3 \text{ cm} \times 2 \text{ cm}$

$A = 6 \text{ cm}^2$

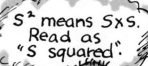

S^2 means $S \times S$. Read as "S squared".

cm² is a short way to write square centimeter.

EXERCISES
Give each area.

1.

3 cm
3 cm

2.
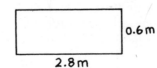
0.6 m
2.8 m

3.
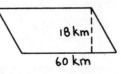
18 km
60 km

4.
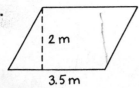
2 m
3.5 m

5.
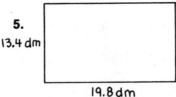
13.4 dm
19.8 dm

6.
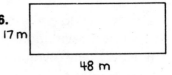
17 m
48 m

First measure the dimensions to the nearest mm.
Then compute the area.

7.

8.

9.
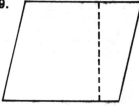

$$
\begin{array}{r}
4.1 \\
6.8 \\
\hline
3{\scriptstyle 2}8 \\
246 \\
\hline
27.88
\end{array}
\qquad
\begin{array}{r}
11,50 \\
27.88
\end{array}
$$

Solve.

10. Some carpet costs $11.50 per square meter. How much would the carpet cost for a rectangular room 4.1 meters by 6.8 meters?

11. A square lot measuring 25 meters on a side is to be seeded with grass seed. One kilogram of seed will cover 200 square meters. If grass seed costs $3.52 per kilogram, how much will it cost to seed the lot?

12. A floor tile 20 cm by 20 cm costs 38¢. How much would it cost to tile the floor of a 9-meter-by-5-meter recreation room?

13. Get a piece of graph paper. See how many different shapes you can draw that have the same area.

14. A carpet layer is to carpet two rectangular rooms, one 5 m by 8 m and another 3.1 m by 6 m. If he charges $1.80 per square meter, how much will he charge for the two rooms?

More about area

The area of the triangle is half the area
of the parallelogram.

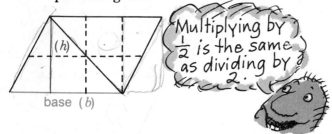

base (b)

 Formula

$$A = \frac{1}{2} \times (b \times h)$$

$$A = \frac{1}{2} \times (3 \text{ cm} \times 2 \text{ cm})$$

$$A = \frac{1}{2} \times 6 \text{ cm}^2$$

$$A = 3 \text{ cm}^2$$

Formula

$$A = \frac{1}{2} \times (b_1 + b_2) \times h$$

$$A = \frac{1}{2} \times (4 \text{ cm} + 2 \text{ cm}) \times 2 \text{ cm}$$

$$A = \frac{1}{2} \times 12 \text{ cm}^2$$

$$A = 6 \text{ cm}^2$$

The area of the trapezoid is half the area
of the parallelogram.

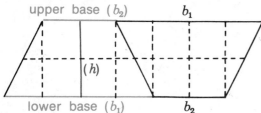

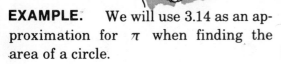

Notice that if you cut a circle into pieces as shown, the pieces
will fit together to form a figure that looks like a rectangle. The length of the rectangle is $\frac{1}{2}$ the circumference
($\pi \times d$, or $\pi \times 2 \times r$) of the circle. The height of the rectangle is the radius (r) of the circle.

$\pi \times r$

Formula

$A = \pi \times r \times r$, or
$A = \pi \times r^2$

EXAMPLE. We will use 3.14 as an approximation for π when finding the
area of a circle.

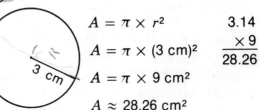

$A = \pi \times r^2$

$A = \pi \times (3 \text{ cm})^2$

$A = \pi \times 9 \text{ cm}^2$

$A \approx 28.26 \text{ cm}^2$

$$\begin{array}{r} 3.14 \\ \times 9 \\ \hline 28.26 \end{array}$$

142

EXERCISES

Give each area.

1.
3m
8m

2.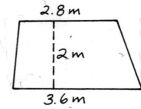
2.8 m
2 m
3.6 m

3.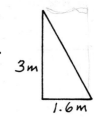
3m
1.6 m

4.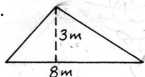
4 cm

5. 108 km

6.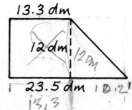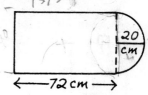
13.3 dm
12 dm 12 DM
23.5 dm 10.2
13,3

7.
3 m
3m
3m
11 m

8.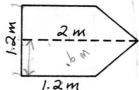
1.2 m
2 m
.6 m
1.2 m

9.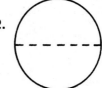
20 cm
←——72 cm——→

First measure each dimension to the nearest mm. Then compute the area.

10.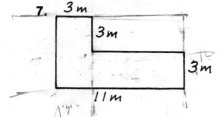

11.

12.

Solve.

13. A triangular flower garden has a base of 42 decimeters and a height of 23 decimeters. What is its area?

14. A pizza house sells large pizzas (30 cm in diameter) for $4.80 and medium pizzas (15 cm in diameter) for $3.20. Which is the better buy?

15. A revolving lawn sprinkler sprays water a distance of 10 meters. How many square meters of lawn will it sprinkle without being moved?

16. A redwood deck in the shape of a trapezoid has a height of 4 meters and bases of 5 meters and 8.1 meters. If a liter of stain covers 7 square meters, will 4 liters be enough to stain the deck?

143

Practice exercises

Complete.

1. 1 km = ___?___ m
2. 3 km = ___?___ m
3. 4.7 km = ___?___ m

4. 1 m = ___?___ cm
5. 23 m = ___?___ cm
6. 2.91 m = ___?___ cm

7. 1 m = ___?___ mm
8. 2 m = ___?___ mm
9. 4.1 m = ___?___ mm

10. 1 cm = ___?___ mm
11. 15 cm = ___?___ mm
12. 3.21 cm = ___?___ mm

13. 10 mm = ___?___ cm
14. 20 mm = ___?___ cm
15. 14 mm = ___?___ cm

16. 4.2 mm = ___?___ cm
17. 4.2 cm = ___?___ mm
18. 523 cm = ___?___ m

19. 421 mm = ___?___ m
20. 4210 mm = ___?___ m
21. 456 m = ___?___ km

Give each perimeter (or circumference) and area.

22.

10 cm

23.
9 m

12 m

24.
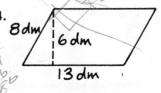
8 dm   6 dm
13 dm

25.

10 cm

26.
9 m
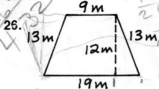
13 m   12 m   13 m
19 m

27.
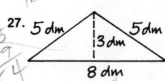
5 dm   5 dm
3 dm
8 dm

Tell whether the situation involves perimeter or area.

28. fencing a yard
29. cultivating a garden
30. carpeting a floor

Solve.

31. The area of a rectangular lot is 1229.1 m². What is its width if its length is 48.2 m?

★ 32. Eighty-three meters of fencing were used to fence in a square garden. What is the area of the garden?

 Divide the area of the circle by the area of the square that it is in.

12 cm

15 mm

7.9 m

144

Mathematics and science

The picture shows that an object was dropped (not thrown) from the top of a water tower. The distance in meters that a free-falling object drops is given by the formula:

$$d = 4.9 \times t^2$$

where t is the time in seconds. (The formula assumes that there is no air resistance.) Using the formula, we can find how far the object fell in the first 3 seconds.

$$d = 4.9 \times t^2$$
$$d = 4.9 \times 3^2 \quad (4.9 \times 9)$$
$$d = 44.1$$

So the object fell 44.1 meters in the first 3 seconds.

The velocity (speed) of a free-falling object increases as the object falls. We can find the velocity (V) after the object has been falling for a given time (t) by using this formula:

$V = 9.8\,t$ This formula gives the velocity in meters per second.

EXERCISES

How far would a free-falling object fall in each of these times?

1. 2 s   2. 4 s   3. 2.5 s   4. 5 s   5. 7.2 s   6. 0.5 minute

What would be the velocity of a free-falling object at the end of each of these times?

7. 5 s   8. 3 s   9. 30 s   10. 6.5 s   11. 8.2 s   12. 16.4 s

Solve.

13. How long would it take a free-falling object to fall 490 meters?

14. How much would the velocity of a free-falling object increase between 3 seconds and 8 seconds?

★15. One kilometer an hour is about 0.28 meter per second. How far would a free-falling object have to fall to have a velocity of 10 kilometers an hour?

145

Surface area of a prism

A rectangular prism
has 6 faces.

A triangular prism
has 5 faces.

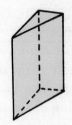

The **bases** of a prism are 2 faces that are the same size and shape and that are in parallel planes.

The **surface area** of a prism is the sum of the areas of all the faces.

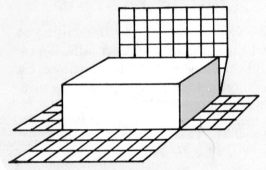

The surface area is 136 cm².

The area of each face is:

top	---	32 cm²
bottom	---	32 cm²
right	---	12 cm²
left	---	12 cm²
front	---	24 cm²
back	---	24 cm²

EXERCISES
Give the surface area of each rectangular prism.

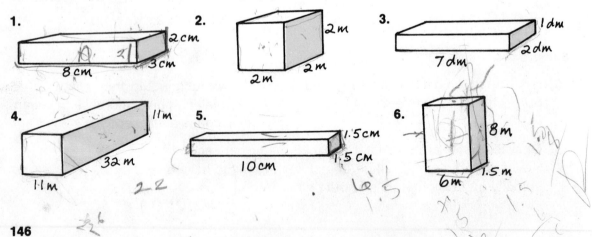

1.
8 cm   3 cm   2 cm

2.
2 m   2 m   2 m

3.
7 dm   1 dm   2 dm

4.
11 m   32 m   11 m

5.
10 cm   1.5 cm   1.5 cm

6.
6 m   8 m   1.5 m

146

Give the surface area of each triangular prism. Notice that each triangle is a right triangle (has a right angle).

7.
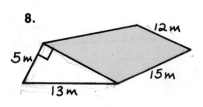
5cm
3cm
6cm
4cm

8.
12m
5m
15m
13m

9.
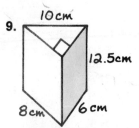
10cm
12.5cm
8cm
6cm

Solve.

10. A rectangular box is to be gift-wrapped. One base of the box is a rectangle 18 cm by 24 cm. The height of the box is 14 cm. How much paper will it take to cover the box?

11. A wastebasket shaped like a rectangular prism is made of metal. The bottom is a 20-cm square and the height is 30 cm. How many square centimeters of metal did it take to make the basket?

12. Get a rectangular box. Measure each dimension to the nearest centimeter and compute the surface area.

EXCURSION ▪◧◪◧◪◧◪◧◪◧◪◧◪◧◪◧◪◧◪◧◪◧◪◧▪
The large block was made by stacking 27 white blocks together. All faces of the large block were then painted green.

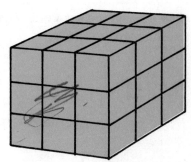

How many small blocks have

0 green faces?   1 green face?   2 green faces?
3 green faces?   4 green faces?

Surface area of a cylinder

Here is a cylinder:

To find its surface area, we might think about cutting it apart like this:

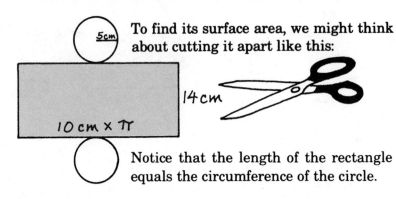

Notice that the length of the rectangle equals the circumference of the circle.

To find the surface area, we can add the areas of the circles and the area of the rectangle.

Area of Each Circle

$A = \pi \times r^2$

$A \approx 3.14 \times (5\text{ cm})^2$

$A \approx 78.5\text{ cm}^2$

So, the area of both circles is about 157 square centimeters.

Area of Rectangle

$A = l \times w$

$A = (10\text{ cm} \times \pi) \times 14\text{ cm}$

$A \approx (10\text{ cm} \times 3.14) \times 14\text{ cm}$

$A \approx 31.4\text{ cm} \times 14\text{ cm}$

$A \approx 439.6\text{ cm}^2$

$$157\text{ cm}^2 + 439.6\text{ cm}^2 = 596.6\text{ cm}^2$$

The surface area of the cylinder is about 596.6 cm².

EXERCISES
Give the surface area of each cylinder. Use 3.14 as an approximation for π.

1.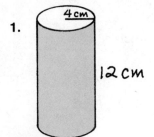

2.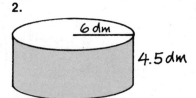

3.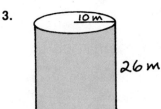

4.

6 cm
15.4 cm

5.

2 m
4.3 m

6.

18 cm
20.6 cm

How much cardboard is in each cereal box? Use 3.14 as an approximation for π.

7.

PUFFO
Breakfast
CEREAL

2 dm
0.6 dm
1.4 dm

8.

6 cm

ROLLED
OATS

SHOT FROM
CATAPULT

22.8 cm

Solve.

9. A crepe-paper border is to be placed around some rectangular tables that measure 1 meter by 2 meters. How many meters of crepe paper will be needed for 7 tables?

10. A fence is to be built around a rectangular lot that is 22 m long and 13 m wide. If fencing costs $3.25 a meter, how much will it cost to fence the lot?

11. A triangular sail has a base of 5 meters and a height of 8 meters. How many square meters of sail is that?

12. A dog is leashed to a stake. If the leash is 4 meters long, how many square meters does the dog have to roam?

★**13.** A goat is tied to one corner of a barn by a 15-meter rope. The barn is 12 m wide by 18 m long. How much area does the goat have to roam?

12 m
18 m
15 m

 How much must be shaved off the radius of a circular metal plate with a radius of 7.5 cm to get a circular plate with an area of 175 cm²?

149

Volume of a prism

To find the volume of the box, we pick a
unit 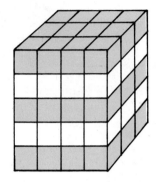 , a cubic centimeter (cm³),
and see how many cubes it takes to fill
the box. There are 12 cm³ in each layer
and there are 5 layers. So the volume is
60 cm³.

We can also find the volume by this
formula.

$$V = l \times w \times h \quad \boxed{\text{Formula}}$$

$$V = 4\,\text{cm} \times 3\,\text{cm} \times 5\,\text{cm}$$

$$V = 60\,\text{cm}^3$$

Notice that the volume of a rectangular prism is equal to the
area of a base times the height. So the volume can also be
found by using the formula $V = B \times h$. (*B* stands for the area
of a base.)

To find the volume of a triangular prism,
multiply the area of a base (*B*) by the
height (*h*).

$$V = B \times h \quad \boxed{\text{Formula}}$$

$$V = \tfrac{1}{2} \times (3\,\text{cm} \times 4\,\text{cm}) \times 7\,\text{cm}$$

$\overparen{\text{6 square cm}}$ $V = 6\,\text{cm}^2 \times 7\,\text{cm}$

$\overparen{\text{42 cubic cm}}$ $V = 42\,\text{cm}^3$

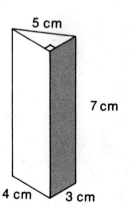

5 cm

7 cm

4 cm   3 cm

EXERCISES

Give each volume.

1.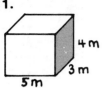
4 m
3 m
5 m

2.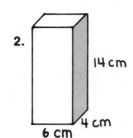
14 cm
4 cm
6 cm

3.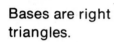
6 dm
3 dm 3 dm

Bases are right triangles.

4.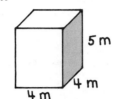
5 m
4 m
4 m

5.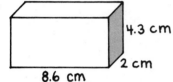
4.3 cm
2 cm
8.6 cm

6.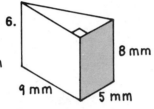
8 mm
9 mm 5 mm

Bases are right triangles.

Solve.

7. A trench 0.6 meter wide, 1.2 meters deep, and 10 meters long was dug for a water main. How many cubic meters of earth were removed?

8. A box that is 8 centimeters wide, 12 centimeters long, and 4.5 centimeters high is to be filled with sand. How many cubic centimeters of sand are needed?

9. A rectangular form that measures 120 decimeters long, 50 centimeters wide, and 24 decimeters high is to be filled with concrete. If concrete costs $36 a cubic meter, what will be the total cost of the concrete?

10. Find the volume of your classroom in cubic meters. Make your measurements to the nearest 0.1 meter.

Multiply.

1. 4.5
× 2.1

2. 0.58
× 5.2

3. 7.4
× 0.36

4. 5.3
× 2.9

5. 1.78
× 8.3

6. 8.96
× 1.42

7. 79.5
× 0.206

Volume of a cylinder

Remember that you can find the volumes of prisms like these by multiplying the area of a base (B) by the height (h).

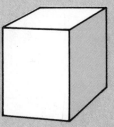

The volume of a cylinder can be found in the same way. Use 3.14 as an approximation for π.

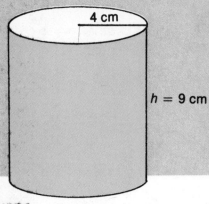

$V = B \times h$

$V = (\pi \times r^2) \times h$

$V = (\pi \times 16 \text{ cm}^2) \times 9 \text{ cm}$

$V \approx (3.14 \times 16 \text{ cm}^2) \times 9 \text{ cm}$

$V \approx 50.24 \text{ cm}^2 \times 9 \text{ cm}$

$V \approx 452.16 \text{ cm}^3$

EXERCISES

Give the volume of each cylinder. Use 3.14 as an approximation for π.

1.
4 cm
5 cm

2.
1 m
7.5 m

3.
2 mm
2 mm

4.
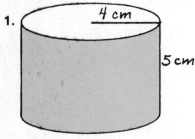
3 m
5.2 m

5.
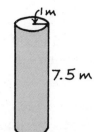
5 mm
4 mm

6.
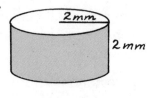
3.6 cm
4.8 cm

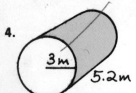

Solve. (Use 3.14 as an approximation for π.)

7. What is the volume of the can?

0.5cm
1.1cm

8. How many cubic centimeters of water would this pipe hold?

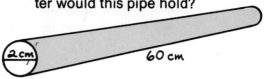
2cm
60 cm

9. How much metal would be needed to make a tin can having a radius of 6 cm and a height of 16 cm?

10. The volume of a tin can is 113.04 cubic cm. The radius of the can is 3 cm. What is its height?

11. Two cylinders have a radius of 4 cm each. One cylinder is 3 cm high and the other is 6 cm high. What are the volumes?

12. Two cylinders have a height of 8 cm each. One cylinder has a radius of 2 cm and the other has a radius of 4 cm. What are their volumes?

13. A cylinder-shaped water tower has a radius of 4.2 m and a height of 24.5 m. How many cubic meters of water does it hold?

14. What is the volume of the largest cylinder contained in a 6-cm cube? *Hint:* First draw a picture.

15. Get some prisms and cylinders. Measure each dimension to the nearest centimeter and compute the volumes.

 How many cm³ of metal are there in this block? (The hole goes all the way through.)

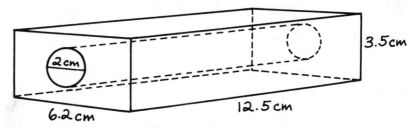
2cm
3.5cm
6.2 cm
12.5 cm

Liquid volume and weight

A unit for measuring liquid volume is
the **liter** (**L**). A liter is 1000 cubic centimeters.

1 liter (L)

The **milliliter** (**mL**) is used to measure
small liquid volumes. A milliliter is 1
cubic centimeter.

1000 mL = 1 L   240

or   1 mL = 0.001 L   .24

200 mL

EXERCISES
Choose the correct liquid volume.

1.

   a. 1.9 L
   b. 1.9 mL

2.

   a. 355 L
   b. 355 mL

Complete.

3. 1 L = __?__ mL

4. 2 L = __?__ mL

5. 1.5 L = __?__ mL

6. 1.3 L = __?__ mL

7. 0.258 L = __?__ mL

8. 0.34 L = __?__ mL

9. 1000 mL = __?__ L

10. 3000 mL = __?__ L

11. 1800 mL = __?__ L

12. 900 mL = __?__ L

13. 750 mL = __?__ L

14. 124 mL = __?__ L

15. Can you find a container that holds about 1 liter?

16. Estimate the volumes of several containers. Check your
    estimates by filling each container.

A unit for measuring weight is the
gram (g).

A smaller unit for measuring weight is
the **milligram (mg).**

$$1000 \text{ mg} = 1 \text{ g}$$

or $\quad 1 \text{ mg} = 0.001 \text{ g}$

A larger unit for measuring weight is
the **kilogram (kg).**

$$1 \text{ kg} = 1000 \text{ g}$$
or $\quad 1 \text{ g} = 0.001 \text{ kg}$

1 kilogram

1 gram

500
milligrams

EXERCISES
Choose the correct answer.

17. **a.** 5.5 mg
    b. 5.5 g
    c. 5.5 kg

18. **a.** 400 mg
    b. 400 g
    c. 400 kg

19. **a.** 1.8 mg
    b. 1.8 g
    c. 1.8 kg

Complete.

20. 1 g = __?__ mg

21. 8 g = __?__ mg

22. 15 g = __?__ mg

23. 2000 mg = __?__ g

24. 1500 mg = __?__ g

25. 800 mg = __?__ g

26. 1 kg = __?__ g

27. 2.1 kg = __?__ g

28. 0.845 kg = __?__ g

29. 3000 g = __?__ kg

30. 2400 g = __?__ kg

31. 560 g = __?__ kg

32. Try to find an object that weighs about 1 kilogram.

33. Estimate the weights of some objects. Check your esti-
mates by weighing each object.

155

Length—customary units

Here are some customary
units for measuring length.

12 inches (in. or ") = 1 foot (ft)
3 ft (') = 1 yard (yd)
1760 yd = 1 mile (mi)

These examples show how to change from one
unit to another.

1. Change 2 miles to yards. There are
    1760 yd in 1 mile.
    So, multiply 1760 by 2.

2. Change 57 in. to feet and inches.
    There are 12 in. in 1 foot.
    So, divide 57 by 12.

```
 1760
  ×2
 3520        2 mi = 3520 yd
```

```
      4
12)57
    -48      57 in. = 4 ft 9 in.
      9
```

EXERCISES
Complete.

1. 9 ft = __?__ in.

2. 6 yd = __?__ ft

3. 6 yd = __?__ in.

4. 3 mi = __?__ yd

5. 1 mi = __?__ ft

6. 8 yd = __?__ in.

7. 108 in. = __?__ ft

8. 140 in. = __?__ ft __?__ in.

9. 48 ft = __?__ yd

10. 76 ft = __?__ yd __?__ ft

11. 92 in. = __?__ ft __?__ in.

12. 150 in. = __?__ ft __?__ in.

13. 2 ft 3 in. = __?__ in.

14. 5 yd 1 ft = __?__ ft

15. 2 yd 5 in. = __?__ in.

Add. Regroup whenever possible.

Regroup 12 in. for 1 ft.

16.   4 ft 9 in.
+ 2 ft 5 in.
$\overline{7\text{ ft }2\text{ in.}}$

17.   7 ft 8 in.
+ 3 ft 7 in.

18.   9 ft 6 in.
+ 5 ft 9 in.

19.   5 yd 2 ft
+ 2 yd 1 ft

20.   3 yd 2 ft
+ 5 yd 2 ft

21.   4 yd 2 ft 8 in.
+3 yd 2 ft 2 in.

22.   3 yd 1 ft 8 in.
+2 yd 2 ft 5 in.

23.   2 yd 2 ft 7 in.
+1 yd 1 ft 6 in.

Subtract.

24.   3 ft
− 1 ft   8 in.
$\overline{1\text{ ft }4\text{ in.}}$

25.   8 ft 5 in.
− 3 ft 9 in.

26.   7 ft 2 in.
− 4 ft 9 in.

27.   6 yd 2 ft
− 4 yd 1 ft

28.   8 yd 1 ft
− 3 yd 2 ft

29.   5 yd
− 2 yd 1 ft

30.   3 yd 2 ft 8 in.
−1 yd 1 ft 9 in.

31.   11 yd 2 ft 4 in.
−6 yd 8 in.

Give each perimeter.

32.

9 ft 6 in.

33.

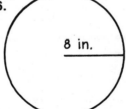

1 ft 7 in.

3 ft 8 in.

34.

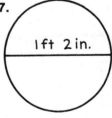

4 yd

1 yd 2 ft

3 yd 2 ft

Give the circumference. Use 3.14 as an approximation for π.

35.   8 in.

36.   8 in.

37.   1 ft 2 in.

Solve.

38. The base paths of a baseball field form a square. How far is it around the bases if the bases are 90 feet apart?

39. Measure the length and width of a rectangular room to the nearest inch. Compute its perimeter.

157

Area—customary units

When measurements are given in more than one unit, change
to a single unit before multiplying. Study this example.

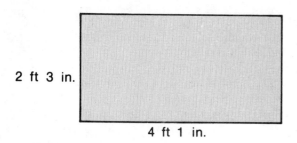

2 ft 3 in.

4 ft 1 in.

$A = l \times w$

$A = 2 \text{ ft } 3 \text{ in. } \times 4 \text{ ft } 1 \text{ in.}$

$A = 27 \text{ in. } \times 49 \text{ in.}$

$A = 1323 \text{ in.}^2$

EXERCISES
Give each area. Use 3.14 as an approximation for π.

1.
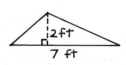
11 in.

2.
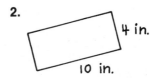
4 in.
10 in.

3.
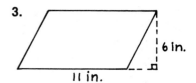
6 in.
11 in.

4.

2 ft
7 ft

5.
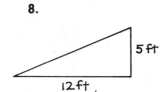
6 ft
4 ft
10 ft

6.
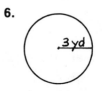
3 yd

7.
3 yd
4 yd

8.
5 ft
12 ft

9.
6 yd
5 yd
8 yd

10.
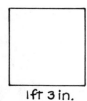
1 ft 3 in.

11.
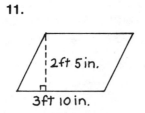
2 ft 5 in.
3 ft 10 in.

12.

1 ft 3 in.

13. How many square inches are in one square foot?

14. How many square feet are in one square yard?

15. How many square inches are in one square yard?

16. Measure the length and width of a rectangular room to the nearest foot. Compute the area. Change to square yards. (Round your answer to the nearest square yard.)

Give the surface area. Use 3.14 as an approximation for π.

17.

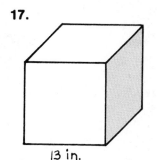

13 in.

18.

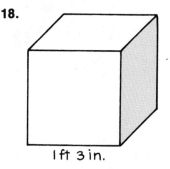

1 ft 3 in.

19.

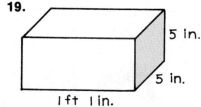

5 in.

5 in.

1 ft 1 in.

20.

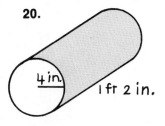

4 in.

1 ft 2 in.

Solve. Use 3.14 as an approximation for π.

21. What is the area in square feet of a circular garden with a diameter of 10 yards?

22. How many square inches of cardboard are used to make a cereal box that is $2\frac{1}{2}$ in. thick, 10 in. wide, and 12 in. high and has an overlapping flap that measures 10 in. by $1\frac{1}{2}$ in.?

Mathematics in careers

Carpet layers generally are paid for each square yard of carpet they lay. They often charge extra for carpeting a small room such as a bath or for carpeting stairs.

EXERCISES

Copy and complete these bills.

1.

JACKSON'S CARPET SERVICE		
Living room	15 yd² @ $2.25 yd²	
Dining room	12 yd² @ $2.25 yd²	
Hall	4 yd² @ $2.25 yd²	
Stairs	10 steps @ $1.25 step	
	Total	

2.

JACKSON'S CARPET SERVICE		
Living room	14 yd² @ $2.25 yd²	
Bedroom	10 yd² @ $2.25 yd²	
Bath	3 yd² @ $3.75 yd²	
Hall	5 yd² @ $2.25 yd²	
Stairs	11 steps @ $1.25 step	
	Total	

Carpet layers have to compute area to determine the amount of carpet laid. (Since they charge by the square yard, each computed area must be in *square yards*.) The area of each "shaded room" shown below was computed and rounded up to the nearest square yard.

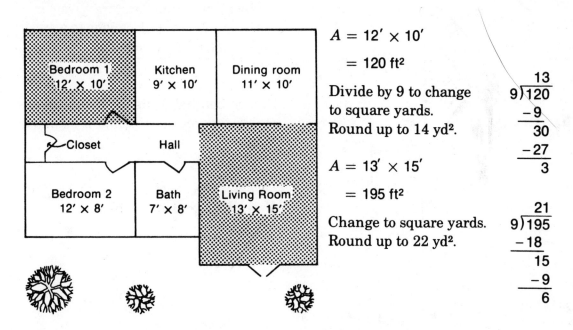

$A = 12' \times 10'$

$= 120 \text{ ft}^2$

Divide by 9 to change to square yards.
Round up to 14 yd².

$$\begin{array}{r} 13 \\ 9\overline{)120} \\ -9 \\ \hline 30 \\ -27 \\ \hline 3 \end{array}$$

$A = 13' \times 15'$

$= 195 \text{ ft}^2$

Change to square yards.
Round up to 22 yd².

$$\begin{array}{r} 21 \\ 9\overline{)195} \\ -18 \\ \hline 15 \\ -9 \\ \hline 6 \end{array}$$

Using the rate of $2.25 a square yard, compute the charge for laying the carpet in each of the following rooms. Round each area up to the nearest square yard.

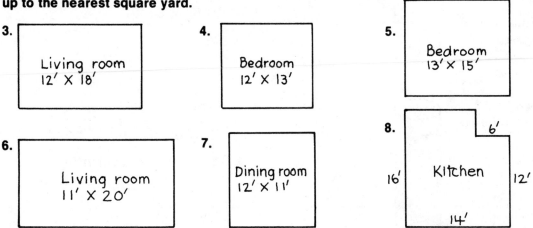

3. Living room 12' × 18'

4. Bedroom 12' × 13'

5. Bedroom 13' × 15'

6. Living room 11' × 20'

7. Dining room 12' × 11'

8. Kitchen — 16', 6', 12', 14'

Volume—customary units

Study these examples.

> **Important:**
>
> When measurements are given in more than one unit, change to a single unit before multiplying.

Remember that V stands for volume, B stands for area of base, and h stands for height.

EXAMPLE 1.

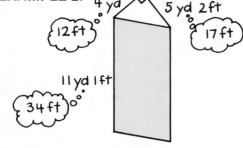

$V = B \times h$

$V = (15 \text{ in.} \times 9 \text{ in.}) \times 10 \text{ in.}$

$V = 135 \text{ in.}^2 \times 10 \text{ in.}$

$V = 1350 \text{ in.}^3$

EXAMPLE 2.

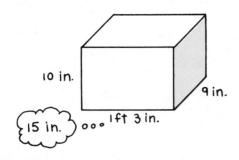

$V = B \times h$

$V = \frac{1}{2} \times (17 \text{ ft} \times 12 \text{ ft}) \times 34 \text{ ft}$

$V = \frac{1}{2} \times 204 \text{ ft}^2 \times 34 \text{ ft}$

$V = 102 \text{ ft}^2 \times 34 \text{ ft}$

$V = 3468 \text{ ft}^3$

EXAMPLE 3.
Use 3.14 for π.

$V = B \times h$

$V = \pi \times (7 \text{ in.} \times 7 \text{ in.}) \times 36 \text{ in.}$

$V \approx 3.14 \times 49 \text{ in.}^2 \times 36 \text{ in.}$

$V \approx 153.86 \text{ in.}^2 \times 36 \text{ in.}$

$V \approx 5538.96 \text{ in.}^3$

EXERCISES

Give each volume.

1.
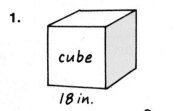
cube

18 in.

2.
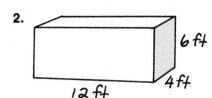
6 ft
4 ft
12 ft

3.
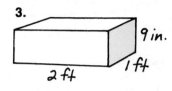
9 in.
1 ft
2 ft

4.
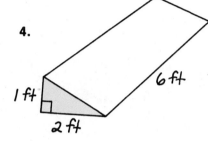
6 ft
1 ft
2 ft

5.
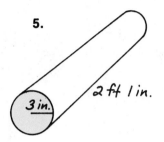
2 ft 1 in.
3 in.

6. 2 yd 1 ft
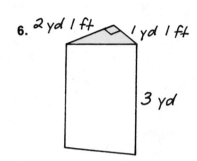
1 yd 1 ft
3 yd

Complete.

7. 1 yd³ = ___?___ ft³   **8.** 1 ft³ = ___?___ in.³   **9.** 1 yd³ = ___?___ in.³

10. Convert your answer for exercise 2 to yd³. Round to the nearest 0.1 yd³.

11. Convert your answer for exercise 3 to ft³. Round to the nearest 0.1 ft³.

Solve.

12. Concrete is sold by the cubic yard. How many cubic yards of concrete are needed for a basement wall that is 3 yd high, 10 yd long, and 0.25 yd thick?

13. A concrete garage floor is 23 ft by 23 ft and 3 in. thick. How many cubic yards of concrete were used?

14. Measure the dimensions of a rectangular room (perhaps your classroom) to the nearest ft. Compute the volume in ft³. Convert the volume to yd³ and round to the nearest 0.1 yd³.

Liquid volume and weight—customary units

2 cups (c) = 1 pint (pt)

2 pints = 1 quart (qt)

2 quarts = 1 half-gallon

2 half-gallons = 1 gallon (gal)

EXERCISES

Complete.

1. 24 pt = __?__ qt   **2.** 8 c = __?__ pt   **3.** 4 qt = __?__ gal

4. 3 qt = __?__ c   **5.** 2 gal = __?__ qt   **6.** 6 pt = __?__ c

7. 1 gal = __?__ pt   **8.** 2 qt = __?__ half-gallon   **9.** 12 c = __?__ qt

10. 16 pt = __?__ qt   **11.** 2 qt = __?__ c   **12.** 3 gal = __?__ half-gallons

13. 3 pt 1 c = __?__ c   **14.** 3 gal 2 qt = __?__ qt   **15.** 8 qt 1 pt = __?__ pt

In the metric system, dry material such as grain is measured with the same units used for liquids. In the customary system, different units are used for dry measure.

2 pints (pt) = 1 quart (qt)
8 quarts = 1 peck (pk)
4 pecks = 1 bushel (bu)

Complete.

16. 6 pt = __?__ qt   **17.** 16 qt = __?__ pk

18. 3 bu = __?__ pk   **19.** 5 pk = __?__ qt

Excursion

Suppose that you have a 3-qt container and a 5-qt container. How could you use the containers to measure out 4 qt of water?

Here are some units used for measuring weight.

16 ounces (oz) = 1 pound (lb)

2000 pounds (lb) = 1 ton (T)

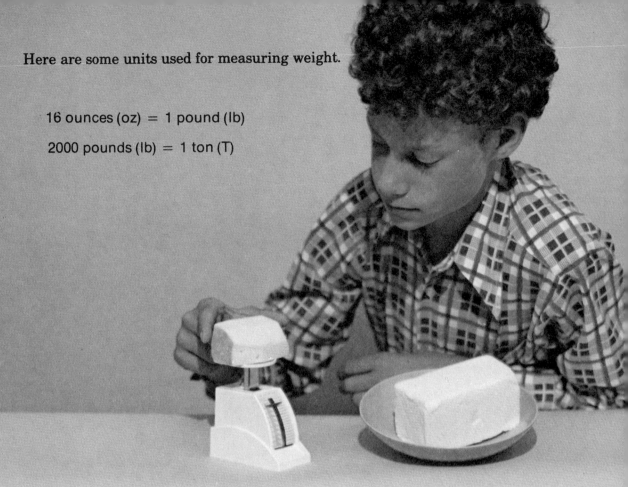

Complete.

20. 4 lb = __?__ oz   **21.** 3 T = __?__ lb   **22.** 256 oz = __?__ lb

23. 8000 lb = __?__ T   **24.** 24 lb = __?__ oz   **25.** 288 oz = __?__ lb

26. 3 lb 6 oz = __?__ oz   **27.** 4 lb 9 oz = __?__ oz   **28.** 12 lb 3 oz = __?__ oz

Solve.

29. A chili recipe calls for 2 lb of ground beef. If you had 1 lb 3 oz of ground beef, how much more would you need?

30. A truck weighing 21,400 lb came to a bridge with this sign:

> **Closed to traffic**
> **over**
> **10 tons**

Should the truck cross the bridge?

CHAPTER CHECKUP

Complete. [pages 134–137]

1. 30 mm = <u> ? </u> cm

2. 200 cm = <u> ? </u> m

3. 135 cm = <u> ? </u> dm

4. 68 cm = <u> ? </u> m

5. 2.1 km = <u> ? </u> m

6. 82.4 mm = <u> ? </u> dm

Give the perimeter (or circumference) and the area. Use 3.14 as an approximation for π. [pages 138–143, 158–159]

7.

8.

9.

10.

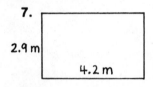

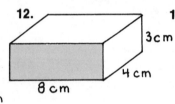

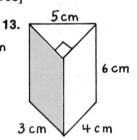

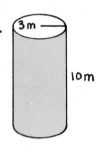

Give the surface area and the volume. Use 3.14 as an approximation for π. [pages 146–153, 159, 162–163]

11.

12.

13.

14.

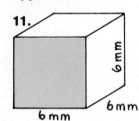

Complete. [pages 154–155]

15. 1 L = <u> ? </u> mL

16. 2 L = <u> ? </u> mL

17. 450 mL = <u> ? </u> L

18. 1 g = <u> ? </u> mg

19. 560 g = <u> ? </u> kg

20. 0.73 kg = <u> ? </u> g

Complete. [pages 156–157]

21. 3 ft = <u> ? </u> in.

22. 7 yd = <u> ? </u> ft

23. 18 yd = <u> ? </u> in.

24. 58 in. = <u> ? </u> ft <u> ? </u> in.

25. 15 ft = <u> ? </u> yd <u> ? </u> ft

26. 2 mi = <u> ? </u> yd

Complete. [pages 164–165]

27. 5 qt = <u> ? </u> pt

28. 4 gal = <u> ? </u> qt

29. 48 pt = <u> ? </u> gal

30. 2 T = <u> ? </u> lb

31. 12 lb = <u> ? </u> oz

32. 56 oz = <u> ? </u> lb <u> ? </u> oz

Project

A metric unit for measuring land area is the **hectare**. A square that is 100 meters on a side has an area of 1 hectare. The hectare is used to measure areas of such regions as parks and farms. Working in a group, lay out a hectare on your school grounds. Estimate the total area of your school grounds in hectares.

Answer these questions.

1. How many square meters are in a hectare?

2. How many hectares are in a square kilometer?

167

CHAPTER REVIEW

Complete.

16.35 km = ___?___ m

/km/hm/dam/m/

1 6,3 5 0. Km

1. 723.1 m = ___?___ km

2. 52.7 m = ___?___ cm

3. 423 mm = ___?___ m

4. 53 cm = ___?___ m

5. 2.6 L = ___?___ mL

6. 423.6 mg = ___?___ g

7. 2.7 kg = ___?___ g

8. 2.7 g = ___?___ kg

9. 48.3 m = ___?___ cm

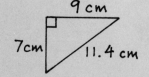

$P = 11.4\ \text{cm} + 9\ \text{cm} + 7\ \text{cm}$

$= 27.4\ \text{cm}$

9 cm

7cm   11.4 cm

$A = \frac{1}{2} \times b \times h$

$= \frac{1}{2} \times 7\ \text{cm} \times 9\ \text{cm}$

$= 31.5\ \text{cm}^2$

Give the surface area. Use 3.14 for π.

Give the volume. Use 3.14 for π.

Give each perimeter. Use 3.14 for π.

10.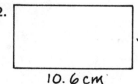

5.2 cm

10.6 cm

11.

16 mm

Give each area. Use 3.14 for π.

12.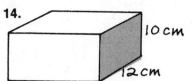

5.2 cm

10.6 cm

13.

16 mm

14.

10 cm

12 cm

20 cm

15.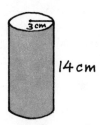

3 cm

14 cm

16.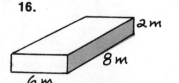

2 m

8 m

6 m

17.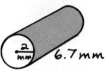

2 mm

6.7 mm

168

Error of measurement

Suppose that you measured each of these segments to the nearest centimeter.

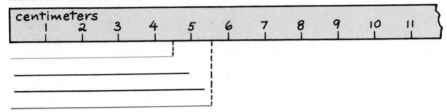

Each length would be recorded as 5 cm. In each case there is some error in the measurement—the difference between the true length and the recorded length. The **greatest possible error** (g.p.e.) occurs in the measurements of the blue segment and the red segment. The greatest possible error is always half of the unit used. In this case the g.p.e. is 0.5 cm.

If we use a smaller unit, we have less error.
Compare these two measurements.

Recorded measure   7 m
unit used: meter
   g.p.e.: 0.5 m

shortest possible true length: 6.5 m
longest possible true length: 7.5 m

Recorded measure   7.00 m
unit used: 0.01 m (1 cm)
   g.p.e.: 0.005 m (0.5 cm)

shortest possible true length: 6.995 m
longest possible true length: 7.005 m

EXERCISES
Give the g.p.e., the shortest possible true length, and the longest possible true length for each of these recorded measurements.

1. 15 m   **2.** 8 cm   **3.** 3.5 m   **4.** 20.45 m

5. 5.2 km   **6.** 6.0 cm   **7.** 18.5 mm   **8.** 15.00 m

9. A measurement is given as 8 m ± 0.5 m.
The g.p.e. is 0.5 m.
   a. What is the shortest possible true length?   **b.** What is the longest possible true length?

Form W X

13 a b c d 33 a b c d 13 a b c d 3 a b c d 29 a b c d
14 a b c d 34 a b c d 14 a b c d 4 a b c d 30 a b c d
15   a b c   a b c   a b c 31 a b c d

MAJOR CHECKUP
Standardized Format

Choose the correct letter.

1. Give the standard numeral for fifty-seven tenths.

    a. 0.57
    b. 0.057
    c. 57
    d. none of these

2. Round 53.499 to the nearest whole number.

    a. 53
    b. 54
    c. 53.5
    d. none of these

3. Give the sum.

$$6.2 + 3.8 + 0.57$$

    a. 1.57
    b. 15.7
    c. 10.57
    d. none of these

4. Give the difference.

$$20.04 - 6.77$$

    a. 13.27
    b. 14.37
    c. 23.27
    d. none of these

5. Multiply.

$$\begin{array}{r} 2.48 \\ \times 0.13 \\ \hline \end{array}$$

    a. 3.2240
    b. 0.3224
    c. 32.2400
    d. none of these

6. Divide.

$$0.08 \overline{)3.216}$$

    a. 40.2
    b. 4.02
    c. 0.402
    d. none of these

7. Change this measurement to meters.

324 mm

    a. 324,000 m
    b. 3.24 m
    c. 0.324 m
    d. none of these

8. Which of these is a subset of {1, 2, 3, 4}?

    a. {1, 2, 3, 4, 5}
    b. {0, 1, 2}
    c. {3, 4}
    d. none of these

9. Find the area.

    a. 314 mm²
    b. 314 mm³
    c. 62.8 mm²
    d. none of these

10. Give the surface area.

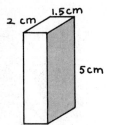

    a. 41 cm²
    b. 15 cm²
    c. 30 cm²
    d. none of these

11. Find the volume.

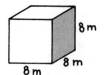

    a. 512 m
    b. 512 m²
    c. 512 m³
    d. none of these

12. Which of these units is the basic unit of liquid volume in the metric system?

    a. meter
    b. liter
    c. gram
    d. none of these

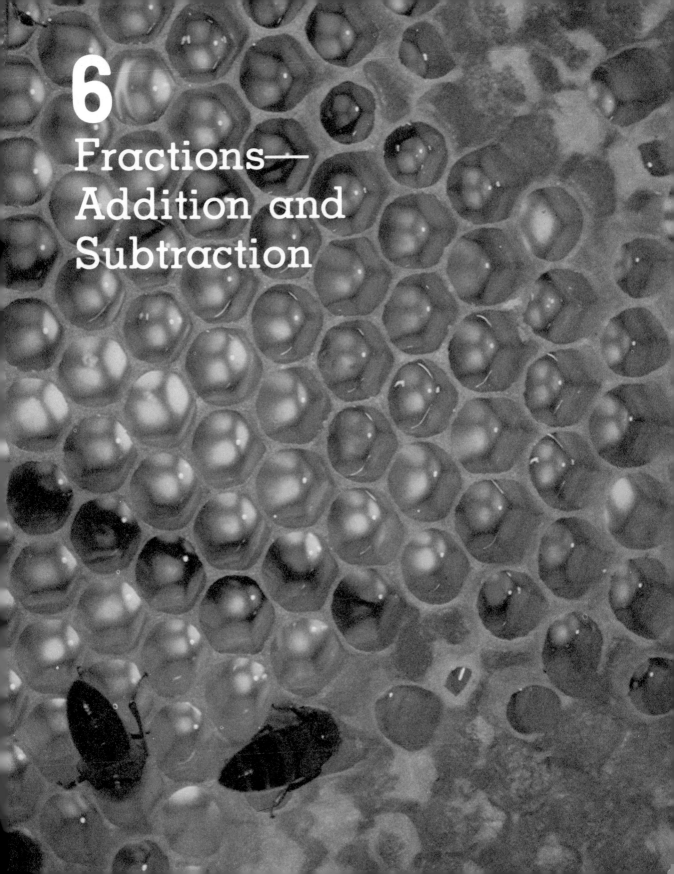

6
Fractions—
Addition and
Subtraction

READY OR NOT ?

What fraction of the region is colored?

1.

2.

3.

4.

5.

What fraction of the objects are colored?

6.

7.

8.

9.

10.

Equivalent fractions

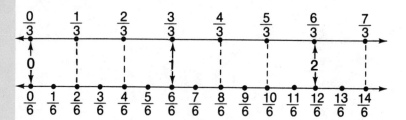

The fractions $\frac{2}{3}$ and $\frac{4}{6}$ name the same number. Fractions that name the same number are called **equivalent fractions**. We write $\frac{2}{3} = \frac{4}{6}$. What other equivalent fractions does the picture show?

EXERCISES

Give two equivalent fractions for each red point.

1.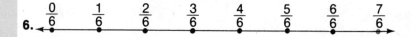

2.

3.

4.

5.

6.

**Give two equivalent fractions for the
part of the eggs that are**

7. white

8. brown

9. in the carton

10. broken

11. not broken

12. white and broken

**Give an equivalent fraction.
Use a number line if you need to.**

13. $\frac{1}{2}$ 14. $\frac{2}{3}$ 15. $\frac{1}{6}$ 16. $\frac{3}{8}$

17. $\frac{3}{2}$ 18. $\frac{1}{7}$ 19. $\frac{2}{9}$ 20. $\frac{0}{2}$

21. $\frac{7}{8}$ 22. $\frac{5}{10}$ 23. $\frac{1}{3}$ 24. $\frac{5}{5}$

25. $\frac{3}{4}$ 26. $\frac{7}{2}$ 27. $\frac{4}{6}$ 28. $\frac{4}{4}$

29. $\frac{1}{8}$ 30. $\frac{1}{4}$ 31. $\frac{3}{9}$ 32. $\frac{4}{12}$

33. $\frac{3}{3}$ 34. $\frac{6}{4}$ 35. $\frac{1}{5}$ 36. $\frac{5}{7}$

37. $\frac{5}{3}$ 38. $\frac{4}{3}$ 39. $\frac{6}{10}$ 40. $\frac{0}{4}$

More about equivalent fractions

Multiplying both numerator and denominator by the same nonzero number gives an equivalent fraction.

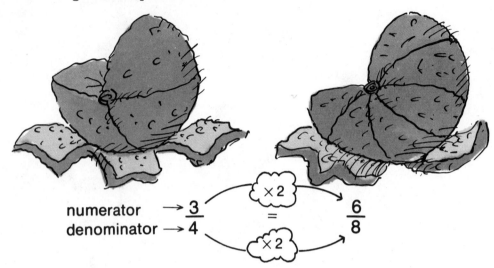

numerator $\rightarrow \dfrac{3}{4}$ $\quad \boxed{\times 2} \quad$ $=$ $\quad \boxed{\times 2} \quad$ $\dfrac{6}{8}$
denominator $\rightarrow$

$\dfrac{2}{3}$ is equivalent to how many twelfths?

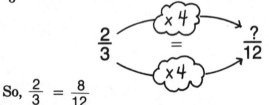

$$\dfrac{2}{3} \quad \boxed{\times 4} \atop \boxed{\times 4} = \dfrac{?}{12}$$

So, $\dfrac{2}{3} = \dfrac{8}{12}$

I would multiply 3 by 4 to get 12. So, I multiply 2 by 4 and get 8.

EXERCISES
Give an equivalent fraction.

1. $\dfrac{1}{3}$ 2. $\dfrac{1}{2}$ 3. $\dfrac{1}{4}$ 4. $\dfrac{3}{2}$ 5. $\dfrac{3}{4}$ 6. $\dfrac{1}{5}$

7. $\dfrac{0}{3}$ 8. $\dfrac{5}{2}$ 9. $\dfrac{3}{5}$ 10. $\dfrac{2}{3}$ 11. $\dfrac{5}{4}$ 12. $\dfrac{4}{3}$

13. $\dfrac{7}{8}$ 14. $\dfrac{5}{9}$ 15. $\dfrac{5}{6}$ 16. $\dfrac{2}{5}$ 17. $\dfrac{3}{8}$ 18. $\dfrac{8}{5}$

Copy and complete.

19. $\dfrac{1}{2} = \dfrac{?}{8}$

20. $\dfrac{2}{2} = \dfrac{?}{8}$

21. $\dfrac{1}{5} = \dfrac{?}{20}$

22. $\dfrac{3}{2} = \dfrac{?}{10}$

23. $\dfrac{1}{4} = \dfrac{?}{16}$

24. $\dfrac{2}{3} = \dfrac{?}{9}$

25. $\dfrac{4}{3} = \dfrac{?}{12}$

26. $\dfrac{1}{3} = \dfrac{?}{6}$

27. $\dfrac{5}{2} = \dfrac{?}{10}$

28. $\dfrac{1}{2} = \dfrac{?}{12}$

29. $\dfrac{1}{3} = \dfrac{?}{12}$

30. $\dfrac{8}{3} = \dfrac{?}{6}$

31. $\dfrac{6}{6} = \dfrac{?}{2}$

32. $\dfrac{2}{3} = \dfrac{?}{12}$

33. $\dfrac{1}{6} = \dfrac{?}{18}$

34. $\dfrac{3}{2} = \dfrac{?}{6}$

35. $\dfrac{2}{3} = \dfrac{?}{6}$

36. $\dfrac{1}{2} = \dfrac{?}{6}$

37. $\dfrac{3}{3} = \dfrac{?}{9}$

38. $\dfrac{1}{3} = \dfrac{?}{15}$

39. $\dfrac{1}{2} = \dfrac{?}{10}$

40. $\dfrac{0}{2} = \dfrac{?}{8}$

41. $\dfrac{4}{3} = \dfrac{?}{6}$

42. $\dfrac{1}{4} = \dfrac{?}{20}$

43. $\dfrac{8}{7} = \dfrac{?}{14}$

44. $\dfrac{5}{2} = \dfrac{?}{8}$

45. $\dfrac{1}{3} = \dfrac{?}{9}$

46. $\dfrac{1}{5} = \dfrac{?}{10}$

47. $\dfrac{1}{4} = \dfrac{?}{8}$

48. $\dfrac{1}{2} = \dfrac{?}{4}$

49. $\dfrac{1}{4} = \dfrac{?}{12}$

50. $\dfrac{3}{2} = \dfrac{?}{4}$

51. $\dfrac{3}{3} = \dfrac{?}{6}$

52. $\dfrac{1}{6} = \dfrac{?}{24}$

53. $\dfrac{0}{2} = \dfrac{?}{6}$

Solve.

54. Which is more, $\dfrac{5}{12}$ of the oranges or $\dfrac{7}{12}$ of the oranges?

55. Which is less, $\dfrac{4}{6}$ of the oranges or $\dfrac{5}{6}$ of the oranges?

56. Which is more, $\dfrac{1}{2}$ or $\dfrac{3}{4}$?

57. Which is less, $\dfrac{5}{6}$ or $\dfrac{3}{4}$?

175

Reducing a fraction to lowest terms

The numerator, 6, and the denominator, 9, are called the **terms** of the fraction.

$$\frac{6}{9} \text{ are blue.}$$

To reduce a fraction to lowest terms, divide both numerator and denominator by their greatest common factor (or divisor).

$$\frac{2}{3} \text{ are blue.}$$

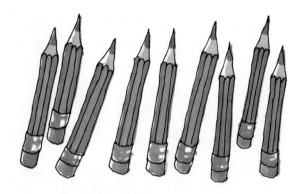

Divide both numerator and denominator by their greatest common divisor, 3.

If you reduce $\frac{4}{2}$ to lowest terms, you get $\frac{2}{1}$, or 2.

EXERCISES

Give the greatest common divisor of the numerator and denominator.

1. $\frac{2}{6}$ 2. $\frac{14}{6}$ 3. $\frac{10}{5}$ 4. $\frac{6}{6}$ 5. $\frac{6}{8}$ 6. $\frac{12}{4}$

7. $\frac{18}{15}$ 8. $\frac{9}{12}$ 9. $\frac{6}{4}$ 10. $\frac{3}{9}$ 11. $\frac{4}{16}$ 12. $\frac{12}{18}$

Reduce each fraction to lowest terms.

13. $\frac{5}{5}$ 14. $\frac{6}{9}$ 15. $\frac{6}{12}$ 16. $\frac{2}{4}$ 17. $\frac{10}{8}$

18. $\frac{10}{12}$ 19. $\frac{4}{16}$ 20. $\frac{2}{8}$ 21. $\frac{2}{6}$ 22. $\frac{6}{10}$

23. $\frac{15}{18}$ 24. $\frac{6}{4}$ 25. $\frac{3}{9}$ 26. $\frac{15}{10}$ 27. $\frac{3}{6}$

28. $\frac{5}{15}$ 29. $\frac{4}{6}$ 30. $\frac{3}{12}$ 31. $\frac{4}{8}$ 32. $\frac{18}{15}$

33. $\frac{9}{6}$ 34. $\frac{0}{4}$ 35. $\frac{4}{12}$ 36. $\frac{16}{32}$ 37. $\frac{10}{15}$

Who am I?

38. I am a fraction. My numerator is 3 and my denominator is 7.

39. I am equivalent to $\frac{4}{8}$. My denominator is 2.

40. I am equivalent to $\frac{3}{2}$. My numerator is 6.

41. I am equivalent to $\frac{3}{2}$. My denominator is 6.

Reduce to lowest terms. $\frac{9702}{14553}$

Multiply.

1. 37.1×2.3

2. 7.39×4.8

3. 85.2×61

4. 8.61×80

5. 58.3×3.7

6. 7.04×7.4

7. 6.26×0.29

8. 55.2×8.3

9. 68.4×0.94

10. 4.39×60

11. 91.6×5.5

12. 0.429×0.36

Comparing fractions

Some students decided to build a birdhouse for a shop project. To build the birdhouse, they had to compare fractions. They found fractions with the same denominator easy to compare. For example:

$$\frac{1}{8} < \frac{3}{8}$$

To compare fractions with different denominators, we find equivalent fractions that have the same (common) denominator.

$$\frac{3}{5}, \frac{6}{10} \qquad \frac{1}{2}, \frac{2}{4}, \frac{3}{4}, \frac{4}{8}, \frac{5}{10}$$

$$\frac{3}{5} > \frac{1}{2}$$

Here is a shortcut.

Step 1. Find the least common denominator.

$$\frac{5}{2} \bullet \frac{7}{3}$$

$$6$$

Step 2. Change to equivalent fractions.

$$\frac{15}{6} \quad \frac{5}{2} \bullet \frac{7}{3} \quad \frac{14}{6}$$

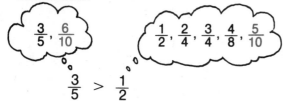

The least common multiple of the denominators is the least common denominator.

Step 3. Compare.

$$\frac{15}{6} \quad \frac{5}{2} > \frac{7}{3} \quad \frac{14}{6}$$

EXERCISES

< or >?

1. $\frac{4}{6} < \frac{5}{6}$

2. $\frac{3}{8} \bullet \frac{3}{10}$

3. $\frac{9}{4} \bullet \frac{7}{4}$

4. $\frac{5}{7} \bullet \frac{2}{7}$

5. $\frac{5}{9} \bullet \frac{4}{9}$

6. $\frac{2}{2} \bullet \frac{3}{2}$

7. $\frac{5}{3} \bullet \frac{4}{3}$

8. $\frac{7}{5} \bullet \frac{7}{6}$

9. $\frac{7}{8} \bullet \frac{5}{8}$

10. $\frac{0}{8} \bullet \frac{1}{8}$

Give the least common denominator.

11. $\frac{1}{2}, \frac{1}{3}$ 12. $\frac{2}{3}, \frac{3}{4}$ 13. $\frac{5}{2}, \frac{8}{5}$ 14. $\frac{4}{3}, \frac{6}{5}$ 15. $\frac{3}{4}, \frac{5}{6}$ 16. $\frac{7}{6}, \frac{11}{9}$

17. $\frac{7}{5}, \frac{8}{7}$ 18. $\frac{2}{3}, \frac{5}{8}$ 19. $\frac{5}{6}, \frac{7}{8}$ 20. $\frac{5}{12}, \frac{1}{3}$ 21. $\frac{7}{9}, \frac{4}{8}$ 22. $\frac{5}{6}, \frac{2}{1}$

<, = , or >? *Hint:* **Find the least common denominator.**

$\left(\frac{2}{3}, \frac{4}{6}\right)$ $\left(\frac{1}{4}, \frac{2}{8}\right)$ $\left(\frac{2}{3}, \frac{4}{6}, \frac{6}{9}\right)$ $\left(\frac{1}{3}, \frac{2}{6}, \ldots, \frac{7}{21}\right)$ $\left(\frac{2}{7}, \frac{4}{14}, \frac{6}{21}\right)$

23. $\frac{2}{3} \bullet \frac{5}{6}$ 24. $1\frac{1}{4} \bullet \frac{3}{8}$ 25. $\frac{26}{39} \bullet \frac{5}{9}$ 26. $\frac{17}{32} \bullet \frac{2}{7}$ 27. $\frac{3}{2} \bullet \frac{5}{3}$

28. $\frac{3}{8} \bullet \frac{1}{2}$ 29. $\frac{1}{3} \bullet \frac{3}{10}$ 30. $\frac{1}{2} \bullet \frac{5}{8}$ 31. $\frac{1}{6} \bullet \frac{1}{8}$ 32. $\frac{5}{2} \bullet \frac{5}{3}$

33. $\frac{2}{9} \bullet \frac{1}{3}$ 34. $\frac{2}{5} \bullet \frac{3}{8}$ 35. $\frac{6}{8} \bullet \frac{3}{4}$ 36. $\frac{3}{5} \bullet \frac{1}{2}$ 37. $\frac{0}{3} \bullet \frac{0}{6}$

38. $\frac{15}{12} \bullet \frac{5}{4}$ 39. $\frac{3}{10} \bullet \frac{1}{4}$ 40. $\frac{1}{5} \bullet \frac{1}{4}$ 41. $\frac{4}{4} \bullet \frac{2}{2}$ 42. $\frac{5}{6} \bullet \frac{7}{8}$

43. $\frac{7}{8} \bullet \frac{3}{5}$ 44. $\frac{4}{3} \bullet \frac{3}{4}$ 45. $\frac{5}{9} \bullet \frac{7}{12}$ 46. $\frac{9}{16} \bullet \frac{5}{8}$ 47. $\frac{7}{5} \bullet \frac{9}{7}$

Solve.

48. Will a $\frac{3}{4}$-inch nail go through a $\frac{1}{2}$-inch-thick board?

49. The small hole for the perch stick had to be $\frac{1}{4}$ inch in diameter. Would a $\frac{3}{8}$-inch drill bit be too large or too small?

50. The hole for the birds to enter had to be $\frac{7}{8}$ inch or larger. Would a $\frac{13}{16}$-inch drill bit make a large enough hole? No

179

Adding fractions

To add two fractions having the same denominator, add the numerators and use the common denominator.

$$\frac{7}{8} + \frac{3}{8} = \frac{10}{8}$$

$$= \frac{5}{4} \quad \text{lowest terms}$$

When the fractions have different denominators, you must change to equivalent fractions with common denominators.

Step 1. Find the least common denominator.

$$\frac{2}{5} + \frac{5}{3} = \frac{}{15} + \frac{}{15}$$

Step 2. Change to equivalent fractions.

$$\frac{2}{5} + \frac{5}{3} = \frac{6}{15} + \frac{25}{15}$$

Step 3. Add.

$$\frac{2}{5} + \frac{5}{3} = \frac{6}{15} + \frac{25}{15}$$

$$= \frac{31}{15}$$

EXERCISES
Add. Reduce fractions to lowest terms.

1. $\frac{1}{3} + \frac{1}{3}$

2. $\frac{3}{8} + \frac{1}{8}$

3. $\frac{1}{6} + \frac{1}{6}$

4. $\frac{5}{6} + \frac{5}{6}$

5. $\frac{3}{8} + \frac{3}{8}$

6. $\frac{5}{9} + \frac{2}{9}$

7. $\frac{3}{10} + \frac{1}{10}$

8. $\frac{2}{7} + \frac{2}{7}$

Add. Reduce answers to lowest terms. *Hint:* **First find the least common denominator.**

9. $\frac{1}{2} + \frac{5}{6}$ 10. $\frac{1}{4} + \frac{1}{2}$ 11. $\frac{1}{2} + \frac{3}{4}$ 12. $1 + \frac{3}{2}$

13. $\frac{1}{2} + \frac{1}{6}$ 14. $\frac{1}{4} + \frac{1}{3}$ 15. $\frac{5}{6} + \frac{1}{8}$ 16. $\frac{3}{8} + \frac{2}{5}$

17. $\frac{2}{3} + \frac{1}{2}$ 18. $\frac{2}{3} + 3$ 19. $\frac{1}{6} + \frac{1}{5}$ 20. $\frac{1}{6} + \frac{3}{4}$

21. $\frac{0}{4} + \frac{3}{2}$ 22. $\frac{1}{15} + \frac{2}{5}$ 23. $\frac{3}{5} + \frac{1}{10}$ 24. $\frac{2}{3} + \frac{1}{9}$

25. $\frac{1}{10} + \frac{2}{3}$ 26. $2 + \frac{1}{4}$ 27. $\frac{2}{2} + \frac{3}{8}$ 28. $\frac{3}{10} + \frac{3}{4}$

Add. Give answers in lowest terms.

29. $\frac{3}{5}$ $+\frac{1}{6}$ 30. $\frac{1}{4}$ $+\frac{1}{8}$ 31. $\frac{3}{4}$ $+\frac{3}{8}$ 32. $\frac{0}{6}$ $+\frac{2}{3}$ 33. $\frac{5}{9}$ $+\frac{1}{3}$ 34. $\frac{3}{5}$ $+\frac{5}{3}$

35. $\frac{7}{8}$ $+\frac{1}{4}$ 36. $\frac{3}{3}$ $+\frac{1}{2}$ 37. $\frac{5}{7}$ $+\frac{2}{3}$ 38. $\frac{5}{6}$ $+\frac{2}{3}$ 39. $\frac{5}{9}$ $+\frac{2}{3}$ 40. $\frac{5}{6}$ $+\frac{1}{4}$

41. $\frac{1}{4}$ $+\frac{5}{9}$ 42. $\frac{3}{8}$ $+\frac{1}{6}$ 43. $\frac{2}{3}$ $+\frac{3}{2}$ 44. $\frac{5}{12}$ $+\frac{1}{3}$ 45. $\frac{7}{8}$ $+\frac{3}{4}$ 46. $\frac{3}{4}$ $+\frac{7}{12}$

Solve.

47. John found $\frac{1}{2}$ pound of mushrooms in the morning and $\frac{1}{4}$ pound in the afternoon. How much did he find in all?

48. Terry used $\frac{2}{3}$ cup of sugar in one recipe and $\frac{3}{4}$ cup in another. How much sugar did he use?

49. Mary typed for $\frac{2}{5}$ of an hour before school and $\frac{3}{4}$ of an hour after school. How long did she type in all?

50. Jerry read $\frac{1}{3}$ of a book on Monday and $\frac{1}{4}$ of the book on Tuesday. What fraction of the book did he read during the two days?

181

Subtracting fractions

To subtract fractions having the same denominator, subtract the numerators and use the common denominator.

$$\frac{3}{4} - \frac{1}{4} = \frac{2}{4}$$
$$= \frac{1}{2}$$

Reduced to lowest terms.

When the two denominators are different, find the least common denominator and change to equivalent fractions.

$$\frac{1}{2} - \frac{1}{3} = \frac{3}{6} - \frac{2}{6}$$
$$= \frac{1}{6}$$

EXERCISES
Subtract. Reduce answers to lowest terms.

1. $\dfrac{5}{8} - \dfrac{1}{8}$ 2. $\dfrac{7}{6} - \dfrac{5}{6}$ 3. $\dfrac{1}{3} - \dfrac{1}{3}$ 4. $\dfrac{7}{5} - \dfrac{2}{5}$ 5. $\dfrac{6}{7} - \dfrac{1}{7}$

6. $\dfrac{4}{3} - \dfrac{3}{3}$ 7. $\dfrac{4}{8} - \dfrac{1}{8}$ 8. $\dfrac{2}{5} - \dfrac{1}{5}$ 9. $\dfrac{5}{9} - \dfrac{4}{9}$ 10. $\dfrac{5}{4} - \dfrac{2}{4}$

11. $\dfrac{7}{5} - \dfrac{4}{5}$ 12. $\dfrac{7}{9} - \dfrac{1}{9}$ 13. $\dfrac{7}{8} - \dfrac{0}{8}$ 14. $\dfrac{5}{3} - \dfrac{1}{3}$ 15. $\dfrac{7}{4} - \dfrac{4}{4}$

Subtract. Reduce answers to lowest terms. *Hint:* **First find the least common denominator.**

16. $\dfrac{1}{3} - \dfrac{2}{9}$ 17. $\dfrac{5}{6} - \dfrac{5}{9}$ 18. $\dfrac{5}{7} - \dfrac{1}{3}$ 19. $2 - \dfrac{1}{4}$ 20. $\dfrac{2}{3} - \dfrac{1}{6}$

21. $\dfrac{5}{3} - \dfrac{6}{5}$ 22. $\dfrac{7}{6} - \dfrac{2}{3}$ 23. $\dfrac{5}{4} - \dfrac{2}{3}$ 24. $\dfrac{3}{4} - \dfrac{1}{3}$ 25. $\dfrac{5}{6} - \dfrac{1}{3}$

26. $\dfrac{3}{4} - \dfrac{2}{3}$ 27. $\dfrac{3}{4} - \dfrac{5}{8}$ 28. $\dfrac{3}{8} - \dfrac{1}{4}$ 29. $\dfrac{1}{2} - \dfrac{1}{6}$ 30. $1 - \dfrac{1}{2}$

31. $\dfrac{4}{5} - \dfrac{2}{3}$ 32. $\dfrac{3}{4} - \dfrac{1}{2}$ 33. $3 - \dfrac{3}{4}$ 34. $\dfrac{1}{2} - \dfrac{0}{8}$ 35. $\dfrac{5}{4} - \dfrac{2}{2}$

Subtract. Give answers in lowest terms.

36. $\begin{array}{r} \frac{8}{9} \\ -\frac{3}{4} \\ \hline \end{array}$ 37. $\begin{array}{r} \frac{3}{4} \\ -\frac{5}{8} \\ \hline \end{array}$ 38. $\begin{array}{r} \frac{3}{4} \\ -\frac{3}{10} \\ \hline \end{array}$ 39. $\begin{array}{r} \frac{3}{4} \\ -\frac{1}{6} \\ \hline \end{array}$ 40. $\begin{array}{r} \frac{2}{5} \\ -\frac{3}{8} \\ \hline \end{array}$ 41. $\begin{array}{r} \frac{5}{6} \\ -\frac{3}{8} \\ \hline \end{array}$

42. $\begin{array}{r} \frac{9}{5} \\ -\frac{2}{3} \\ \hline \end{array}$ 43. $\begin{array}{r} \frac{5}{9} \\ -\frac{1}{2} \\ \hline \end{array}$ 44. $\begin{array}{r} \frac{2}{3} \\ -\frac{1}{4} \\ \hline \end{array}$ 45. $\begin{array}{r} \frac{5}{4} \\ -\frac{5}{8} \\ \hline \end{array}$ 46. $\begin{array}{r} \frac{5}{6} \\ -\frac{0}{4} \\ \hline \end{array}$ 47. $\begin{array}{r} \frac{9}{4} \\ -\frac{3}{2} \\ \hline \end{array}$

Solve.

48. Had $\dfrac{3}{4}$ cup of flour. Used $\dfrac{2}{3}$ cup. How much was left?

49. Need $\dfrac{3}{2}$ cups of sugar. Have $\dfrac{3}{4}$ cup. How much more sugar is needed?

50. Should bake $\dfrac{1}{2}$ hour. Have baked $\dfrac{1}{4}$ hour. How much longer to bake?

Excursion

Complete this magic square.

$\frac{2}{3}$		$\frac{1}{2}$
	$\frac{5}{12}$	
		$\frac{1}{6}$

Practice exercises

Give each sum in lowest terms.

1. $\frac{1}{2}$
$+\frac{2}{3}$

2. $\frac{1}{3}$
$+\frac{1}{2}$

3. $\frac{5}{3}$
$+\frac{5}{4}$

4. $\frac{2}{3}$
$+\frac{5}{9}$

5. $\frac{2}{3}$
$+\frac{3}{2}$

6. $\frac{1}{3}$
$+\frac{3}{5}$

7. $\frac{5}{8}$
$+\frac{1}{4}$

8. $\frac{0}{2}$
$+\frac{3}{8}$

9. $\frac{2}{3}$
$+\frac{3}{4}$

10. $\frac{6}{5}$
$+\frac{3}{10}$

11. $\frac{5}{6}$
$+\frac{1}{2}$

12. $\frac{3}{4}$
$+\frac{1}{8}$

13. $\frac{1}{4}$
$+\frac{3}{8}$

14. $\frac{4}{4}$
$+\frac{3}{3}$

15. $\frac{1}{4}$
$+\frac{1}{2}$

16. $\frac{1}{3}$
$+\frac{7}{8}$

17. $\frac{1}{5}$
$+\frac{3}{7}$

18. $\frac{1}{4}$
$+\frac{5}{12}$

19. $\frac{1}{2}$
$+\frac{5}{8}$

20. $\frac{7}{10}$
$+\frac{5}{6}$

21. $\frac{4}{4}$
$+\frac{7}{15}$

22. $\frac{4}{5}$
$+\frac{2}{3}$

23. $\frac{1}{3}$
$+\frac{3}{4}$

24. $\frac{2}{3}$
$+\frac{3}{8}$

Give each difference in lowest terms.

25. $\frac{1}{2}$
$-\frac{1}{4}$

26. $\frac{7}{8}$
$-\frac{3}{4}$

27. $\frac{3}{4}$
$-\frac{5}{8}$

28. $\frac{1}{2}$
$-\frac{1}{3}$

29. $\frac{5}{6}$
$-\frac{2}{3}$

30. $\frac{7}{2}$
-2

31. $\frac{3}{10}$
$-\frac{1}{5}$

32. $\frac{3}{4}$
$-\frac{3}{8}$

33. $\frac{3}{4}$
$-\frac{1}{4}$

34. $\frac{7}{9}$
$-\frac{0}{2}$

35. $\frac{1}{2}$
$-\frac{3}{8}$

36. $\frac{7}{4}$
-1

37. $\frac{2}{3}$
$-\frac{3}{8}$

38. 1
$-\frac{2}{3}$

39. 2
$-\frac{5}{4}$

40. $\frac{5}{8}$
$-\frac{5}{8}$

41. $\frac{5}{9}$
$-\frac{1}{3}$

42. $\frac{5}{4}$
$-\frac{5}{8}$

43. $\frac{2}{3}$
$-\frac{1}{3}$

44. $\frac{1}{2}$
$-\frac{4}{9}$

45. $\frac{3}{4}$
$-\frac{1}{2}$

46. $\frac{2}{3}$
$-\frac{1}{4}$

47. $\frac{8}{9}$
$-\frac{3}{4}$

48. $\frac{3}{4}$
$-\frac{2}{3}$

Mathematics and science

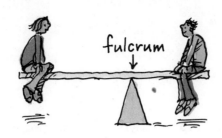

fulcrum

Notice that the boy and the girl are in balance.
When they are in balance, these products are equal:

| boy's weight | × | his distance from fulcrum | = | girl's weight | × | her distance from fulcrum |

Problem: The boy weighs 60 kg and is seated 2 m from the fulcrum.
How much does the girl weigh if she is seated 3 m from the fulcrum?

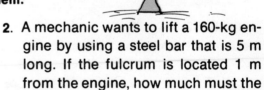

Solution:
$$60 \times 2 = w \times 3$$
$$120 = w \times 3$$
$$40 = w$$

What do you multiply by 3 to get 120?

I DUNNO— WHAT?

Answer: 40 kg

EXERCISES
Solve. You may first want to picture each problem.

1. A boy weighing 50 kg is seated 3 m from the fulcrum of a seesaw. How far would a boy weighing 75 kilograms have to sit from the fulcrum for the seesaw to balance?

2. A mechanic wants to lift a 160-kg engine by using a steel bar that is 5 m long. If the fulcrum is located 1 m from the engine, how much must the mechanic weigh to lift the engine?

3. A girl weighing 40 kg is seated 1.5 m from the fulcrum of a seesaw. When another girl is seated 2 m from the fulcrum, the seesaw is in balance. How much does the other girl weigh?

★ 4. A man weighing 80 kg wants to lift a rock that weighs 400 kg. If he places the fulcrum 2 m from the rock, how long a lever does he need to lift the rock?

Mixed numbers

fraction → $\frac{5}{2}$ = $2\frac{1}{2}$ ← mixed number

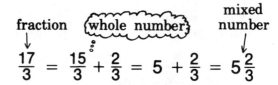

Changing a Mixed Number to a Fraction

mixed number   fraction

$5\frac{3}{4} = 5 + \frac{3}{4} = \frac{20}{4} + \frac{3}{4} = \frac{23}{4}$

I multiply 4 and 5 to get the number of fourths in 5. Then I add 3 to get how many fourths in all.

$5\frac{3}{4} = \frac{23}{4}$ $(4 \times 5) + 3$

Changing a Fraction to a Mixed Number

fraction   (whole number)   mixed number

$\frac{17}{3} = \frac{15}{3} + \frac{2}{3} = 5 + \frac{2}{3} = 5\frac{2}{3}$

I divide 17 by 3 to get the whole number part. The remainder tells how many thirds in the fraction part.

$$\begin{array}{r} 5 \\ 3\overline{)17} \\ -15 \\ \hline 2 \end{array}$$ $\frac{17}{3} = 5\frac{2}{3}$

EXERCISES
Give a mixed number and a fraction for each red point.

1.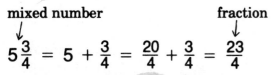
2.
3.
4.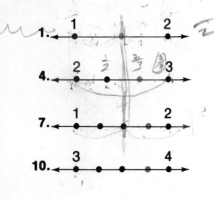
5.
6.
7.
8.
9.
10.
11.
12.

Change each mixed number to a fraction.

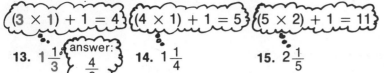

$(3 \times 1) + 1 = 4$ $(4 \times 1) + 1 = 5$ $(5 \times 2) + 1 = 11$

13. $1\frac{1}{3}$ answer: $\frac{4}{3}$

14. $1\frac{1}{4}$

15. $2\frac{1}{5}$

16. $1\frac{3}{4}$

17. $2\frac{3}{5}$

18. $2\frac{2}{5}$

19. $4\frac{3}{5}$

20. $4\frac{3}{10}$

21. $3\frac{1}{3}$

22. $3\frac{1}{4}$ 23. $2\frac{3}{8}$ 24. $5\frac{1}{5}$ 25. $6\frac{2}{3}$ 26. $1\frac{7}{8}$

27. $6\frac{3}{4}$ 28. $2\frac{5}{6}$ 29. $3\frac{5}{8}$ 30. $2\frac{4}{9}$ 31. $4\frac{3}{5}$

Change each fraction to a whole number or a mixed number.

32. $\frac{5}{3}$ 33. $\frac{7}{2}$ 34. $\frac{5}{4}$ 35. $\frac{5}{2}$ 36. $\frac{11}{4}$

37. $\frac{9}{8}$ 38. $\frac{6}{6}$ 39. $\frac{9}{5}$ 40. $\frac{15}{5}$ 41. $\frac{7}{6}$

42. $\frac{9}{4}$ 43. $\frac{11}{8}$ 44. $\frac{7}{3}$ 45. $\frac{9}{2}$ 46. $\frac{8}{3}$

47. $\frac{25}{6}$ 48. $\frac{21}{3}$ 49. $\frac{10}{2}$ 50. $\frac{10}{3}$ 51. $\frac{0}{3}$

Who am I?

52. I am a fraction equivalent to $3\frac{1}{2}$. My denominator is 4.

53. I am a fraction equivalent to $2\frac{3}{5}$. I am in lowest terms.

Excursion ▪●▪●▪●▪●▪●▪●▪●▪●▪●▪●▪●▪●▪●▪●▪●▪●

Using four 4s, write expressions for the numbers 1 through 8. Here are the first two:

$\frac{44}{44} = 1$

$\frac{4}{4} + \frac{4}{4} = 2$

Divide.

1. $3\overline{)15.9}$

2. $6\overline{)15.6}$

3. $2\overline{)15.6}$

4. $9\overline{)85.5}$

5. $6\overline{)2.28}$

6. $5\overline{)2.35}$

7. $5\overline{)6.75}$

8. $3\overline{)85.2}$

9. $4\overline{)0.824}$

10. $4\overline{)146.8}$

11. $3\overline{)17.82}$

12. $2\overline{)1.472}$

Adding mixed numbers

Here is how to find the sum of two mixed numbers.

EXAMPLE 1.

Step 1. Add fractions.

Step 2. Add whole numbers.

$$2\frac{2}{5}$$
$$+1\frac{1}{5}$$
$$\overline{3\frac{3}{5}}$$

EXAMPLE 2.

Step 1. Write fractions with a common denominator.

Step 2. Add fractions.

Step 3. Add whole numbers.

$$3\frac{2}{3} = 3\frac{8}{12}$$
$$+5\frac{1}{4} = +5\frac{3}{12}$$
$$\overline{8\frac{11}{12}}$$

You can regroup as you do with whole numbers.

EXAMPLE 3.

Step 1. Write fractions with a common denominator.

Step 2. Add fractions.

Step 3. Add whole numbers.

Step 4. Regroup so that the fraction is less than 1.

$$7\frac{2}{3} = 7\frac{4}{6}$$
$$+4\frac{1}{2} = +4\frac{3}{6}$$
$$\overline{11\frac{7}{6}} = 12\frac{1}{6}$$

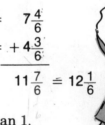

EXERCISES
Add. Remember to give the fraction part in lowest terms.

1. $3\frac{1}{4}$
   $+4\frac{1}{4}$

2. $8\frac{1}{7}$
   $+3\frac{4}{7}$

3. $5\frac{1}{2}$
   $+6\frac{1}{2}$

4. $9\frac{3}{8}$
   $+6\frac{1}{8}$

5. $10\frac{1}{6}$
   $+6\frac{5}{6}$

6. $8\frac{3}{8}$
   $+7\frac{3}{8}$

7. $4\frac{1}{4}$
   $+3\frac{1}{2}$

8. $3\frac{5}{6}$
   $+3\frac{1}{3}$

9. $12\frac{1}{3}$
   $+5\frac{2}{3}$

10. $6\frac{1}{2}$
    $+7\frac{2}{3}$

11. $6\frac{3}{4}$
    $+8\frac{1}{8}$

12. $13\frac{2}{5}$
    $+6$

13. $6\frac{1}{2}$
$+4\frac{5}{6}$

14. $4\frac{5}{8}$
$+3\frac{1}{2}$

15. $2\frac{1}{2}$
$+\frac{5}{8}$

16. $16\frac{3}{7}$
$+4\frac{1}{3}$

17. $12\frac{3}{4}$
$+5\frac{3}{8}$

18. $17\frac{2}{5}$
$+11\frac{3}{4}$

19. $15\frac{3}{5}$
$+8\frac{1}{2}$

20. $12\frac{2}{3}$
$+11\frac{3}{4}$

21. $16\frac{5}{8}$
$+13\frac{2}{3}$

22. $23\frac{4}{5}$
$+14$

23. $20\frac{5}{8}$
$+6\frac{5}{6}$

24. $24\frac{3}{4}$
$+19\frac{5}{8}$

Solve.

CHOCOLATES — $2.40 a pound

(1 pound + ½ pound)

RIBBON 48¢ a yard

25. How much will $1\frac{1}{2}$ pounds cost?

26. How much will $6\frac{2}{3}$ yards cost?

27. Jerry baby-sat $2\frac{1}{2}$ hours one evening and $1\frac{3}{4}$ hours the next evening. How many hours did he baby-sit in all?

28. The rainfall in May was $4\frac{3}{4}$ inches and in June it was $5\frac{1}{4}$ inches. What was the total rainfall for the two months?

29. Mary baked $2\frac{3}{4}$ dozen chocolate cookies and $3\frac{1}{3}$ dozen peanut butter cookies. How many dozen cookies did she bake? How many cookies did she bake?

30. During the first 3 days of a trip the Hunt family drove $5\frac{1}{2}$, $6\frac{3}{4}$, and $4\frac{1}{3}$ hours. How many hours did they drive during the 3 days?

Excursion ●■●■●■●■●■●■●■●■●■●■●■●■●■●■●■●■●■●

Ancient Egyptians expressed fractional numbers as a sum of unit fractions with *different* denominators. Here are some examples:

$$\frac{2}{5} = \frac{1}{3} + \frac{1}{15}$$
$$\frac{3}{5} = \frac{1}{3} + \frac{1}{15} + \frac{1}{5} \text{ or } \frac{1}{2} + \frac{1}{10}$$

How might they have expressed these fractions?

$$\frac{2}{7}, \frac{3}{7}, \frac{4}{9}, \frac{5}{9}$$

Subtracting mixed numbers

Here is how to find the difference of two mixed numbers.

EXAMPLE 1.

Step 1. Subtract fractional numbers.

Step 2. Subtract whole numbers.

$$3\frac{5}{7}$$
$$-1\frac{2}{7}$$
$$\overline{\quad\;2\frac{3}{7}}$$

EXAMPLE 2.

Step 1. Write fractions with a common denominator.

Step 2. Subtract fractional numbers.

Step 3. Subtract whole numbers.

$$5\frac{2}{3} = 5\frac{4}{6}$$
$$-2\frac{1}{2} = -2\frac{3}{6}$$
$$\overline{\qquad\quad 3\frac{1}{6}}$$

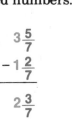
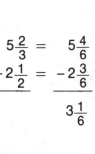

Sometimes you will need to regroup before subtracting the fractions.

EXAMPLE 3.

Step 1. Not enough fifths.
Regroup 1 into $\frac{5}{5}$.

Step 2. Subtract.

$$9\frac{2}{5} = 8\frac{7}{5}$$
$$-6\frac{3}{5} = -6\frac{3}{5}$$
$$\overline{\qquad\quad 2\frac{4}{5}}$$

You can show regrouping as you did with whole numbers.

$$\overset{8}{\cancel{9}}\frac{\overset{7}{\cancel{2}}}{5}$$
$$-6\frac{3}{5}$$
$$\overline{\quad 2\frac{4}{5}}$$

EXERCISES
Subtract. Remember to give the fraction part in lowest terms.

1. $8\frac{3}{4}$ 2. $9\frac{7}{8}$ 3. $6\frac{1}{2}$ 4. $15\frac{3}{4}$ 5. $8\frac{5}{9}$ 6. $15\frac{5}{7}$
   $-2\frac{1}{4}$ $-3\frac{3}{8}$ $-3\frac{1}{6}$ $-8\frac{3}{8}$ $-1\frac{1}{3}$ $-9\frac{1}{7}$

7. $11\frac{3}{4}$ 8. $9\;\;\;8\frac{5}{5}$ 9. 12 10. 6 11. 8 12. $11\frac{6}{7}$
   $-2\frac{1}{3}$ $-1\frac{3}{5}$ $-3\frac{1}{4}$ $-2\frac{5}{8}$ $-3\frac{2}{3}$ $-7\frac{1}{2}$

13. $8\frac{5}{6}$
    $-2\frac{1}{6}$

14. $6\frac{1}{4}$
    $-5\frac{3}{4}$

15. $16\frac{3}{8}$
    $-5\frac{5}{8}$

16. $12\frac{3}{4}$
    -10

17. $6\frac{3}{8}$
    $-2\frac{3}{4}$

18. $18\frac{3}{8}$
    $-2\frac{3}{4}$

19. $9\frac{2}{5}$
    $-6\frac{1}{2}$

20. $24\frac{1}{3}$
    $-18\frac{1}{2}$

21. 16
    $-5\frac{7}{8}$

22. $26\frac{7}{8}$
    $-4\frac{3}{4}$

23. 18
    $-9\frac{1}{2}$

24. $23\frac{3}{8}$
    -12

Solve.

25. One week Alvin watched TV for $6\frac{1}{4}$ hours and Beth watched TV for $3\frac{3}{4}$ hours. How many more hours did Alvin watch TV?

26. John long-jumped $16\frac{1}{4}$ feet and Kevin long-jumped $14\frac{2}{3}$ feet. How many feet farther did John jump?

27. Susan had $78\frac{1}{2}$ feet of kite string. She gave $18\frac{3}{4}$ feet of it to a friend. How many feet of string did she have left?

Give the perimeter of each figure.

28.
$4\frac{1}{2}$ ft
$2\frac{3}{4}$ ft

29.
$2\frac{7}{8}$ ft
$5\frac{1}{4}$ ft
6 ft

30.
$1\frac{7}{8}$ ft
$1\frac{7}{8}$ ft
$4\frac{1}{8}$ ft
$3\frac{1}{8}$ ft

Keeping Skills Sharp

Divide.

1. $2.6\overline{)15.938}$

2. $0.52\overline{)37.856}$

3. $4.1\overline{)21.894}$

4. $0.73\overline{)22.338}$

5. $8.9\overline{)814.35}$

6. $6.5\overline{)21.645}$

7. $4.4\overline{)36.3}$

8. $0.27\overline{)25.974}$

9. $0.64\overline{)3.6544}$

10. $113\overline{)20.679}$

11. $22.6\overline{)117.972}$

12. $0.438\overline{)0.279882}$

Practice exercises

Add.

1. $5\frac{2}{3}$
   $+7\frac{1}{3}$

2. 6
   $+8\frac{3}{5}$

3. $7\frac{3}{4}$
   $+9\frac{1}{4}$

4. $7\frac{1}{5}$
   $+8\frac{1}{8}$

5. $8\frac{3}{4}$
   $+8\frac{1}{8}$

6. $5\frac{5}{9}$
   $+9\frac{1}{3}$

7. $8\frac{1}{8}$
   $+9\frac{1}{4}$

8. $6\frac{5}{8}$
   $+6$

9. $9\frac{1}{2}$
   $+9\frac{1}{3}$

10. $8\frac{2}{3}$
    $+5\frac{1}{4}$

11. $12\frac{7}{8}$
    $+8\frac{1}{4}$

12. $13\frac{5}{8}$
    $+5\frac{1}{2}$

13. $19\frac{3}{4}$
    $+6\frac{2}{5}$

14. $17\frac{3}{4}$
    $+3\frac{3}{8}$

15. $18\frac{5}{6}$
    $+7\frac{1}{3}$

16. $12\frac{2}{3}$
    $+10\frac{5}{9}$

17. $15\frac{3}{8}$
    $+13\frac{7}{8}$

18. $23\frac{3}{4}$
    $+15\frac{1}{2}$

19. $25\frac{5}{8}$
    $+18\frac{3}{4}$

20. $30\frac{2}{3}$
    $+12\frac{3}{4}$

Subtract.

21. $8\frac{4}{5}$
    $-4\frac{1}{5}$

22. $9\frac{8}{9}$
    $-3\frac{2}{9}$

23. $7\frac{2}{3}$
    $-1\frac{1}{6}$

24. $9\frac{1}{2}$
    $-\frac{1}{3}$

25. $7\frac{7}{8}$
    $-2\frac{3}{4}$

26. $6\frac{9}{10}$
    $-3\frac{2}{5}$

27. $5\frac{3}{4}$
    $-2\frac{1}{3}$

28. $8\frac{5}{6}$
    -3

29. $5\frac{3}{4}$
    $-2\frac{5}{8}$

30. $9\frac{3}{5}$
    -6

31. 11
    $-4\frac{2}{3}$

32. 13
    $-8\frac{1}{4}$

33. $12\frac{1}{4}$
    $-3\frac{1}{8}$

34. $15\frac{1}{3}$
    $-9\frac{1}{2}$

35. $18\frac{1}{8}$
    $-9\frac{3}{4}$

36. $22\frac{1}{2}$
    $-8\frac{3}{4}$

37. 24
    $-9\frac{3}{5}$

38. $25\frac{1}{4}$
    $-11\frac{2}{5}$

39. $29\frac{1}{3}$
    $-16\frac{5}{6}$

40. 27
    $-18\frac{7}{8}$

Mathematics and world geography
Canada

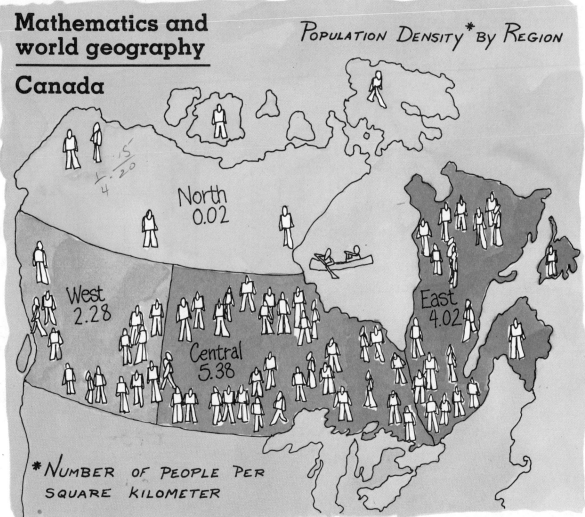

POPULATION DENSITY* BY REGION

North 0.02

West 2.28

Central 5.38

East 4.02

*NUMBER OF PEOPLE PER SQUARE KILOMETER

1. Which area has the greatest population density?

2. Which area has the least population density?

3. The area of the East is 2,080,332 square kilometers. What is the population of the East?

4. The area of the North is 3,917,044 square kilometers. What is the population of the North?

5. The population of the West is 5,251,000. What is the area of the West?

6. The population of the Central region is 9,357,000. What is the area of the Central region?

7. What is the total population of Canada? (Use exercises 3–6.)

8. What is the total area of Canada? (Use exercises 3–6.)

Problem solving

1. During a physical education class each student made 3 long jumps. The longest jump was recorded. Jan jumped 10' 2$\frac{1}{2}$", 11' 3$\frac{1}{4}$", and 10' 8$\frac{1}{4}$". What was her longest jump?

2. John's longest jump was 10' 8$\frac{1}{2}$". How much farther was Jan's longest jump? (See exercise 1.)

> Regrouped 1 foot for 12 inches.

$$11' 3\frac{1}{4}'' = \quad 10' 15\frac{1}{4}''$$
$$-10' 8\frac{1}{2}'' = -10' \quad 8\frac{1}{2}''$$

3. Mike's three jumps were 11' 1$\frac{1}{2}$", 10' 11$\frac{3}{4}$", and 11' 1$\frac{1}{2}$". Terry's three jumps were 10' $\frac{1}{2}$", 11' $\frac{3}{4}$", and 11' 4$\frac{1}{4}$". What was each boy's longest jump? How much farther was Terry's longest jump?

4. Bill's shortest jump was 9' 4$\frac{1}{2}$". His longest jump was 1' 7$\frac{3}{4}$" longer than his shortest jump. How far was his longest jump?

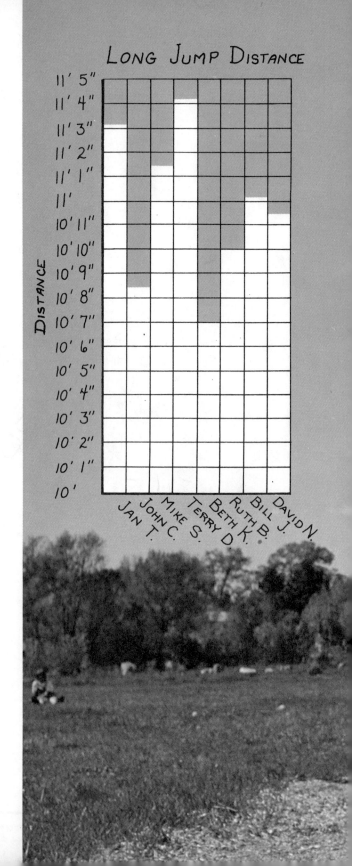

LONG JUMP DISTANCE

DISTANCE

11' 5"
11' 4"
11' 3"
11' 2"
11' 1"
11'
10' 11"
10' 10"
10' 9"
10' 8"
10' 7"
10' 6"
10' 5"
10' 4"
10' 3"
10' 2"
10' 1"
10'

JAN T.
JOHN C.
MIKE S.
TERRY D.
BETH K.
RUTH B.
BILL J.
DAVID N.

194

Refer to the graph to answer the following questions.

5. What was the longest jump?

6. Who had the shortest jump?

7. How many jumped more than 11 ft?

8. How many jumped farther than Ruth?

9. How much farther did Bill jump than John?

10. Who jumped 2 in. farther than David?

11. Who had the fifth longest jump?

12. What was the difference between the longest and shortest jumps?

CHAPTER CHECKUP

Give each sum in lowest terms. [pages 176–177, 180–181]

1. $\frac{1}{5} + \frac{3}{5}$
2. $\frac{1}{4} + \frac{1}{2}$
3. $\frac{3}{8} + \frac{1}{4}$
4. $\frac{1}{3} + \frac{1}{4}$

5. $\frac{3}{4} + \frac{2}{3}$
6. $\frac{7}{8} + \frac{5}{4}$
7. $\frac{5}{9} + \frac{2}{3}$
8. $\frac{0}{6} + \frac{3}{5}$

Give each difference in lowest terms. [pages 176–177, 182–184]

9. $\frac{5}{9} - \frac{2}{9}$
10. $\frac{7}{8} - \frac{3}{8}$
11. $\frac{5}{6} - \frac{1}{2}$
12. $\frac{3}{2} - \frac{3}{4}$

13. $\frac{5}{7} - \frac{0}{3}$
14. $\frac{1}{2} - \frac{1}{3}$
15. $\frac{3}{4} - \frac{2}{3}$
16. $\frac{5}{6} - \frac{5}{8}$

[pages 186–187]

Copy and complete. 17. 18. 19. 20. 21. 22. 23. 24. 25.

	17.	18.	19.	20.	21.	22.	23.	24.	25.
Fraction	$\frac{3}{2}$	$\frac{5}{3}$	$\frac{11}{4}$	$\frac{9}{5}$	$\frac{15}{6}$				
Mixed number						$2\frac{1}{2}$	$3\frac{1}{4}$	$4\frac{2}{3}$	$1\frac{3}{5}$

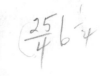

Add. [pages 188–189]

26. $3\frac{1}{5}$
$+2\frac{2}{5}$

27. $5\frac{1}{4}$
$+2\frac{1}{2}$

28. $6\frac{5}{8}$
$+3\frac{3}{4}$

29. $9\frac{5}{8}$
$+4\frac{3}{8}$

30. $6\frac{2}{5}$
$+3\frac{3}{4}$

31. 8
$+5\frac{2}{7}$

Subtract.

32. $8\frac{5}{9}$
$-3\frac{4}{9}$

33. $9\frac{3}{4}$
$-2\frac{1}{2}$

34. $8\frac{1}{2}$
$-5\frac{1}{3}$

35. $7\frac{1}{2}$
$-1\frac{3}{4}$

36. $7\frac{2}{3}$
$-5\frac{5}{6}$

37. 6
$-3\frac{7}{8}$

Solve. [pages 194–195]

38. A bread recipe calls for $\frac{3}{4}$ cup of white flour and $\frac{1}{2}$ cup of whole wheat flour. How much flour does the recipe call for?

39. Alice had $\frac{5}{8}$ yard of ribbon. She used $\frac{1}{2}$ yard on a dress. What fraction of a yard did she have left?

196

Project

1. Have each of your classmates jump from a line, measure the length of the jump in centimeters, and record the distance.

2. Have each classmate divide the length of the jump by his or her height and find the quotient to the nearest tenth.

EXAMPLE.

$$
\begin{array}{r}
1.17 \\
152 \overline{)178.00} \\
\underline{152} \\
26\ 0 \\
\underline{15\ 2} \\
10\ 80 \\
\underline{10\ 64} \\
16
\end{array}
$$

height → in cm

length of jump in cm

3. Graph the results on a graph like this:

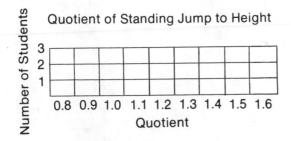

Quotient of Standing Jump to Height

Number of Students

3
2
1

0.8 0.9 1.0 1.1 1.2 1.3 1.4 1.5 1.6

Quotient

4. Repeat steps 1–3 for a running long jump.

197

CHAPTER REVIEW

$\frac{3}{4} + \frac{2}{3} = \frac{9}{12} + \frac{8}{12} = \frac{17}{12}$

$\frac{5}{3} - \frac{2}{5} = \frac{25}{15} - \frac{6}{15} = \frac{19}{15}$

Regroup $\frac{9}{8}$ for $1\frac{1}{8}$

$3\frac{1}{2} = 3\frac{4}{8}$
$+2\frac{5}{8} = +2\frac{5}{8}$
_____ _____
$6\frac{1}{8}$

Regroup 1 for $\frac{12}{12}$

$6\frac{1}{3} = 6\frac{4}{12} = 5\frac{16}{12}$
$-2\frac{3}{4} = -2\frac{9}{12} = -2\frac{9}{12}$
_____ _____
$3\frac{7}{12}$

Give the least common denominator.

1. $\frac{1}{3}$, $\frac{1}{4}$ 2. $\frac{2}{3}$, $\frac{1}{2}$ 3. $\frac{3}{8}$, $\frac{3}{4}$ 4. $\frac{2}{5}$, $\frac{1}{3}$

5. $\frac{5}{6}$, $\frac{3}{8}$ 6. $\frac{4}{9}$, $\frac{2}{3}$ 7. $\frac{5}{2}$, $\frac{3}{5}$ 8. $\frac{7}{4}$, $\frac{5}{6}$

Add. Reduce answers to lowest terms.

9. $\frac{2}{9} + \frac{3}{9}$ 10. $\frac{3}{8} + \frac{1}{8}$ 11. $\frac{3}{4} + \frac{1}{2}$

12. $\frac{5}{6} + \frac{1}{3}$ 13. $\frac{2}{3} + \frac{5}{4}$ 14. $\frac{7}{6} + \frac{5}{8}$

Subtract. Reduce answers to lowest terms.

15. $\frac{5}{6} - \frac{1}{6}$ 16. $\frac{1}{2} - \frac{1}{3}$ 17. $\frac{5}{8} - \frac{1}{4}$

18. $\frac{11}{12} - \frac{3}{4}$ 19. $\frac{5}{2} - \frac{5}{6}$ 20. $\frac{7}{3} - \frac{0}{5}$

Add.

21. $3\frac{1}{3}$ $+2\frac{1}{3}$ 22. $4\frac{1}{4}$ $+3\frac{1}{2}$ 23. $5\frac{1}{2}$ $+2\frac{1}{3}$

24. $6\frac{1}{2}$ $+3\frac{5}{8}$ 25. $4\frac{5}{6}$ $+2\frac{1}{3}$ 26. $5\frac{3}{4}$ $+3\frac{2}{3}$

Subtract.

27. $8\frac{5}{9}$ $-2\frac{1}{9}$ 28. $7\frac{3}{4}$ $-3\frac{1}{4}$ 29. $9\frac{5}{8}$ $-4\frac{1}{4}$

30. $6\frac{1}{3}$ $-1\frac{1}{2}$ 31. $8\frac{2}{3}$ $-2\frac{5}{6}$ 32. $7\frac{1}{8}$ $-3\frac{5}{16}$

CHAPTER CHALLENGE

1. Make a 4 × 4 square like the one shown.
2. Work the following exercises and replace each letter by its number.

a	b	c	d
e	f	g	h
i	j	k	l
m	n	o	p

Give

a. the greatest common factor of 15 and 18.

b. the sum of $\frac{5}{8}$ and $\frac{6}{8}$.

c. the sum of 1 and $\frac{1}{4}$.

d. the sum of $1\frac{1}{4}$ and $1\frac{3}{8}$.

e. the number that is $\frac{3}{8}$ less than 2.

f. the number that is $\frac{3}{4}$ less than 3.

g. the number that is $\frac{3}{8}$ greater than 2.

h. the only even prime number.

i. the number that is $1\frac{1}{2}$ greater than $\frac{5}{8}$.

j. the number that is $\frac{7}{12}$ greater than $1\frac{1}{6}$.

k. the difference of $3\frac{3}{8}$ and $1\frac{1}{2}$.

l. the difference of 3 and $\frac{1}{2}$.

m. the difference of $4\frac{5}{8}$ and $3\frac{1}{8}$.

n. the number that is $\frac{1}{2}$ greater than the sum of 1 and $1\frac{3}{8}$.

o. the number that is $\frac{1}{4}$ less than the difference of $5\frac{1}{8}$ and $2\frac{1}{8}$.

p. the number that is $\frac{3}{8}$ greater than the difference of 1 and $\frac{1}{4}$.

3. If you didn't make any mistakes, your completed square should be a magic square. That is, the sum of the numbers in each row, column, and diagonal should be the same. Check to see whether your square is magic.

MAJOR CHECKUP
Standardized Format

Choose the correct letter.

1. 535,000,000 rounded to the nearest ten million is

    a. 530,000,000
    b. 535,000,000
    c. 500,000,000
    d. none of these

2. Divide.

$136\overline{)14282}$

    a. 15 R2
    b. 155 R2
    c. 105 R2
    d. none of these

3. Add.

    2.93
    .08
    25.6
  +7.42

    a. 36.03
    b. 24.93
    c. 35.03
    d. none of these

4. Find this difference.

37.6 − 2.54

    a. 1322
    b. 12.2
    c. 35.06
    d. none of these

5. Multiply.

    5.84
  ×6.5

    a. 37.96
    b. 63.24
    c. 3.796
    d. none of these

6. Divide.

$2.6\overline{)7.93}$

    a. 3.05
    b. 0.35
    c. 3.5
    d. none of these

7. Find the perimeter.

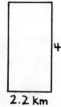

4.5 km
2.2 km

    a. 6.7 km
    b. 13.4 km
    c. 9.9 km
    d. none of these

8. Find the area.

6.3 m 10.5 m 8.4 m

    a. 25.2 m²
    b. 52.92 m²
    c. 26.46 m²
    d. none of these

9. Find the surface area of of this cube.

5 cm

    a. 25 cm²
    b. 125 cm²
    c. 100 cm²
    d. none of these

10. Find the volume.

Use 3.14 as an approximation for π.

3 cm
10 cm

    a. 282.6 cm³
    b. 28.26 cm³
    c. 259.788 cm³
    d. none of these

11. The greatest common factor of 9 and 12 is

    a. 36
    b. 9
    c. 3
    d. none of these

12. Which of these numbers is prime?

    a. 9
    b. 21
    c. 31
    d. 36

MIDYEAR TEST

Add or subtract.

1. 9461
    + 3953

2. 786
    237
    + 89

3. 6248
    − 2519

4. 7002
    − 3594

Multiply or divide.

5. 596
    × 58

6. 7218
    × 309

7. 8)1624

8. 94)36085

Round 563.8905 to the nearest

9. hundredth

10. tenth

11. one

12. thousandth

Add or subtract.

13. 2.9
    + 5.78

14. 8.846
    5.92
    + 1.396

15. 450.3
    − 318.4

16. 34
    − 15.75

Multiply or divide.

17. 9.84
    × 62

18. 12.8
    × 10.3

19. 5)3.965

20. 1.25)43.285

Solve.

21. What was Garcia's best time?

22. What is the difference between Northrup's best and worst times?

23. Find Jackson's average time.

24. Find the average time for the third dash. Give answer to the nearest 0.01 of a second.

Results of 50-Meter Dash			
Name	Time in Seconds of 3 Dashes		
	1st	2nd	3rd
Davis	12.5	13.0	12.8
Garcia	13.4	12.9	13.3
Howard	14.3	13.6	13.4
Jackson	13.5	13.6	13.1
Northrup	14.3	13.9	13.7
Trotter	13.6	14.2	13.8

Continued on the next page

Ch. 1

Ch. 2

Ch. 3

201

Complete.

25. The greatest common factor of 18 and 24 is __?__.

26. The prime factorization of 60 is __?__.

27. The least common multiple of 6 and 9 is __?__.

Solve each equation.

28. $n - 8 = 9$ 29. $n + 18 = 39$ 30. $25 + n = 25$

Complete.

31. 40 mm = __?__ cm   32. 900 cm = __?__ m

33. 3.6 km = __?__ m   34. 570 mm = __?__ m

Give the perimeter (circumference).
Use 3.14 as an approximation for π.

35.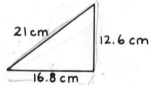
21 cm 12.6 cm 16.8 cm

36.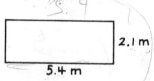
2.1 m 5.4 m

37.
8.2 cm

Give the area.
Use 3.14 as an approximation for π.

38.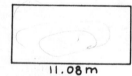
5.61 m 11.08 m

39.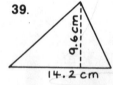
9.6 cm 14.2 cm

40.
1.5 m

41. Find the surface area.

42. Find the volume.

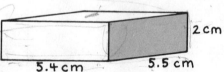
2 cm 5.4 cm 5.5 cm

Give each sum or difference in lowest terms.

43. $\dfrac{2}{5} + \dfrac{1}{5}$

44. $\dfrac{3}{4} + \dfrac{2}{3}$

45. $\dfrac{5}{8} - \dfrac{3}{8}$

46. $\dfrac{3}{2} - \dfrac{2}{3}$

47. $5\dfrac{1}{3}$
$+ 2\dfrac{1}{2}$

48. $6\dfrac{3}{4}$
$+ 4\dfrac{5}{8}$

49. $7\dfrac{1}{3}$
$- 2\dfrac{3}{8}$

50. 9
$- 4\dfrac{3}{5}$

7 Fractions—Multiplication and Division

This is a unit square.

What fraction of a unit square is colored?

1.

2.

3.

4.

5.

6.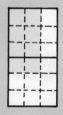

Multiplying fractions

We can multiply to find what part of the square is green.

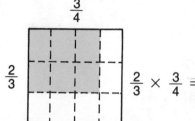

$$\frac{2}{3} \times \frac{3}{4} = \frac{6}{12} \leftarrow \text{green parts} \atop \leftarrow \text{total parts}$$

To multiply two fractions, multiply the numerators to get the numerator of the product, and multiply the denominators to get the denominator of the product.

EXERCISES
Multiply.

1. $\frac{2}{3} \times \frac{1}{2}$

2. $\frac{1}{2} \times \frac{1}{3}$

3. $\frac{2}{3} \times \frac{2}{3}$

4. $\frac{1}{2} \times \frac{3}{5}$

5. $\frac{1}{3} \times \frac{3}{4}$

6. $\frac{4}{5} \times \frac{3}{2}$

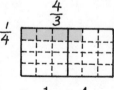

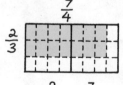

7. $\frac{1}{4} \times \frac{4}{3}$

8. $\frac{2}{3} \times \frac{7}{4}$

204

Multiply. Reduce answers to lowest terms.

9. $\frac{1}{4} \times \frac{1}{5}$ 10. $\frac{7}{8} \times \frac{2}{3}$ 11. $\frac{1}{8} \times \frac{1}{7}$ 12. $\frac{3}{1} \times \frac{2}{3}$

13. $\frac{3}{8} \times \frac{2}{3}$ 14. $\frac{8}{5} \times \frac{3}{4}$ 15. $\frac{3}{5} \times \frac{5}{3}$ 16. $\frac{0}{3} \times \frac{4}{5}$

17. $\frac{3}{7} \times \frac{2}{3}$ 18. $4 \times \frac{5}{6}$ 19. $\frac{1}{2} \times \frac{3}{8}$ 20. $\frac{2}{3} \times \frac{3}{10}$

21. $\frac{7}{8} \times \frac{8}{7}$ 22. $\frac{4}{7} \times \frac{2}{5}$ 23. $\frac{3}{4} \times 5$ 24. $\frac{3}{2} \times \frac{5}{2}$

25. $\frac{3}{4} \times \frac{4}{3}$ 26. $\frac{3}{4} \times \frac{8}{7}$ 27. $\frac{5}{7} \times \frac{4}{6}$ 28. $\frac{3}{5} \times \frac{2}{2}$

29. $\frac{3}{5} \times \frac{1}{4}$ 30. $\frac{5}{2} \times \frac{2}{3}$ 31. $\frac{5}{9} \times \frac{3}{1}$ 32. $\frac{5}{9} \times \frac{3}{2}$ $\frac{15}{18}$ $\frac{5}{6}$

33. $\frac{3}{10} \times \frac{5}{6}$ 34. $\frac{4}{5} \times \frac{4}{5}$ 35. $5 \times \frac{2}{3}$ 36. $\frac{7}{8} \times 2$

37. $\frac{7}{4} \times 4$ 38. $\frac{2}{3} \times \frac{0}{3}$ 39. $\frac{0}{8} \times 5$ $\frac{6}{8}$ 40. $4 \times \frac{5}{4}$

41. $3 \times \frac{4}{5}$ 42. $\frac{4}{5} \times \frac{3}{8}$ 43. $\frac{3}{8} \times \frac{5}{6}$ 44. $\frac{0}{5} \times \frac{1}{2}$

45. $\frac{2}{3} \times \frac{3}{2}$ 46. $\frac{5}{12} \times \frac{3}{5}$ 47. $\frac{7}{5} \times \frac{5}{3}$ 48. $\frac{7}{10} \times \frac{2}{5}$

Multiply across and multiply down. Give answers in lowest terms.

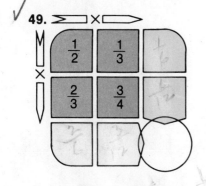

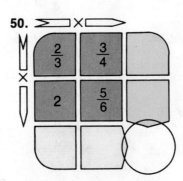

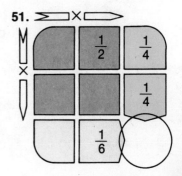

Fraction of a number

The Denim Den is having a sale on blue jeans. One style of jeans is regularly $24. To find the sale price, we take $\frac{3}{4}$ of $24.

$$\frac{3}{4} \text{ of } \$24 = \$18$$

To find $\frac{3}{4}$ of 24, I first divide 24 by 4 to find $\frac{1}{4}$ of 24. Then I multiply that by 3, getting 18.

SALE
all jeans
$\frac{3}{4}$ of
Marked price

Finding a fraction of a number can be thought of as a multiplication problem.

$$\frac{3}{4} \text{ of } 24 = \frac{3}{4} \times 24$$
$$= \frac{72}{4}$$
$$= 18$$

EXERCISES
Compute.

1. $\frac{1}{2}$ of 18

2. $\frac{1}{3}$ of 21

3. $\frac{1}{5}$ of 60

4. $\frac{1}{4}$ of 20

5. $\frac{1}{8}$ of 32

6. $\frac{1}{6}$ of 54

7. $\frac{1}{3}$ of 18.3

8. $\frac{2}{3}$ of 3.18

9. $\frac{4}{9}$ of 38.7

10. $\frac{1}{4}$ of 264

11. $\frac{2}{4}$ of 264

12. $\frac{3}{4}$ of 264

13. $\frac{5}{8}$ of 24

14. $\frac{3}{8}$ of 16

15. $\frac{5}{4}$ of 100

16. $\frac{3}{2}$ of 140

17. $\frac{5}{6}$ of 30

18. $\frac{7}{8}$ of 56

19. $\frac{2}{3}$ of 36

20. $\frac{3}{2}$ of 36

21. $\frac{6}{5}$ of 40

22. $\frac{3}{10}$ of 54.6

23. $\frac{4}{5}$ of 3.75

24. $\frac{2}{2}$ of 9.38

Here are some price tags from the Denim Den. Compute the sale prices. *Remember:* **The sale price is $\frac{3}{4}$ of the regular price. Round each price to the nearest cent.**

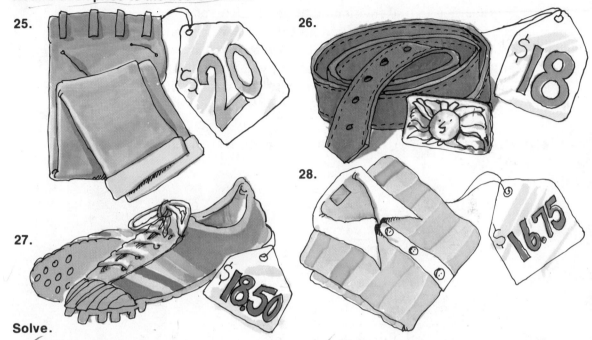

25.

26.

27.

28.

Solve.

29. Sarah wants to buy a new bicycle that cost $96.99. Her father will pay $\frac{1}{3}$ of the price. How much money will Sarah need for her share?

30. Joe can throw a football $\frac{2}{5}$ of the length of a football field (100 yards). How many yards can he throw a football?

31. A club wants to sell 120 tickets for a chili supper. They have sold $\frac{5}{6}$ of their tickets. How many tickets do they have left to sell?

32. To get to school, Alex ran $\frac{3}{8}$ of a mile. How many yards is that?

33. There are 464 students in a school. Five-eighths of them are girls. How many boys are in the school?

34. Mr. Adams earns $720 per month. How much money would he save in a year if he saved $\frac{1}{8}$ of his earnings?

35. A furlong, $\frac{1}{8}$ of a mile, is used for horse racing. How many yards long is a 7-furlong race?

★36. Carol earns $1.75 per hour. She saves $\frac{5}{7}$ of that. How many hours must she work to save $25?

More about equivalent fractions

Earlier, you learned to find fractions that are equivalent to a given fraction by multiplying or dividing both numerator and denominator by the same number (not 0). Now that you know how to multiply fractions, you can look at equivalent fractions in another way. The multiplying by 1 property tells you that if you multiply a number by 1, you get that same number.

You also know that $\frac{2}{2}$, $\frac{3}{3}$, $\frac{4}{4}$, etc., are all equal to 1. Let's put these ideas together.

$$\frac{3}{4} = \frac{3}{4} \times 1 = \frac{3}{4} \times \frac{2}{2} = \frac{6}{8}$$
equivalent fractions

$$\frac{7}{3} = \frac{7}{3} \times 1 = \frac{7}{3} \times \frac{4}{4} = \frac{28}{12}$$
equivalent fractions

Explain each step in the examples above.

Equivalent fractions →

X	$\frac{2}{2}$	$\frac{3}{3}$	$\frac{4}{4}$	$\frac{5}{5}$	$\frac{6}{6}$	$\frac{7}{7}$	$\frac{8}{8}$
$\frac{1}{2}$	$\frac{2}{4}$	$\frac{3}{6}$	$\frac{4}{8}$	$\frac{5}{10}$	$\frac{6}{12}$	$\frac{7}{14}$	$\frac{8}{16}$
$\frac{1}{3}$	$\frac{2}{6}$	$\frac{3}{9}$	$\frac{4}{12}$	$\frac{5}{15}$	$\frac{6}{18}$	$\frac{7}{21}$	$\frac{8}{24}$
$\frac{2}{3}$	$\frac{4}{6}$	$\frac{6}{9}$	$\frac{8}{12}$	$\frac{10}{15}$	$\frac{12}{18}$	$\frac{14}{21}$	$\frac{16}{24}$

EXERCISES

Multiply. Give each product in lowest terms.

1. $\frac{1}{4} \times \frac{2}{2}$

2. $\frac{2}{3} \times \frac{3}{3}$

3. $\frac{1}{3} \times \frac{5}{5}$

4. $\frac{3}{2} \times \frac{4}{4}$

5. $\frac{5}{2} \times \frac{6}{6}$

6. $\frac{1}{2} \times \frac{5}{5}$

7. $\frac{4}{3} \times \frac{8}{8}$

8. $\frac{5}{4} \times \frac{2}{2}$

9. $\frac{5}{3} \times \frac{3}{4}$

10. $\frac{3}{5} \times \frac{2}{3}$

11. $\frac{1}{5} \times \frac{4}{5}$

12. $\frac{4}{5} \times \frac{2}{3}$

13. $\frac{5}{6} \times \frac{4}{4}$

14. $\frac{1}{6} \times \frac{3}{5}$

15. $\frac{7}{2} \times \frac{2}{5}$

16. $\frac{7}{5} \times \frac{1}{6}$

Give each product in lowest terms.

17. $3 \times \dfrac{3}{4}$

18. $\dfrac{1}{2} \times \dfrac{1}{3}$

19. $\dfrac{1}{3} \times 6$

20. $4 \times \dfrac{3}{4}$

21. $\dfrac{3}{8} \times \dfrac{4}{5}$

22. $\dfrac{2}{3} \times \dfrac{3}{5}$

23. $\dfrac{7}{8} \times \dfrac{4}{3}$

24. $\dfrac{5}{9} \times \dfrac{2}{2}$

25. $\dfrac{2}{2} \times 3$

26. $\dfrac{1}{4} \times 7$

27. $\dfrac{5}{8} \times \dfrac{5}{8}$

28. $\dfrac{5}{9} \times \dfrac{3}{5}$

29. $\dfrac{5}{8} \times \dfrac{3}{3}$

30. $\dfrac{7}{2} \times \dfrac{4}{3}$

31. $\dfrac{6}{7} \times \dfrac{2}{3}$

32. $\dfrac{5}{8} \times \dfrac{12}{5}$

33. $\dfrac{1}{2} \times 2$

34. $\dfrac{3}{2} \times \dfrac{2}{3}$

Give the sale price of each item.

SALE ²⁄₃ of marked price

35. 39¢

36. 15¢ Eraser

37. Glue 48¢

38. 78¢

39. 45¢

Subtract. Reduce answers to lowest terms.

1. $\dfrac{3}{4} - \dfrac{1}{4}$

2. $\dfrac{1}{2} - \dfrac{1}{8}$

3. $2 - \dfrac{2}{3}$

4. $1 - \dfrac{2}{5}$

5. $\dfrac{3}{4} - \dfrac{3}{8}$

6. $\dfrac{5}{6} - \dfrac{1}{2}$

7. $\dfrac{1}{2} - \dfrac{1}{3}$

8. $\dfrac{1}{3} - \dfrac{1}{4}$

9. $\dfrac{3}{4} - \dfrac{2}{3}$

10. $\dfrac{3}{2} - \dfrac{2}{3}$

11. $\dfrac{7}{8} - \dfrac{5}{6}$

12. $\dfrac{4}{3} - \dfrac{3}{8}$

Reciprocals

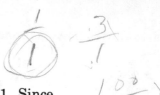

Two numbers are **reciprocals** if their product is 1. Since
$\frac{2}{3} \times \frac{3}{2} = 1$, $\frac{2}{3}$ and $\frac{3}{2}$ are reciprocals.

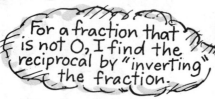

$\frac{3}{5} \times \frac{5}{3}$

EXERCISES
Give the reciprocal of each number.

1. 3   2. $\frac{1}{2}$ 3. $\frac{1}{9}$ 4. $\frac{5}{8}$ 5. $\frac{2}{3}$ 6. $\frac{6}{7}$ 7. $\frac{3}{5}$ 8. $\frac{2}{9}$

9. $\frac{3}{4}$ 10. $\frac{4}{3}$ 11. $\frac{11}{12}$ 12. 6 13. $\frac{13}{2}$ 14. $\frac{15}{9}$ 15. 15   16. 100

Who am I?

17. I do not have a reciprocal.   18. I am my own reciprocal.

Complete.

19. $\frac{2}{3} \times ? = 1$ 20. $? \times \frac{1}{2} = 1$ 21. $5 \times ? = 1$

22. $1 \times ? = 1$ 23. $\frac{3}{4} \times ? = 1$ 24. $? \times \frac{9}{5} = 1$

25. $? \times \frac{1}{3} = 1$ 26. $\frac{5}{8} \times ? = 1$ 27. $12 \times ? = 1$

28. $4 \times ? = 1$ 29. $16 \times ? = 1$ 30. $\frac{1}{18} \times ? = 1$

31. $\frac{5}{9} \times ? = 1$ 32. $? \times \frac{7}{5} = 1$ 33. $? \times \frac{13}{4} = 1$

34. $\frac{2}{5} \times ? = 1$ 35. $? \times \frac{9}{2} = 1$ 36. $? \times \frac{7}{8} = 1$

37. $3 \times ? = 1$ 38. $? \times 10 = 1$ 39. $? \times \frac{3}{5} = 1$

40. $? \times 6 = 1$ 41. $? \times \frac{1}{6} = 1$ 42. $\frac{1}{8} \times ? = 1$

43. $\frac{5}{6} \times ? = 1$ 44. $\frac{10}{9} \times ? = 1$ 45. $? \times \frac{10}{11} = 1$

First complete. Then compare your answers in each exercise.

46.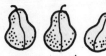

a. How many $\frac{1}{2}$s in 3?

b. $3 \div \frac{1}{2} = ?$

c. $3 \times 2 = ?$

47.

a. How many $\frac{1}{3}$s in 2?

b. $2 \div \frac{1}{3} = ?$

c. $2 \times 3 = ?$

48.

a. How many $\frac{2}{3}$s in 2?

b. $2 \div \frac{2}{3} = ?$

c. $2 \times \frac{3}{2} = ?$

49.

a. How many $\frac{3}{4}$s in 3?

b. $3 \div \frac{3}{4} = ?$

c. $3 \times \frac{4}{3} = ?$

50.

a. How many $\frac{2}{5}$s in $\frac{4}{5}$?

b. $\frac{4}{5} \div \frac{2}{5} = ?$

c. $\frac{4}{5} \times \frac{5}{2} = ?$

51.

a. How many $\frac{2}{3}$s in $\frac{8}{3}$?

b. $\frac{8}{3} \div \frac{2}{3} = ?$

c. $\frac{8}{3} \times \frac{3}{2} = ?$

Complete.

52. Look at exercise 48. Dividing by $\frac{2}{3}$ is the same as multiplying by ___?___.

53. Look at exercise 49. Dividing by $\frac{3}{4}$ is the same as multiplying by ___?___.

54. Look at exercise 50. Dividing by $\frac{2}{5}$ is the same as multiplying by the reciprocal of ___?___.

55. Look at exercise 51. Dividing by $\frac{2}{3}$ is the same as multiplying by the reciprocal of ___?___.

 What is the reciprocal of 0.125? Of 0.0125?

Dividing by a fraction

Suppose that it takes $\frac{3}{4}$ of a pound of salt mixed with ice to freeze one container of ice cream. How many containers of ice cream can be frozen with $5\frac{1}{2}$-pound boxes of salt?

$$\frac{5}{2} \div \frac{3}{4} = ?$$

To solve this, you can think about cutting the boxes in half to get $\frac{1}{4}$-lb boxes and then grouping 3 of the $\frac{1}{4}$-lb boxes together.

There is enough salt to freeze $3\frac{1}{3}$, or $\frac{10}{3}$, containers of ice cream.

$$\frac{5}{2} \div \frac{3}{4} = \frac{10}{3}$$

To divide by a fraction, you can multiply by its reciprocal.

reciprocals

$$\frac{5}{2} \div \frac{3}{4} = \frac{5}{2} \times \frac{4}{3}$$
$$= \frac{20}{6}$$
$$= \frac{10}{3}$$

EXERCISES
Complete.

1. To divide by $\frac{3}{5}$, you can multiply by the reciprocal of __?__.

2. Dividing by $\frac{4}{7}$ is the same as multiplying by the reciprocal of __?__.

3. Dividing by $\frac{6}{5}$ is the same as multiplying by __?__.

4. To divide by $\frac{5}{8}$, you can multiply by the reciprocal of __?__.

Divide. Give quotients in lowest terms.

$$\frac{2}{3} \times \frac{1}{2}$$

$$\frac{3}{2} \times \frac{4}{1}$$

$$\frac{3}{4} \times \frac{4}{1}$$

$$\frac{3}{8} \times \frac{1}{2}$$

5. $\frac{2}{3} \div 2$ 6. $\frac{3}{2} \div \frac{1}{4}$ 7. $\frac{3}{4} \div \frac{1}{4}$ 8. $\frac{3}{8} \div 2$

9. $\frac{3}{4} \div \frac{2}{3}$ 10. $\frac{5}{8} \div 3$ 11. $\frac{4}{5} \div \frac{2}{2}$ 12. $8 \div \frac{3}{5}$

13. $5 \div \frac{2}{5}$ 14. $\frac{5}{6} \div \frac{3}{8}$ 15. $\frac{3}{5} \div 4$ 16. $\frac{0}{4} \div \frac{1}{2}$

17. $\frac{5}{9} \div \frac{1}{3}$ 18. $6 \div \frac{1}{2}$ 19. $\frac{6}{5} \div \frac{3}{3}$ 20. $\frac{7}{4} \div \frac{7}{4}$

21. $\frac{3}{8} \div \frac{3}{4}$ 22. $\frac{3}{4} \div \frac{3}{8}$ 23. $\frac{5}{9} \div \frac{2}{3}$ 24. $\frac{2}{3} \div \frac{5}{9}$

25. $\frac{5}{6} \div \frac{2}{3}$ 26. $\frac{2}{3} \div \frac{5}{6}$ 27. $\frac{3}{8} \div \frac{3}{2}$ 28. $\frac{3}{2} \div \frac{3}{8}$

29. $\frac{2}{5} \div \frac{1}{4}$ 30. $\frac{0}{5} \div \frac{5}{6}$ 31. $\frac{5}{9} \div \frac{4}{3}$ 32. $\frac{7}{8} \div \frac{5}{4}$

33. $\frac{5}{4} \div 3$ 34. $\frac{6}{5} \div \frac{1}{10}$ 35. $\frac{8}{3} \div \frac{4}{3}$ 36. $\frac{9}{2} \div \frac{3}{4}$

Solve.

37. How much vanilla is needed to make 2 gallons of ice cream?

38. The recipe calls for $2\frac{1}{2}$ ($\frac{5}{2}$) cups of sugar. How many gallons of ice cream can be made from $1\frac{1}{4}$ ($\frac{5}{4}$) cups of sugar?

    Hint: $\frac{5}{4} \div \frac{5}{2}$

39. Suppose that you have $1\frac{1}{2}$ cups of heavy cream. How much more heavy cream do you need to make a full recipe?

40. Suppose that you have $3\frac{1}{4}$ cups of sugar and want to make 2 gallons of ice cream. How much more sugar do you need?

Vanilla Ice Cream
makes 1 gallon

4 eggs

$2\frac{1}{2}$ cups of sugar

$3\frac{1}{4}$ cups of heavy cream

$2\frac{3}{4}$ tablespoons of vanilla

$6\frac{1}{2}$ cups of whole milk

Beat eggs and sugar until thick.
Blend in cream and vanilla.
Add milk.

Practice exercises

Give each product in lowest terms.

1. $\frac{2}{3} \times \frac{4}{4}$

2. $\frac{3}{10} \times \frac{2}{9}$

3. $\frac{2}{5} \times \frac{4}{7}$

4. $\frac{5}{8} \times \frac{0}{6}$

5. $\frac{1}{8} \times \frac{1}{6}$

6. $\frac{1}{4} \times \frac{1}{2}$

7. $\frac{1}{2} \times \frac{5}{8}$

8. $\frac{4}{4} \times \frac{3}{8}$

9. $\frac{5}{3} \times \frac{2}{2}$

10. $\frac{5}{6} \times \frac{3}{10}$

11. $6 \times \frac{5}{12}$

12. $\frac{5}{3} \times 2$

13. $\frac{7}{9} \times \frac{3}{7}$

14. $2 \times \frac{3}{4}$

15. $\frac{1}{4} \times \frac{2}{2}$

16. $\frac{0}{3} \times \frac{5}{2}$

17. $\frac{3}{8} \times 5$

18. $\frac{5}{8} \times \frac{8}{5}$

19. $\frac{2}{2} \times \frac{3}{2}$

20. $\frac{7}{10} \times \frac{4}{3}$

21. $\frac{5}{6} \times \frac{0}{2}$

22. $\frac{5}{12} \times \frac{3}{8}$

23. $\frac{5}{9} \times \frac{9}{5}$

24. $5 \times \frac{2}{5}$

Give each quotient in lowest terms.

25. $\frac{1}{2} \div \frac{1}{3}$

26. $\frac{1}{3} \div \frac{1}{2}$

27. $\frac{2}{3} \div \frac{2}{3}$

28. $\frac{3}{4} \div \frac{1}{4}$

29. $3 \div \frac{4}{5}$

30. $\frac{3}{4} \div \frac{2}{2}$

31. $\frac{7}{3} \div 2$

32. $\frac{1}{8} \div \frac{9}{5}$

33. $\frac{8}{5} \div \frac{5}{9}$

34. $\frac{0}{6} \div \frac{4}{3}$

35. $\frac{4}{9} \div \frac{1}{3}$

36. $\frac{9}{2} \div \frac{5}{8}$

37. $\frac{8}{7} \div 4$

38. $\frac{1}{2} \div \frac{2}{3}$

39. $2 \div \frac{5}{6}$

40. $\frac{7}{2} \div 4$

41. $\frac{3}{4} \div \frac{1}{8}$

42. $\frac{3}{15} \div \frac{5}{3}$

43. $\frac{5}{16} \div \frac{1}{2}$

44. $\frac{3}{2} \div \frac{3}{14}$

45. $\frac{0}{3} \div \frac{5}{8}$

46. $\frac{9}{5} \div \frac{3}{8}$

47. $\frac{1}{5} \div \frac{15}{4}$

48. $\frac{3}{4} \div \frac{3}{4}$

Multiply across and multiply down. Give answers in lowest terms.

49.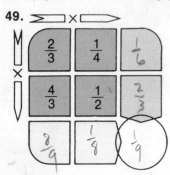

50.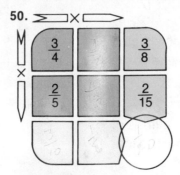

51.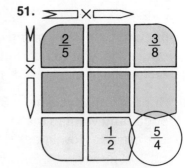

214

Mathematics and world geography

Egypt

1. When the largest of the pyramids was completed, its base was a square about 234 meters on each side and its height was 147 meters. What was the volume of the pyramid? (The formula for the volume of a pyramid is $V = \frac{1}{3} Bh$, where B is the area of the base and h is the height of the pyramid.)

2. For 30 years 100,000 men worked, first to build a roadway for transporting the stone, and then to build the Great Pyramid. If the men worked every day of every year, how many man-days of work did it take to complete the job? (Ignore leap years.)

3. Khufu, the Egyptian king buried in the Great Pyramid, reigned for about 23 years beginning in 2900 B.C. When did his reign end?

4. The circumference of the head of the Sphinx is about 22 meters. Assuming that the head is circular, what is its diameter?

The cancellation shortcut

Here is a shortcut that can often be used when multiplying fractions. It gives the product in lowest terms. The shortcut, called **canceling**, is to divide both numerator and denominator by a common factor *before* doing the multiplication. Here is an example.

EXAMPLE.

$$\frac{3}{8} \times \frac{4}{3} = ?$$

Step 1.
Divide by 3.

$$\frac{\cancel{3}}{8} \times \frac{4}{\cancel{3}} = ?$$

Step 2.
Divide by 4.

$$\frac{\cancel{3}}{\underset{2}{\cancel{8}}} \times \frac{\cancel{4}}{\cancel{3}}$$

Step 3.
Multiply.

$$\frac{\cancel{3}}{\cancel{8}} \times \frac{\cancel{4}}{\cancel{3}} = \frac{1}{2}$$

The product is in lowest terms.

OTHER EXAMPLES.

Divide by 2.
Divide by 2.

$$\frac{\cancel{6}}{\cancel{8}} \times \frac{2}{5} = \frac{3}{10}$$

Divide by 2.
Divide by 3.

$$\frac{9}{12} \times \frac{\cancel{6}}{\cancel{8}} = \frac{9}{16}$$

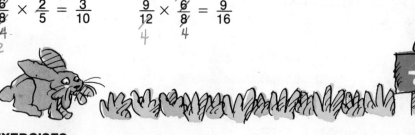

EXERCISES
Multiply.

1. $\frac{3}{5} \times \frac{10}{3}$

2. $\frac{4}{7} \times \frac{14}{12}$

3. $\frac{5}{9} \times \frac{3}{15}$

4. $\frac{7}{5} \times \frac{6}{14}$

5. $\frac{6}{4} \times \frac{8}{9}$

6. $\frac{4}{9} \times \frac{18}{12}$

7. $8 \times \frac{1}{12}$

8. $\frac{16}{9} \times \frac{3}{20}$

9. $12 \times \frac{3}{16}$

10. $\frac{15}{21} \times \frac{14}{10}$

11. $\frac{16}{24} \times \frac{18}{14}$

12. $\frac{15}{32} \times \frac{24}{20}$

13. $\frac{35}{8} \times \frac{12}{20}$

14. $\frac{16}{42} \times \frac{36}{24}$

15. $\frac{16}{7} \times 35$

16. $\frac{45}{14} \times \frac{28}{35}$

Divide. **Example.** $\dfrac{5}{6} \div \dfrac{2}{3} = \dfrac{5}{\cancel{6}_2} \times \dfrac{\cancel{3}^1}{2} = \dfrac{5}{4}$

17. $\dfrac{3}{8} \div \dfrac{5}{6}$

18. $\dfrac{4}{7} \div \dfrac{2}{3}$

19. $\dfrac{6}{9} \div \dfrac{1}{3}$

20. $\dfrac{24}{36} \div 2$

21. $\dfrac{16}{42} \div \dfrac{36}{24}$

22. $\dfrac{45}{13} \div \dfrac{25}{26}$

23. $\dfrac{15}{17} \div \dfrac{15}{17}$

24. $\dfrac{18}{24} \div \dfrac{3}{8}$

25. $8 \div \dfrac{3}{2}$

26. $\dfrac{4}{5} \div 6$

27. $5 \div \dfrac{10}{3}$

28. $\dfrac{3}{4} \div 8$

29. $\dfrac{4}{5} \div \dfrac{5}{4}$

30. $\dfrac{12}{5} \div \dfrac{4}{10}$

31. $\dfrac{4}{5} \div \dfrac{8}{10}$

32. $\dfrac{5}{9} \div \dfrac{15}{3}$

33. $\dfrac{7}{8} \div \dfrac{21}{4}$

34. $\dfrac{24}{25} \div \dfrac{16}{5}$

Change to a fraction.

1. $2\dfrac{1}{2}$ 2. $3\dfrac{1}{4}$

3. $4\dfrac{1}{4}$ 4. $5\dfrac{1}{3}$

5. $2\dfrac{2}{3}$ 6. $2\dfrac{5}{16}$

7. $3\dfrac{3}{4}$ 8. $4\dfrac{2}{5}$

Change to a mixed number.

9. $\dfrac{7}{2}$ 10. $\dfrac{10}{3}$

11. $\dfrac{5}{4}$ 12. $\dfrac{13}{5}$

13. $\dfrac{13}{2}$ 14. $\dfrac{7}{6}$

15. $\dfrac{9}{4}$ 16. $\dfrac{13}{3}$

Solve.

35. There are 32 students in Bill's math class. One day $\dfrac{1}{8}$ of the students were absent. How many students were present?

36. Meg had $\dfrac{5}{6}$ of a yard of wire. She used $\dfrac{1}{2}$ of a yard to hang a picture. What fraction of a yard did she have left?

★37. Jack earned \$4.80. He saved $\dfrac{1}{3}$ of it and spent $\dfrac{1}{2}$ of the rest going to a movie. How much did the movie cost?

Follow the path to find the end number.

38.

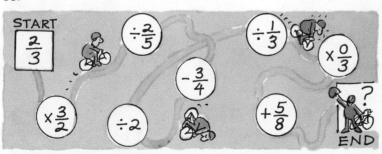

217

Using division

$\frac{2}{3}$ of the nickels in a coin collection are buffalo nickels. If there are 10 buffalo nickels, how many nickels are there in all?

Equation:

$\frac{2}{3}$ of **?** = 10

Solution:

The $\frac{2}{3}$ tells us to think about 2 out of 3 sets with the same number of nickels in each set.

The 10 tells us that there are 10 nickels equally divided between the 2 sets.

Since there are 5 nickels in each set, there are 15 nickels in all.

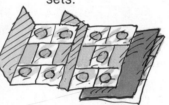

$\frac{2}{3}$ of **?** = 10

$\frac{2}{3}$ of **?** = 10

$\frac{2}{3}$ of **15** = 10

You can just divide to find the missing factor.

$10 \div \frac{2}{3} = 10 \times \frac{3}{2} = 15$

EXERCISES
Solve.

1. $\frac{1}{3}$ of **?** = 4

2. $\frac{1}{4}$ of **?** = 12

3. $\frac{1}{2}$ of **?** = 17

4. $\frac{2}{3}$ of **?** = 24

5. $\frac{3}{8}$ of **?** = 39

6. $\frac{5}{6}$ of **?** = 30

7. $\frac{4}{4}$ of **?** = 48

8. $\frac{3}{2}$ of **?** = 6.42

✓ 9. $\frac{2}{3}$ of **?** = 6.42

10. $\frac{5}{8}$ of **?** = 40

11. $\frac{4}{3}$ of **?** = 48

12. $\frac{3}{2}$ of **?** = 41.4

13. $\frac{1}{3}$ of **?** = 16.3

14. $\frac{5}{7}$ of **?** = 68.5

15. $\frac{5}{9}$ of **?** = 435

16. $\frac{3}{5}$ of ? = 3111   17. $\frac{2}{3}$ of ? = 42   18. $\frac{1}{2}$ of ? = 1.96

19. $\frac{9}{2}$ of ? = 603   20. $\frac{7}{8}$ of ? = 4.83   21. $\frac{2}{2}$ of ? = 12.6

22. $\frac{4}{3}$ of ? = 6.16   23. $\frac{3}{8}$ of ? = 91.2   24. $\frac{5}{3}$ of ? = 0.3815

The sale price of each item is shown on the tag. Find the regular price of each item.

25.
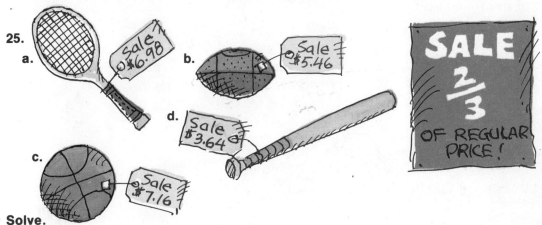

a. Sale $6.98
b. Sale $5.46
c. Sale $7.16
d. Sale $3.64

SALE $\frac{2}{3}$ OF REGULAR PRICE!

Solve.

26. One day Mr. Allan drove 483 kilometers. This was $\frac{3}{8}$ of the total trip. How many kilometers was the total trip?

27. Terry baked $\frac{2}{3}$ of a recipe of cookies. She baked 36 cookies. How many cookies would be in a full recipe?

28. A raincoat is on sale for $\frac{3}{4}$ of its regular price. What is the sale price if the regular price is $18.72?

29. A raincoat is on sale for $\frac{3}{4}$ of its regular price. What is the regular price if the sale price is $18.72?

Find each end number.

30.

START $\frac{2}{3}$ $\times \frac{3}{8}$ $- \frac{1}{4}$ $\div \frac{5}{6}$ $+ \frac{5}{12}$? END

31.
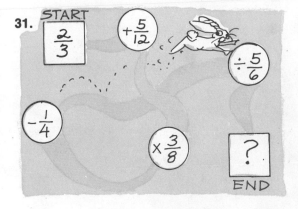

START $\frac{2}{3}$ $+ \frac{5}{12}$ $\div \frac{5}{6}$ $- \frac{1}{4}$ $\times \frac{3}{8}$? END

219

Complex fractions

We can think of the fraction bar as in-
dicating division.

$$\frac{1}{2} = 1 \div 2$$

We can use a fraction to show the quotient of two fractions.

$$\frac{\frac{2}{3}}{\frac{3}{4}}$$

Such a fraction is called a **complex fraction**. To simplify a
complex fraction, divide the fraction in the numerator by the
fraction in the denominator.

$$\frac{\frac{2}{3}}{\frac{5}{6}} = \frac{2}{3} \div \frac{5}{6}$$

$$= \frac{2}{\overset{}{\underset{1}{3}}} \times \frac{\overset{2}{6}}{5}$$

$$= \frac{4}{5}$$

EXERCISES
Simplify each complex fraction.

1. $\dfrac{\frac{1}{5}}{\frac{3}{4}}$ 2. $\dfrac{\frac{7}{3}}{\frac{14}{9}}$ 3. $\dfrac{\frac{5}{9}}{\frac{15}{6}}$ 4. $\dfrac{\frac{6}{9}}{\frac{6}{12}}$ 5. $\dfrac{\frac{5}{3}}{\frac{10}{6}}$ 6. $\dfrac{\frac{8}{5}}{\frac{10}{4}}$

7. $\dfrac{\frac{7}{5}}{\frac{14}{10}}$ 8. $\dfrac{\frac{3}{8}}{\frac{9}{4}}$ 9. $\dfrac{\frac{5}{6}}{\frac{15}{9}}$ 10. $\dfrac{\frac{15}{24}}{\frac{20}{12}}$ 11. $\dfrac{\frac{9}{18}}{\frac{6}{15}}$ 12. $\dfrac{\frac{7}{15}}{\frac{38}{10}}$

220

Simplify.

$$5 \div \frac{2}{3}$$

13. $\dfrac{\frac{5}{3}}{\frac{3}{9}}$ 14. $\dfrac{\frac{7}{5}}{\frac{21}{10}}$ 15. $\dfrac{5}{\frac{2}{3}}$ 16. $\dfrac{3}{\frac{3}{4}}$ 17. $\dfrac{\frac{3}{8}}{9}$ 18. $\dfrac{\frac{7}{8}}{\frac{4}{4}}$

19. $\dfrac{\frac{1}{2}}{\frac{3}{4}}$ 20. $\dfrac{\frac{5}{8}}{\frac{5}{4}}$ 21. $\dfrac{\frac{3}{5}}{\frac{6}{3}}$ 22. $\dfrac{7}{\frac{3}{5}}$ 23. $\dfrac{\frac{2}{3}}{\frac{4}{5}}$ 24. $\dfrac{\frac{5}{12}}{\frac{10}{6}}$

25. $\dfrac{\frac{7}{5}}{3}$ 26. $\dfrac{\frac{7}{8}}{\frac{3}{8}}$ 27. $\dfrac{6}{\frac{3}{4}}$ 28. $\dfrac{\frac{8}{9}}{2}$ 29. $\dfrac{\frac{5}{12}}{\frac{1}{6}}$ 30. $\dfrac{\frac{0}{4}}{\frac{1}{2}}$

Solve.

31. One week Mrs. Rogers bought 46.6 liters of gasoline for 17.9¢ per liter and 59.1 liters of gasoline for 16.9¢ per liter. How much did she spend in all? Round each sale to the nearest cent.

32. One week the daily high Celsius temperature readings were 27°, 31°, 30°, 26°, 32°, 29°, and 28°. Find the average daily high for the week.

33. Rachel wants to attend a summer camp that costs $118. Her parents have agreed to pay $\frac{3}{5}$ if she pays the rest. How much money will Rachel have to pay?

34. From the table, compute the average yearly precipitation in Atlanta.

Average Monthly Precipitation, Atlanta, Georgia.

Month	Precipitation (cm)
January	11.2
February	11.4
March	13.7
April	11.4
May	8.1
June	9.7
July	11.9
August	9.1
September	8.4
October	6.1
November	7.6
December	11.2

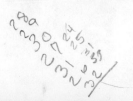
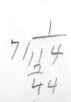

Fractions, mixed numbers, and decimals

Changing decimals to fractions

If you can *read* a decimal correctly, you can easily change a decimal to a fraction. Then you may have to reduce that fraction. Study these examples.

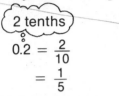

2 tenths

$$0.2 = \frac{2}{10}$$
$$= \frac{1}{5}$$

375 thousandths

$$0.375 = \frac{375}{1000}$$
$$= \frac{3}{8}$$

3 and 25 hundredths

$$3.25 = 3\frac{25}{100}$$
$$= 3\frac{1}{4}$$

Changing fractions to decimals

To change a fraction to a decimal, divide the numerator by the denominator. Study these examples.

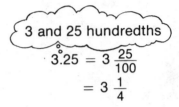

$$\begin{array}{r} 0.4 \\ 5\overline{)2.0} \end{array}$$

$$\frac{2}{5} = 0.4$$

$$\begin{array}{r} 0.75 \\ 4\overline{)3.00} \end{array}$$

$$2\frac{3}{4} = 2.75$$

EXERCISES

Change to a fraction or mixed number.

1. 0.3   2. 0.5   3. 0.8   4. 0.25   5. 0.64   6. 0.80

7. 3.375   8. 3.1   9. 1.08   10. 2.16   11. 1.875   12. 3.48

Change to a decimal.

13. $\frac{1}{2}$ 14. $\frac{7}{8}$ 15. $\frac{1}{4}$ 16. $\frac{1}{8}$ 17. $\frac{3}{8}$ 18. $1\frac{1}{2}$

19. $1\frac{1}{4}$ 20. $\frac{3}{10}$ 21. $2\frac{1}{8}$ 22. $3\frac{1}{4}$ 23. $2\frac{3}{5}$ 24. $\frac{4}{5}$

<, =, or >?

25. $\frac{1}{8}$ ● 0.12   26. $\frac{1}{5}$ ● 0.25   27. $\frac{4}{5}$ ● 0.75   28. $\frac{3}{8}$ ● 0.375

29. $\frac{3}{4}$ ● 0.8   30. $\frac{1}{4}$ ● 0.25   31. $\frac{3}{5}$ ● 0.5   32. $\frac{5}{8}$ ● 0.630

33. $1\frac{1}{2}$ ● 1.6   34. $1\frac{1}{4}$ ● 1.20   35. $3\frac{7}{8}$ ● 3.8   36. $4\frac{2}{5}$ ● 4.4

222

Copy and complete these tables.

37.

Fraction or Mixed Number	$\frac{1}{4}$	$\frac{2}{4}$	$\frac{3}{4}$	$\frac{4}{4}$	$1\frac{1}{4}$	$1\frac{2}{4}$
Decimal						

38.

Fraction or Mixed Number	$\frac{1}{5}$	$\frac{2}{5}$	$\frac{3}{5}$	$\frac{4}{5}$	$\frac{5}{5}$	$1\frac{1}{5}$
Decimal						

39.

Fraction or Mixed Number	$\frac{1}{8}$	$\frac{2}{8}$	$\frac{3}{8}$	$\frac{4}{8}$	$\frac{5}{8}$	$\frac{6}{8}$
Decimal						

Many measurements in customary units are made in half-inches, quarter-inches, eighth-inches, sixteenth-inches, and thirty-second-inches. Often these measurements must be changed to decimals. Tables like this make that job easier.

Fraction	$\frac{1}{2}$	$\frac{1}{4}$	$\frac{1}{8}$	$\frac{1}{16}$	$\frac{1}{32}$
Decimal	0.5	0.25	0.125	0.0625	0.03125

Use the table to change to decimals.

40. $\frac{5}{16}$ 41. $\frac{3}{32}$ 42. $\frac{5}{8}$ 43. $\frac{4}{16}$

44. $\frac{3}{8}$ 45. $\frac{3}{4}$ 46. $3\frac{7}{8}$ 47. $6\frac{1}{4}$

48. $2\frac{5}{32}$ 49. $7\frac{9}{16}$ 50. $12\frac{5}{8}$ 51. $16\frac{15}{16}$

Memorize the decimal values for halves, quarters, and eighths.

1. $\frac{4}{9} + \frac{1}{9}$

2. $\frac{3}{5} + \frac{2}{5}$

3. $\frac{1}{2} + \frac{1}{4}$

4. $\frac{3}{8} + \frac{1}{4}$

5. $\frac{1}{2} + \frac{1}{3}$

6. $\frac{2}{3} + \frac{3}{4}$

7. $\frac{5}{8} + \frac{2}{3}$

8. $\frac{5}{9} + \frac{5}{6}$

9. $\frac{0}{8} + \frac{3}{2}$

10. $\frac{3}{2} + \frac{2}{3}$

223

Repeating decimals

In these two examples, the division never ends!

$\frac{2}{3}$ = ?

$$\begin{array}{r} 0.66 \\ 3\overline{)2.00} \\ -18 \\ \hline 20 \\ -18 \\ \hline 2 \end{array}$$

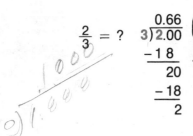

The 6 will keep repeating as long as you keep dividing.

The 36 will keep repeating as long as you keep dividing.

$\frac{15}{11}$ = ?

$$\begin{array}{r} 1.36 \\ 11\overline{)15.00} \\ -11 \\ \hline 40 \\ -33 \\ \hline 70 \\ -66 \\ \hline 4 \end{array}$$

Such decimals are called **repeating** decimals.

There are four ways of writing a repeating decimal.

1. Write 3 dots after the decimal to show that it repeats.

$\frac{2}{3}$ = 0.66 . . . $\frac{15}{11}$ = 1.3636 . . .

This can be confusing because you can't be sure what part repeats.

2. Use a bar over the digits that repeat.

$\frac{2}{3}$ = 0.66 . . . = 0.$\overline{6}$ $\frac{15}{11}$ = 1.3636 . . . = 1.$\overline{36}$

3. Write the answer as a **mixed decimal**.

mixed decimal

$\frac{2}{3}$ = 0.66$\frac{2}{3}$ Read this as "sixty-six and two-thirds hundredths."

This method is not used often, but it will be useful in your work with percents.

4. Round the decimal.

$\frac{2}{3}$ = 0.666 . . . ≈ 0.67 $\frac{15}{11}$ = 1.3636 . . . ≈ 1.364

224

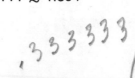

EXERCISES

Change to decimals. Use three dots to write repeating decimals.

1. $\frac{1}{3}$ 2. $\frac{2}{3}$ 3. $\frac{1}{9}$ 4. $\frac{2}{9}$ 5. $\frac{3}{9}$ 6. $\frac{4}{9}$

7. $\frac{5}{9}$ 8. $\frac{6}{9}$ 9. $\frac{7}{9}$ 10. $\frac{8}{9}$ 11. $\frac{1}{6}$ 12. $\frac{5}{6}$

13. $\frac{4}{3}$ 14. $\frac{10}{9}$ 15. $\frac{7}{6}$ 16. $\frac{1}{12}$ 17. $\frac{4}{12}$ 18. $\frac{5}{12}$

19. $\frac{1}{7}$ 20. $\frac{1}{13}$ 21. $\frac{2}{17}$ 22. $\frac{4}{15}$ 23. $\frac{10}{15}$ 24. $\frac{7}{17}$

Change to mixed decimals. Give answers in hundredths.

25. $\frac{1}{3}$ 26. $\frac{1}{8}$ 27. $\frac{5}{6}$ 28. $\frac{3}{8}$ 29. $\frac{1}{9}$ 30. $\frac{4}{9}$

Change to decimals. Round to the nearest hundredth.

31. $\frac{1}{3}$ 32. $\frac{1}{6}$ 33. $\frac{5}{6}$ 34. $\frac{3}{8}$ 35. $\frac{7}{9}$ 36. $\frac{1}{9}$

37. $\frac{1}{12}$ 38. $\frac{11}{12}$ 39. $1\frac{5}{8}$ 40. $\frac{13}{6}$ 41. $2\frac{5}{9}$ 42. $\frac{17}{7}$

<, = , or >?

43. $\frac{1}{3}$ ⬤ 0.3   44. $\frac{1}{3}$ ⬤ 0.33   45. $\frac{1}{3}$ ⬤ 0.333   46. $\frac{1}{3}$ ⬤ 0.3333

47. $\frac{1}{3}$ ⬤ $0.\overline{3}$ 48. $\frac{2}{3}$ ⬤ 0.6   49. $\frac{2}{3}$ ⬤ 0.66   50. $\frac{2}{3}$ ⬤ 0.67

51. $\frac{2}{3}$ ⬤ 0.666   52. $\frac{2}{3}$ ⬤ 0.6666   53. $\frac{2}{3}$ ⬤ $0.\overline{6}$ 54. $\frac{1}{7}$ ⬤ 0.1

55. $\frac{1}{7}$ ⬤ 0.14   56. $\frac{1}{7}$ ⬤ 0.143   57. $\frac{1}{7}$ ⬤ 0.1429   58. $\frac{1}{7}$ ⬤ 0.14285

> Changing fractions to decimals makes it easier to compare them.

Which number is greater?

59. $\frac{3}{8}$ $\frac{4}{7}$ 60. $\frac{3}{5}$ $\frac{2}{3}$ 61. $\frac{1}{3}$ $\frac{2}{5}$ 62. $\frac{3}{4}$ $\frac{4}{5}$

63. $\frac{5}{6}$ $\frac{5}{8}$ 64. $\frac{4}{5}$ $\frac{5}{7}$ 65. $\frac{4}{5}$ $\frac{6}{7}$ 66. $\frac{4}{9}$ $\frac{3}{8}$

 67. $\frac{57}{78}$ $\frac{45}{64}$ 68. $\frac{105}{432}$ $\frac{293}{957}$

Multiplying mixed numbers

A custom T-shirt store charges $9\frac{1}{2}$¢ for each letter they put on a T-shirt. We can multiply to find how much these letters will cost:

SUPERMAN

To multiply, we first change the mixed number to a fraction.

$$8 \times 9\frac{1}{2} = \overset{4}{\cancel{8}} \times \frac{19}{\cancel{2}}_{1}$$
$$= 76$$

So, the letters will cost 76¢.

Here is another way to multiply $9\frac{1}{2}$ by 8.

Step 1. Multiply the fraction.

$$\begin{array}{r} 9\frac{1}{2} \\ \times 8 \\ \hline 4 \end{array}$$

Step 2. Multiply the whole number.

$$\begin{array}{r} 9\frac{1}{2} \\ \times 8 \\ \hline 4 \\ 72 \end{array}$$

Step 3. Add the products.

$$\begin{array}{r} 9\frac{1}{2} \\ \times 8 \\ \hline 4 \\ 72 \\ \hline 76 \end{array}$$

When multiplying two mixed numbers, it is easier to change them to fractions first. Before you multiply, estimate the product by rounding each factor to the nearest whole number.

$$\overset{①}{1\frac{1}{4}} \times \overset{③}{2\frac{2}{3}}$$

The product is about 3.

$$1\frac{1}{4} \times 2\frac{2}{3} = \frac{5}{\cancel{4}_{1}} \times \frac{\cancel{8}^{2}}{3}$$
$$= \frac{10}{3}$$
$$= 3\frac{1}{3}$$

226

EXERCISES

First estimate. Then multiply. Give answers as mixed or whole numbers.

1. $3\frac{3}{4} \times 1\frac{2}{3}$

2. $5\frac{3}{4} \times 2\frac{3}{4}$

3. $3 \times 4\frac{2}{3}$

4. $1\frac{5}{8} \times 3\frac{1}{3}$

5. $5\frac{1}{6} \times 8\frac{1}{5}$

6. $2\frac{1}{2} \times 2\frac{1}{2}$

7. $6\frac{2}{7} \times 4$

8. $9 \times 2\frac{1}{6}$

9. $7\frac{3}{4} \times 9$

10. $3\frac{3}{4} \times 5\frac{1}{6}$

11. $5\frac{3}{4} \times 2\frac{2}{3}$

12. $6\frac{1}{3} \times 4\frac{2}{5}$

13. $4\frac{3}{8} \times 2$

14. $5 \times 2\frac{5}{8}$

15. $3 \times 4\frac{2}{5}$

16. $6\frac{2}{3} \times 8$

17. $1\frac{2}{5} \times 2\frac{3}{8}$

18. $4 \times 4\frac{5}{6}$

19. $3\frac{2}{3} \times 5\frac{1}{2}$

20. $5\frac{3}{8} \times 7\frac{3}{4}$

Compute each total cost. Remember that the letters cost $9\frac{1}{2}$¢ each. Round each cost up to the nearest cent.

21.

22.

23.

24.

Solve.

25. Mrs. Albert plans to drive 55 miles per hour on a trip. At that rate, how far will she travel in $2\frac{3}{4}$ hours?

26. Howard jogs $3\frac{1}{3}$ miles each day. How many miles does he jog in a week?

27. Connie works Saturday mornings for $1.75 an hour. One Saturday she worked from 9:00 A.M. to 11:45 A.M. How much did she earn that Saturday? Give answer to the nearest cent.

28. Bill works every day after school from 4:00 P.M. to 6:15 P.M., and from 10:30 to 3:30 on Saturdays. If he is paid $1.70 an hour, how much does he earn in a week? Give answer to the nearest cent.

Dividing mixed numbers

Two girls hiked from Base Camp to Clear Lake Camp in $2\frac{3}{4}$ hours. We can divide to find how many miles they averaged each hour.

To divide mixed numbers, change each mixed number to an equivalent fraction and divide.

$$8\frac{1}{2} \div 2\frac{3}{4} = \frac{17}{2} \div \frac{11}{4}$$

$$= \frac{17}{\underset{1}{2}} \times \frac{\overset{2}{4}}{11}$$

$$= \frac{34}{11} = 3\frac{1}{11}$$

They averaged $3\frac{1}{11}$ miles per hour.

We can estimate the quotient by rounding each mixed number to the nearest whole number and dividing.

$$\underset{8\frac{1}{2}}{\textcircled{9}} \div \underset{2\frac{3}{4}}{\textcircled{3}}$$

The quotient should be about 3.

228

EXERCISES

First estimate the quotient. Then give the quotient as a mixed number or fraction.

1. $5\frac{1}{2} \div 1\frac{1}{3}$ 2. $3\frac{1}{4} \div 2$ 3. $4\frac{2}{3} \div 1\frac{1}{4}$

4. $6\frac{2}{3} \div 4\frac{1}{5}$ 5. $5 \div 2\frac{1}{3}$ 6. $5\frac{3}{8} \div 4\frac{4}{5}$

7. $8\frac{1}{5} \div 3\frac{3}{4}$ 8. $4\frac{1}{2} \div 2$ 9. $6\frac{1}{2} \div 2\frac{2}{3}$

10. $5\frac{1}{2} \div 2\frac{1}{4}$ 11. $1\frac{1}{3} \div 5$ 12. $5\frac{3}{8} \div 2\frac{1}{3}$

13. $1\frac{3}{4} \div 4\frac{1}{2}$ 14. $3\frac{1}{2} \div 1\frac{1}{8}$ 15. $6\frac{3}{4} \div 3$

16. $5\frac{2}{3} \div 1\frac{1}{4}$ 17. $2\frac{3}{8} \div 1\frac{1}{3}$ 18. $3\frac{1}{2} \div 2\frac{3}{4}$

19. $4 \div 1\frac{1}{9}$ 20. $5 \div 3\frac{5}{8}$ 21. $8\frac{3}{4} \div 3$

22. $6 \div 2\frac{3}{4}$ 23. $4\frac{1}{3} \div 2\frac{1}{2}$ 24. $2 \div 1\frac{1}{2}$

Solve.

25. Laura packed $4\frac{3}{4}$ pounds of food. If she rationed herself to $1\frac{1}{2}$ pounds per day, how many days of food did she pack?

26. Laura and Leslie rented a canoe at Clear Lake for $3\frac{1}{2}$ hours. How much did it cost if the canoe rented for $1.20 an hour?

Work through the path backwards to find the starting number.

27.

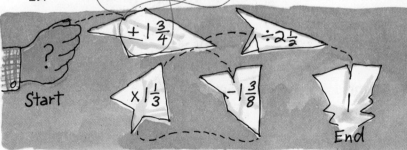

Add or subtract.

1. $4\frac{1}{3}$
$+2\frac{1}{3}$

2. $3\frac{1}{2}$
$+1\frac{1}{4}$

3. $5\frac{1}{2}$
$+2$

4. $2\frac{5}{8}$
$+2\frac{1}{2}$

5. $4\frac{2}{3}$
$+3\frac{5}{6}$

6. $5\frac{3}{8}$
$-4\frac{2}{3}$

7. $4\frac{5}{9}$
$-2\frac{1}{9}$

8. $3\frac{5}{8}$
$-1\frac{1}{4}$

9. $7\frac{1}{2}$
$-4\frac{1}{3}$

10. 6
$-1\frac{1}{2}$

TARGET ONE

$$\frac{1}{3} + \frac{1}{2} = \frac{2}{6} + \frac{3}{6}$$

$$= \boxed{\frac{5}{6}}$$

$$1\frac{1}{2} \times \frac{3}{4} = \frac{3}{2} \times \frac{3}{4}$$

$$= \frac{9}{8}$$

$$= \boxed{1\frac{1}{8}}$$

Which is closer to 1?

1. a. $1\frac{3}{4} \div 1\frac{1}{4}$ **2. a.** $\frac{3}{8} + \frac{3}{4}$ **3. a.** $1\frac{5}{6} - \frac{7}{8}$

   b. $1 - \frac{1}{6}$ **b.** $\frac{3}{4} \times 1\frac{1}{3}$ **b.** $2\frac{1}{4} \div 1\frac{5}{6}$

4. a. $\frac{5}{8} + \frac{1}{3}$ **5. a.** $1\frac{5}{6} - \frac{5}{8}$ **6. a.** $2\frac{1}{4} - 1$

   b. $1\frac{7}{8} - \frac{3}{4}$ **b.** $2 \div 1\frac{7}{8}$ **b.** $1 \div \frac{7}{8}$

Play the game.

1. Make this set of cards.

| $\frac{1}{2}$ | $\frac{1}{3}$ | $\frac{1}{4}$ | $\frac{3}{4}$ | $\frac{3}{8}$ | $\frac{5}{8}$ | $\frac{7}{8}$ | $\frac{1}{6}$ | $\frac{5}{6}$ | 1 | $1\frac{1}{4}$ | $1\frac{1}{3}$ |

| $1\frac{1}{2}$ | $1\frac{3}{4}$ | $1\frac{3}{8}$ | $1\frac{5}{8}$ | $1\frac{7}{8}$ | $1\frac{1}{6}$ | $1\frac{5}{6}$ | 2 | $2\frac{1}{4}$ | $2\frac{1}{3}$ | $2\frac{1}{2}$ | $2\frac{3}{8}$ |

2. Divide the class into two teams.

3. Mix up the cards. A player from each team picks two cards.

4. Each player may either add, subtract, multiply, or divide the two numbers he picks. The player who gets closer to 1 earns a point for his team.

5. After all players have played, the team with the greater total wins the game.

Mathematics in careers

Workers in a greenhouse must often use mathematics in their work. They follow recipes for mixing soil, apply fertilizers according to formulas, and compute costs, prices, and taxes.

Here is a recipe for potting soil.

   2 parts loam

   $1\frac{1}{2}$ parts peat moss

   1 part coarse sand

   1 lb of bone meal for each bushel of mixture

1. A worker mixing potting soil started with 4 bushels of loam. How much peat moss did he need?

2. How much bone meal would be used in a mixture that started with 8 bushels of loam?

3. How much peat moss would be used with 3 bushels of sand?

4. How much loam would be used with 6 bushels of peat moss?

5. A fertilizer marked 5-10-5 is $\frac{5}{100}$ nitrogen, $\frac{10}{100}$ phosphorus, and $\frac{5}{100}$ potash. How much nitrogen is in a 50-lb bag of the fertilizer?

6. How much phosphorus is in a 25-lb bag of fertilizer marked 10-15-15?

Problem solving

A seventh-grade class had a cookie sale to raise money for a field trip. They used the two recipes shown.

Sugar Cookies
makes 4 dozen

$1\frac{1}{2}$ cups powdered sugar

1 cup butter

1 egg

1 teaspoon vanilla

$\frac{1}{2}$ teaspoon almond flavoring

$2\frac{1}{2}$ cups sifted flour

1 teaspoon cream of tartar

1 teaspoon soda

Cream sugar and butter; add egg and flavorings; mix thoroughly. Sift dry ingredients together and stir in. Refrigerate 2 to 3 hours. Preheat oven to 375°. Roll out dough and cut with cookie cutters. Bake 7 to 8 minutes.

Nut 'n' Chip Cookies
makes 3 dozen

$1\frac{1}{2}$ cups whole-wheat flour

$\frac{1}{4}$ cup nonfat dry milk

$\frac{1}{2}$ teaspoon baking soda

$\frac{1}{2}$ teaspoon salt

4 tablespoons butter

$\frac{3}{4}$ cup packed brown sugar

2 eggs

2 tablespoons water

$\frac{1}{2}$ teaspoon vanilla

1 cup semi-sweet chocolate chips

$\frac{1}{2}$ cup walnuts

$\frac{1}{4}$ cup pecans

Thoroughly mix flour, dry milk, soda, and salt. Cream together butter and brown sugar. Blend eggs, water, and vanilla. Add flour mixture and blend well. Stir in chocolate chips and nuts. Drop by teaspoons on a greased cookie sheet. Bake at 375° for 8 to 10 minutes.

A group of students made 10 dozen nut 'n' chip cookies.

1. How many recipes was 10 dozen cookies?

2. How much flour did they use?

3. How much baking soda did they use?

4. How much of the other ingredients did they use?

5. If they had 6 cups of brown sugar before baking the cookies, how much should they have had after baking the cookies?

Another group of students made 10 dozen sugar cookies.

6. How many recipes was 10 dozen cookies?

7. How much powdered sugar did they use?

8. How much butter did they use?

9. How much of the other ingredients did they use?

10. How many sugar cookies can be made with $\frac{3}{4}$ cup of powdered sugar?

11. How many nut 'n' chip cookies can be made with 1 cup of whole-wheat flour?

CHAPTER CHECKUP

Solve. [206–207, 218–219, 232–233]

1. $\frac{1}{2}$ of 16 = ?

2. $\frac{2}{3}$ of 81 = ?

3. $\frac{4}{3}$ of 132 = ?

4. $\frac{1}{3}$ of ? = 8

5. $\frac{5}{8}$ of ? = 65

6. $\frac{3}{2}$ of ? = 921

7. A record that regularly sells for $5.76 is on sale for $\frac{2}{3}$ of its regular price. What is the sale price?

8. A girls' club has raised $120 to buy books for the library. This is $\frac{4}{5}$ of the total money needed. How much is the total amount?

Give each product in lowest terms. [pages 204–205, 216]

9. $\frac{3}{4} \times \frac{1}{2}$

10. $\frac{2}{3} \times 2$

11. $\frac{7}{8} \times \frac{0}{3}$

12. $\frac{5}{9} \times \frac{3}{4}$

13. $\frac{5}{8} \times \frac{8}{5}$

14. $\frac{3}{2} \times \frac{5}{6}$

15. $9 \times \frac{4}{3}$

16. $\frac{8}{3} \times \frac{3}{4}$

Give each quotient in lowest terms. [pages 212–213, 217]

17. $\frac{3}{4} \div \frac{1}{4}$

18. $3 \div \frac{2}{3}$

19. $\frac{4}{3} \div \frac{2}{5}$

20. $\frac{7}{8} \div \frac{3}{4}$

21. $\frac{5}{6} \div \frac{2}{3}$

22. $\frac{7}{8} \div \frac{3}{2}$

23. $\frac{5}{6} \div 4$

24. $\frac{9}{4} \div \frac{3}{8}$

Copy and complete this table. Give fractions in lowest terms. [pages 222–225]

	25.	26.	27.	28.	29.	30.	31.	32.
Fraction	$\frac{6}{10}$		$\frac{1}{4}$			$\frac{3}{2}$	$\frac{5}{4}$	$\frac{2}{3}$
Decimal		0.27		0.3	0.68			

Multiply. Give the product as a mixed or whole number. [pages 226–227]

33. $2\frac{1}{2} \times 3$

34. $4 \times 2\frac{3}{4}$

35. $1\frac{1}{2} \times 3\frac{3}{4}$

36. $2\frac{5}{8} \times 3\frac{2}{3}$

Divide. Give the quotient as a mixed number. [pages 228–229]

37. $8\frac{1}{2} \div 1\frac{3}{4}$

38. $6\frac{2}{3} \div 2$

39. $9\frac{1}{4} \div 2\frac{3}{8}$

40. $10\frac{5}{6} \div 3\frac{2}{3}$

234

Project

1. List the following activities. For a typical school day, estimate the fraction of a whole day (24 hours) spent on each activity.

   a. sleeping   b. eating
   c. going to and from school   d. doing class work
   e. doing homework   f. socializing
   g. watching television   h. other

2. Show how you spend your time by making a circle graph.

   EXAMPLE.

   Suppose $\frac{5}{12}$ of the day is spent sleeping.

   $$\frac{5}{12} \text{ of } 360° = 150°$$

   angle shaded for sleeping

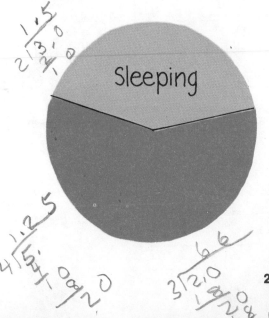

To find a fraction of a quantity, divide by the denominator and multiply by the numerator.

$$\frac{2}{3} \text{ of } 36 = 24$$

Complete.

1. $\frac{1}{4}$ of 20 = ?

2. $\frac{1}{3}$ of 24 = ?

3. $\frac{3}{4}$ of 36 = ?

4. $\frac{3}{2}$ of 18 = ?

5. $\frac{5}{8}$ of 40 = ?

6. $\frac{7}{3}$ of 42 = ?

$$\frac{3}{5} \times \frac{3}{2} = \frac{9}{10}$$

Give each product in lowest terms.

7. $3 \times \frac{1}{2}$

8. $\frac{7}{8} \times \frac{2}{5}$

9. $\frac{2}{3} \times 4$

10. $\frac{3}{4} \times \frac{2}{3}$

11. $\frac{5}{6} \times \frac{6}{5}$

12. $\frac{5}{9} \times \frac{3}{8}$

To divide, multiply by the reciprocal.

$$\frac{4}{3} \div \frac{2}{5} = \frac{4}{3} \times \frac{5}{2}$$
$$= \frac{20}{6}$$
$$= \frac{10}{3}$$

Give each quotient in lowest terms.

13. $\frac{5}{6} \div \frac{1}{2}$

14. $\frac{2}{3} \div 3$

15. $\frac{7}{8} \div \frac{3}{4}$

16. $\frac{5}{9} \div \frac{5}{3}$

17. $4 \div \frac{7}{8}$

18. $\frac{6}{5} \div \frac{5}{9}$

$$2\frac{1}{2} \times 3\frac{3}{4} = \frac{5}{2} \times \frac{15}{4}$$
$$= \frac{75}{8}$$
$$= 9\frac{3}{8}$$

Give each product as a mixed or whole number.

19. $2\frac{1}{2} \times 6$

20. $2\frac{1}{5} \times 3\frac{1}{4}$

21. $8 \times 3\frac{2}{3}$

22. $1\frac{1}{5} \times 5\frac{1}{2}$

23. $9\frac{3}{4} \times 3\frac{1}{3}$

24. $4\frac{3}{5} \times 2\frac{3}{8}$

$$8\frac{2}{3} \div 1\frac{3}{4} = \frac{26}{3} \div \frac{7}{4}$$
$$= \frac{26}{3} \times \frac{4}{7}$$
$$= \frac{104}{21}$$
$$= 4\frac{20}{21}$$

Give each quotient as a mixed number.

25. $9\frac{1}{2} \div 3$

26. $8 \div 2\frac{1}{2}$

27. $5\frac{1}{2} \div 1\frac{1}{4}$

28. $6\frac{3}{5} \div 2\frac{1}{3}$

29. $8\frac{3}{8} \div 1\frac{2}{3}$

30. $6\frac{2}{3} \div 1\frac{2}{5}$

CHAPTER CHALLENGE

You remember that multiplying a number by 1 does not change the number: $16 \times 1 = 16$, $\frac{4}{5} \times 1 = \frac{4}{5}$. You probably also remember that there are lots of ways to write 1: $\frac{2}{2}$, $\frac{8}{8}$, $\frac{65}{65}$, etc. Here are some other ways to write 1, which are different from the ways you already know:

$$\frac{1 \text{ ft}}{12 \text{ in.}} \qquad \frac{12 \text{ in.}}{1 \text{ ft}} \qquad \frac{1 \text{ yd}}{3 \text{ ft}} \qquad \frac{16 \text{ oz}}{1 \text{ lb}} \qquad \frac{2 \text{ c}}{1 \text{ pt}}$$

Fractions like these are called **conversion fractions**. They can be used to convert a measurement from one unit to another unit.

EXAMPLE 1. Convert 32 feet to inches.

Choose an appropriate conversion fraction.	Cancel units.	Multiply.

$$32 \text{ ft} \times \frac{12 \text{ in.}}{1 \text{ ft}} = \qquad 32 \not{\text{ft}} \times \frac{12 \text{ in.}}{1 \not{\text{ft}}} = \qquad 384 \text{ in.}$$

Choose a conversion fraction whose denominator is the unit you began with and whose numerator is the unit you wish to end with.

You may use more than one conversion fraction.

EXAMPLE 2. Convert 80,000 ounces to tons.

$$\overset{\overset{5}{5000}}{80{,}000 \not{\text{oz}}} \times \frac{1 \not{\text{lb}}}{\underset{1}{16 \not{\text{oz}}}} \times \frac{1 \text{ T}}{\underset{2}{2000 \not{\text{lb}}}} = \frac{5}{2}\text{T} = 2\frac{1}{2}\text{T}$$

EXERCISES

Complete. Use conversion fractions.

1. $16 \text{ pt} = \underline{?} \text{ gal}$ 2. $16 \text{ gal} = \underline{?} \text{ pt}$ 3. $6 \text{ qt} = \underline{?} \text{ c}$ 4. $6 \text{ c} = \underline{?} \text{ qt}$

5. $3 \text{ ft}^2 = \underline{?} \text{ in.}^2$ 6. $6 \text{ ft}^2 = \underline{?} \text{ yd}^2$ 7. $1 \text{ mi} = \underline{?} \text{ in.}$ 8. $2 \text{ yd}^3 = \underline{?} \text{ ft}^3$
$\widehat{\text{ft} \times \text{ft}} \quad \widehat{\text{in.} \times \text{in.}}$

9. $283 \text{ km} = \underline{?} \text{ m}$ 10. $283 \text{ m} = \underline{?} \text{ km}$ 11. $12 \text{ kg} = \underline{?} \text{ mg}$ 12. $12 \text{ mg} = \underline{?} \text{ kg}$

237

Form W X

13				33				13				3				29			
a	b	c	d	a	b	c	d	a	b	c	d	a	b	c	d	a	b	c	d
14				34				14				4				30			
a	b	c	d	a	b	c	d	a	b	c	d			c	d	a	b	c	d
15																31			
		a	b	c	a	b	c						a	b	c	a	b	c	d

MAJOR CHECKUP
Standardized Format

Choose the correct letter.

1. Round 5.3692 to the nearest thousandth.

    a. 5.370
    b. 5.37
    c. 5.369
    d. none of these

2. Find the sum.

    $82.5 + 6.98$

    a. 89.48
    b. 15.23
    c. 152.3
    d. none of these

3. Find the difference.

    $38.2 - 3.45$

    a. 34.75
    b. 2.55
    c. 347.5
    d. none of these

4. Multiply.

    5.42×31.4

    a. 170.188
    b. 160.088
    c. 4.336
    d. none of these

5. Divide.

    $0.23\overline{)2.944}$

    a. 0.128
    b. 12.8
    c. 1.28
    d. none of these

6. 5.23 m = _____?_____ cm

    a. 52.3
    b. 0.523
    c. 523
    d. none of these

7. Find the area. Use 3.14 as an approximation for π.

    a. 3.14 cm²
    b. 12.56 cm²
    c. 6.28 cm²
    d. none of these

8. Find the volume.

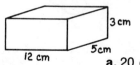

    a. 20 cm³
    b. 63 cm³
    c. 180 cm³
    d. none of these

9. What is the least common multiple of 9 and 12?

    a. 3
    b. 18
    c. 36
    d. none of these

10. Which number is composite?

    a. 2
    b. 11
    c. 29
    d. none of these

11. Add.

    $5\frac{3}{4} + 2\frac{1}{3}$

    a. $7\frac{1}{12}$
    b. $8\frac{1}{12}$
    c. $7\frac{5}{12}$
    d. none of these

12. Subtract.

    $8\frac{1}{3} - 2\frac{5}{8}$

    a. $6\frac{7}{24}$
    b. $6\frac{17}{24}$
    c. $5\frac{17}{24}$
    d. none of these

8
Ratios and Percent

What fraction of the marbles are red?

1.

2.

3.

4.

Copy and complete.

5. $\frac{1}{2} = \frac{?}{4}$

6. $\frac{2}{3} = \frac{?}{6}$

7. $\frac{3}{4} = \frac{?}{12}$

8. $\frac{4}{3} = \frac{?}{12}$

9. $\frac{3}{2} = \frac{?}{18}$

10. $\frac{3}{8} = \frac{12}{?}$

11. $\frac{9}{4} = \frac{36}{?}$

12. $\frac{5}{6} = \frac{30}{?}$

Ratio

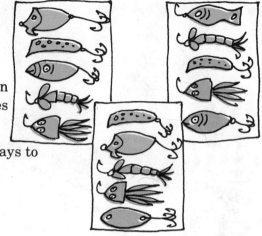

The **ratio** of green lures to blue lures is 6 to 9.

Here are some ways to write the ratio.

6 to 9 $\frac{6}{9}$ 6 : 9

We can read each ratio as "6 to 9." Here are some equal ratios that could also be used.

Looking at 1 card of lures:

2 to 3 $\frac{2}{3}$ 2 : 3

Looking at 2 cards of lures:

4 to 6 $\frac{4}{6}$ 4 : 6

We can find equal ratios by finding equivalent fractions.

$$\frac{2}{3} = \frac{4}{6} = \frac{6}{9} \qquad 2:3 = 4:6 = 6:9$$

EXERCISES

Give the ratio of

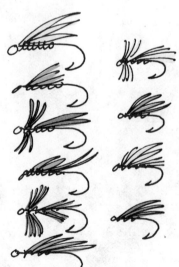

1. large flies to small flies.

2. small flies to large flies.

3. blue flies to red flies.

4. small red to large red.

5. small yellow to large blue.

6. blue to not blue.

7. not red to red.

8. red to small yellow.

240

Give each ratio as a fraction in lowest terms.

9. $5:10$ 10. 6 to 4   11. 12 to 8   12. $9:24$ 13. $8:6$ 14. 16 to 36

Copy and complete.

15. $\dfrac{1}{3} = \dfrac{12}{?}$ 16. $\dfrac{7}{2} = \dfrac{?}{8}$ 17. $\dfrac{8}{5} = \dfrac{40}{?}$ 18. $\dfrac{4}{3} = \dfrac{12}{?}$

19. $\dfrac{5}{8} = \dfrac{15}{?}$ 20. $\dfrac{7}{8} = \dfrac{42}{?}$ 21. $\dfrac{4}{8} = \dfrac{?}{48}$ 22. $\dfrac{6}{5} = \dfrac{?}{30}$

23. $\dfrac{6}{5} = \dfrac{30}{?}$ 24. $\dfrac{5}{8} = \dfrac{?}{16}$ 25. $\dfrac{3}{4} = \dfrac{24}{?}$ 26. $\dfrac{2}{3} = \dfrac{18}{?}$

Solve.

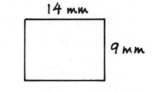

27. **a.** What is the "length to width" ratio?
   b. What is the "width to length" ratio?

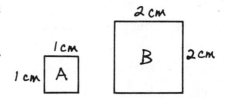

28. **a.** What is the ratio of the perimeter of A to the perimeter of B?
   b. What is the ratio of the area of A to the area of B?
   c. Are the ratios equal?

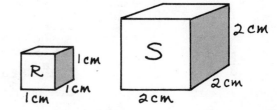

29. **a.** What is the ratio of the volume of R to the volume of S?
   b. What is the ratio of the surface area of R to the surface area of S?
   c. Are the ratios equal?

What is the ratio of the length of the small cube to the length of the large cube?

What is the ratio of the volume of the small cube to the volume of the large cube?

1.

3.2cm
6.4cm

2.

0.17cm

0.34cm

Proportions

An equation stating that two ratios are equal is called a **proportion**. Each proportion has a related multiplication equation.

Proportion	Multiplication equation
$\dfrac{3}{4} = \dfrac{9}{12}$	$3 \times 12 = 4 \times 9$

The two products 3×12 and 4×9 are often called **cross products**. The cross products and the ratios have a special relationship:

> If the ratios are equal, so are the cross products
>
> and
>
> if the cross products are equal, so are the ratios.

Since the cross products are equal, the ratios are equal.

Since the cross products are not equal, the ratios are not equal.

$$\frac{3}{5} = \frac{6}{10}$$

These facts give us an easy way to solve a proportion.

$$\frac{5}{9} \neq \frac{1}{2}$$

SHORTCUT WORKING

EXAMPLE. Solve: $\dfrac{3}{7} = \dfrac{12}{n}$

Step 1. Write the related multiplication equation.

$$3n = 7 \times 12$$

Step 2. Solve the multiplication equation.

$$3n = 7 \times 12$$
$$3n = 84$$
$$n = 28$$

$$\begin{array}{r} 28 \\ 3\overline{)84} \end{array}$$

Check: $\dfrac{3}{7} = \dfrac{12}{28}$

242

EXERCISES

= or ≠ ?

1. $\frac{3}{4}$ ● $\frac{6}{8}$ 2. $\frac{2}{1}$ ● $\frac{3}{2}$ 3. $\frac{9}{8}$ ● $\frac{6}{5}$

4. $\frac{6}{9}$ ● $\frac{4}{6}$ 5. $\frac{3}{6}$ ● $\frac{4}{8}$ 6. $\frac{9}{6}$ ● $\frac{6}{4}$

7. $\frac{6}{5}$ ● $\frac{7}{6}$ 8. $\frac{7}{7}$ ● $\frac{8}{8}$ 9. $\frac{9}{12}$ ● $\frac{6}{8}$

Copy and complete.

10. $\frac{5}{2} = \frac{n}{3}$ 11. $\frac{5}{6} = \frac{4}{n}$

    $2n = 5 \times 3$ $5n = 6 \times 4$

    $n = \underline{\quad?\quad}$ $n = \underline{\quad?\quad}$

Hint: Divide 15 by 2.

12. $\frac{n}{8} = \frac{3}{5}$ 13. $\frac{4}{n} = \frac{6}{9}$

    $5n = \underline{\quad?\quad}$ $6n = \underline{\quad?\quad}$

    $n = \underline{\quad?\quad}$ $n = \underline{\quad?\quad}$

Solve each proportion.

14. $\frac{n}{3} = \frac{5}{9}$ 15. $\frac{7}{n} = \frac{4}{6}$ 16. $\frac{4}{8} = \frac{2}{n}$

17. $\frac{6}{n} = \frac{4}{3}$ 18. $\frac{9}{n} = \frac{7}{4}$ 19. $\frac{8}{n} = \frac{5}{6}$

20. $\frac{n}{8} = \frac{6}{5}$ 21. $\frac{3}{3} = \frac{n}{3}$ 22. $\frac{n}{8} = \frac{3}{4}$

23. $\frac{5}{16} = \frac{n}{11}$ 24. $\frac{17}{23} = \frac{n}{15}$ 25. $\frac{8}{5} = \frac{6}{n}$

26. $\frac{13}{38} = \frac{24}{n}$ 27. $\frac{9}{100} = \frac{n}{50}$ 28. $\frac{n}{100} = \frac{5}{6}$

Proportions in problem solving

The first man to fly nonstop across the Atlantic alone was Charles A. Lindbergh.

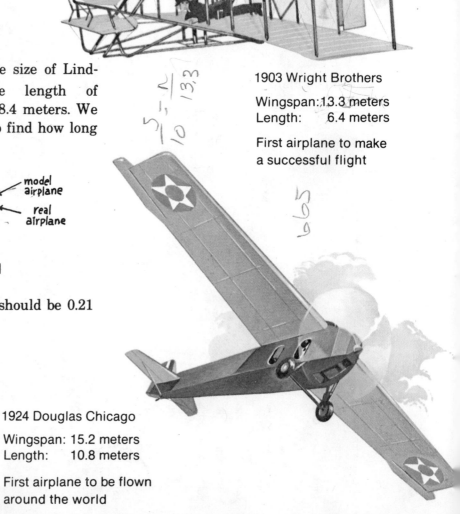

A model is to be $\frac{1}{40}$ the size of Lindbergh's airplane. The length of Lindbergh's airplane is 8.4 meters. We can solve a proportion to find how long the model should be.

model
airplane → ← model airplane
real airplane → $\frac{1}{40} = \frac{n}{8.4}$ ← real airplane

$$40n = 8.4$$

$$n = 0.21$$

The length of the model should be 0.21 meters.

1903 Wright Brothers

Wingspan: 13.3 meters
Length: 6.4 meters

First airplane to make a successful flight

1924 Douglas Chicago

Wingspan: 15.2 meters
Length: 10.8 meters

First airplane to be flown around the world

EXERCISES
Solve.

1. A model of the Wright brothers' plane is to be $\frac{1}{10}$ the size of the real airplane. Find its wingspan and length.

2. What are the wingspan and length of a model Douglas Chicago if it is $\frac{1}{25}$ the actual size?

3. Compute the wingspan and length of a Fokker T-2 model if it is $\frac{1}{80}$ the actual size.

4. What is the ratio of wingspan to length of the Fokker Josephine Ford? What is the length of a model that has a wingspan of 3.0 meters?

5. To get a special shade of green for painting the Douglas Chicago, 2 bottles of midnight blue are mixed with 3 bottles of canary yellow. How much canary yellow should be mixed with 1 bottle of midnight blue to get the same color?

6. A model of the Wright brothers' airplane is to be 0.5 meter long. What should the wingspan be?

1923 Fokker T-2

Wingspan: 24.3 meters
Length: 15.0 meters

First airplane to fly nonstop across the United States

1926 Fokker Josephine Ford

Wingspan: 19.3 meters
Length: 15.0 meters

First airplane to fly over the North Pole

Rates

Here a proportion is used to solve a problem involving **rates**. You might think of a rate as a ratio of two quantities.

In 1932 Hubert Opperman set a 24-hour distance record for a bicycle rider when he rode 1380 kilometers. At that rate, how far did he ride in 7 hours?

```
0 km          n km                          1380 km
●─────────────●───────────────────────────────●
0 h           7 h                            24 h
```

$$\underset{\text{hours}}{\overset{\text{kilometers}}{\frac{1380}{24}}} = \frac{n}{7}$$

$$24n = 9660$$

$$n = 402.5$$

He rode 402.5 km in 7 h.

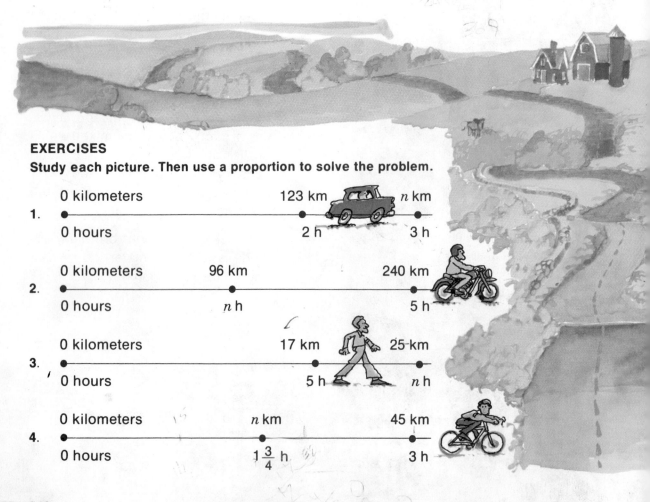

EXERCISES

Study each picture. Then use a proportion to solve the problem.

1.
```
0 kilometers              123 km      n km
●───────────────────────────●──────────●
0 hours                      2 h        3 h
```

2.
```
0 kilometers      96 km              240 km
●───────────────────●──────────────────●
0 hours            n h                5 h
```

3.
```
0 kilometers              17 km    25 km
●───────────────────────────●────────●
0 hours                      5 h     n h
```

4.
```
0 kilometers              n km          45 km
●───────────────────────────●─────────────●
0 hours                    1 3/4 h        3 h
```

246

Use the given rate to solve each problem. Round each answer to the nearest tenth.

5. 30 kilometers in 7 hours
   How far in 3 hours?

6. 62 kilometers in 2.5 hours
   How far is 4 hours?

7. 96 kilometers in 1.6 hours
   How long to go 60 kilometers?

8. 168 kilometers in 3.25 hours
   How long to go 240 kilometers?

Solve.

9. A 0.5-kilogram package of hamburger costs $2.00. At that rate what would a 0.8-kilogram package of hamburger cost?

10. 1.6 kilograms of apples cost $1.19. What would 2.3 kilograms of apples cost?

11. In 3 days, members of the Drama Society sold 72 tickets to their play. At that rate, how many tickets would they sell in 5 days?

12. An automobile used 15.3 liters of gasoline to go 80 kilometers. How much gasoline would it use to go 142 kilometers? Give your answer to the nearest tenth liter.

13. Jill earned $3.35 for baby-sitting $3\frac{1}{2}$ hours. How much would she earn for $1\frac{3}{4}$ hours? Give your answer to the nearest cent.

14. Jeff mowed $\frac{2}{3}$ of a lawn in 52 minutes. At that rate, how long would it take him to mow the whole lawn?

Excursion ❚❙❚❙❚❙❚❙❚❙❚❙❚❙❚❙❚❙❚❙❚❙❚❙❚❙❚❙

Get a paper cup and toss it onto the floor 50 times.

What fraction of the tosses landed on the bottom? On the top? On the side? Estimate how many times in 1000 tosses the cup would land on its top, bottom, and side.

Scale drawing

A map is an example of a scale drawing. For example, 1 centimeter on the map stands for 5.5 kilometers on the trail.

Barabo

Yorke

$1 cm = 5.5 km$

East Fork

Huntsville

Since we know the scale, we can measure a distance on the map and solve a proportion to find the corresponding distance on a trail.

EXAMPLE.

The distance from Barabo to East Fork on the map is 6 centimeters. How long is the trail from Barabo to East Fork?

The distance from Barabo to East Fork is 33 kilometers.

cm on map

$$\frac{1}{5.5} = \frac{6}{n}$$

km on trail

$n = 6 (5.5)$

$= 33$

EXERCISES

1. On the map, measure the distance between Barabo and Yorke to the nearest millimeter. Compute the distance from Barabo to Yorke.

2. What is the actual distance from Huntsville to Yorke?

3. What is the actual straight-line distance from East Fork to Yorke?

Here is the floor plan of a house.

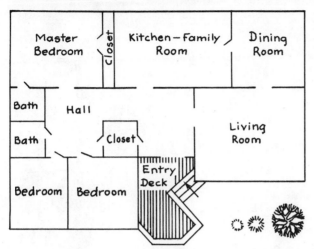

Scale: 1 cm = 2.5 meters

Find each of the following lengths by carefully measuring the drawing and solving a proportion.

4. the length of the living room

5. the width of the kitchen–family room

6. the dimensions (length and width) of the dining room

Solve.

7. The floor of the kitchen–family room is to be covered with tile costing $9.95 a square meter. How much will the tile cost?

8. The floors of the living and dining rooms are to be carpeted. If the carpet costs $12.75 a square meter, how much will the carpet cost for these two rooms?

Decide on a scale and draw a floor plan of your classroom.

Give each quotient in lowest terms.

1. $3 \div \frac{3}{4}$

2. $\frac{2}{5} \div \frac{2}{3}$

3. $\frac{5}{9} \div \frac{2}{5}$

4. $\frac{8}{5} \div \frac{4}{3}$

5. $\frac{3}{8} \div 5$

6. $\frac{3}{2} \div \frac{9}{4}$

7. $\frac{7}{4} \div \frac{3}{8}$

8. $\frac{9}{4} \div \frac{1}{2}$

9. $\frac{6}{5} \div 3$

10. $\frac{9}{8} \div \frac{3}{4}$

Practice exercises

Solve.

1. $\dfrac{5}{2} = \dfrac{n}{4}$

2. $\dfrac{6}{n} = \dfrac{3}{5}$

3. $\dfrac{28}{12} = \dfrac{n}{3}$

4. $\dfrac{8}{n} = \dfrac{24}{18}$

5. $\dfrac{n}{6} = \dfrac{15}{30}$

6. $\dfrac{3}{4} = \dfrac{15}{n}$

7. $\dfrac{13}{8} = \dfrac{39}{n}$

8. $\dfrac{12}{42} = \dfrac{n}{7}$

9. $\dfrac{3}{5} = \dfrac{n}{6}$

10. $\dfrac{7}{9} = \dfrac{4}{n}$

11. $\dfrac{5}{2} = \dfrac{8}{n}$

12. $\dfrac{7}{9} = \dfrac{3}{n}$

13. $\dfrac{6}{4} = \dfrac{5}{n}$

14. $\dfrac{n}{12} = \dfrac{9}{5}$

15. $\dfrac{3}{8} = \dfrac{n}{2}$

16. $\dfrac{7}{16} = \dfrac{4}{n}$

17. $\dfrac{n}{8} = \dfrac{3}{7}$

18. $\dfrac{5}{2} = \dfrac{n}{9}$

19. $\dfrac{n}{6} = \dfrac{1}{8}$

20. $\dfrac{8}{5} = \dfrac{n}{9}$

21. $\dfrac{n}{1\frac{1}{2}} = \dfrac{3}{4}$

22. $\dfrac{\frac{2}{3}}{4} = \dfrac{5}{n}$

23. $\dfrac{2\frac{1}{2}}{3} = \dfrac{n}{6}$

24. $\dfrac{4}{n} = \dfrac{1\frac{1}{2}}{2}$

25. $\dfrac{3\frac{2}{3}}{4} = \dfrac{7\frac{1}{3}}{n}$

26. $\dfrac{n}{2\frac{3}{4}} = \dfrac{4}{5}$

27. $\dfrac{1\frac{1}{4}}{2} = \dfrac{\frac{3}{4}}{n}$

28. $\dfrac{n}{\frac{5}{8}} = \dfrac{\frac{1}{5}}{3}$

Use a proportion to solve each problem.

29. Joan jogged 400 m in 2 minutes. At that rate, how long would it take her to jog 1500 m?

30. Jerry hiked 1.6 km in 14 minutes. At that rate, how long would it take him to hike 7.2 km?

31. If 11.2 liters of gasoline cost $2.25, how much do 16 liters cost? Round your answer to the nearest cent.

32. Bill wants to make a scale drawing of an airplane. He decides to use the scale 1 cm = 1.5 m. How long should his drawing be if the length of the airplane is 20.5 m?

Mathematics in careers

Concrete contractors construct such things as foundations, walls, walks, patios, driveways, and roads. Concrete is made from portland cement, sand, gravel, and water. Portland cement comes in a 94-pound bag, which holds 1 cubic foot of cement. The ratio of the ingredients depends on the use of the concrete.

EXERCISES

Use your completed table in exercises 2 and 3.

1. Copy and complete the following table.

Makes 1 Cubic Yard of Concrete			
Mix ratio cement:sand: gravel	Portland cement (ft³)	Sand (ft³)	$\frac{3}{4}$-inch gravel (ft³)
$1:1:1\frac{3}{4}$	10	10	$17\frac{1}{2}$
$1:3:5$	$4\frac{1}{2}$		
$1:2\frac{1}{2}:3\frac{1}{2}$	6		

3. The $1:2\frac{1}{2}:3\frac{1}{2}$ mix can be used for driveways. How much of each material is needed for a driveway having a volume of 5 cubic yards?

2. It is recommended that the $1:3:5$ mix be used for footings (the bases on which foundation walls rest). How many cubic feet of each material are needed for a footing having a volume of 3 cubic yards?

4. Here is a scale drawing of a patio.

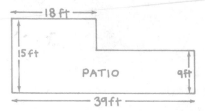

If concrete costs $38 a cubic yard, how much will a 4-inch slab for this patio cost? Round the volume up to the nearest $\frac{1}{2}$ cubic yard.

Percent

So far, you have learned three ways to write about hundredths: words, fractions, and decimals. Now we add a fourth way—percents. **Percent** means "per hundred." We write about percents with a percent sign:

$$\%$$

Here is an example.

A seventh-grade student surveyed 100 students to find out their favorite individual sports.

The graph shows that 21 out of 100 students liked tennis best. Here are some ways to write about that.

21 hundredths of the students liked tennis best.

$\frac{21}{100}$ of the students liked tennis best.

0.21 of the students liked tennis best.

21% of the students liked tennis best.

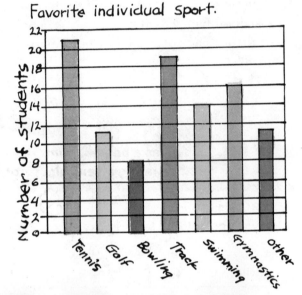

Favorite individual sport.

EXERCISES

Refer to the graph above. What part of the total number of students liked the given sport best? Write the answers as fractions, decimals, and percents.

1. golf **2.** bowling **3.** swimming

4. What does 100% mean?

Copy and complete.

	5.	6.	7.	8.	9.	10.
Decimal	0.41	0.37	0.13	0.73	0.87	0.06
Fraction						
Percent						

Write as a percent.

11. 0.37   **12.** 0.42   **13.** 0.63   **14.** 0.40   **15.** 0.82   **16.** 0.56

17. 0.72   **18.** 0.35   **19.** 0.60   **20.** 0.90   **21.** 0.10   **22.** 0.09

23. 0.03   **24.** 0.05   **25.** 0.01   **26.** 0.25   **27.** 0.18   **28.** 0.45

Write each fraction as a percent. *Hint:* **First change to an equivalent fraction having a denominator of 100.**

29. $\frac{1}{2} \cdot \frac{50}{100}$ **30.** $\frac{1}{4} \cdot \frac{?}{100}$ **31.** $\frac{3}{4} \cdot \frac{?}{100}$ **32.** $\frac{2}{5} \cdot \frac{?}{100}$

33. $\frac{1}{5}$ **34.** $\frac{3}{10}$ **35.** $\frac{4}{4}$ **36.** $\frac{3}{5}$ **37.** $\frac{9}{10}$ **38.** $\frac{4}{5}$

39. $\frac{3}{2}$ **40.** $\frac{5}{4}$ **41.** $\frac{5}{2}$ **42.** $\frac{7}{4}$ **43.** $\frac{1}{10}$ **44.** $\frac{1}{20}$

Write each percent as a fraction in lowest terms.

45. 10% $\frac{10}{100}$ **46.** 20%   **47.** 50%   **48.** 60%   **49.** 75%   **50.** 80%

51. 5%   **52.** 32%   **53.** 48%   **54.** 64%   **55.** 25%   **56.** 65%

Here are the results of a comic-strip survey of seventh-grade students. What percent read

57. no comic strip?

58. two comic strips?

59. more than four?

60. more than one?

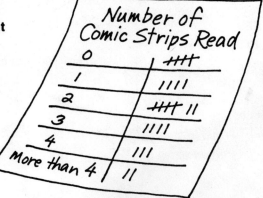

Number of Comic Strips Read

0	++++
1	IIII
2	++++ II
3	IIII
4	III
More than 4	II

253

More about percents

Percents are used in many ways. When you have to compute with percents you must change them to fractions or decimals.

To change a percent to a decimal, move the decimal point two places to the left and drop the percent sign.

28.3% = .28.3% = 0.283

37% = .37.% = 0.37

100% = 1.00.% = 1.00

4% = 0.04.% = 0.04

To change a decimal to a percent, move the decimal point 2 places to the right and write a percent sign.

0.52 = 0.52.% = 52%

0.314 = 0.31.4% = 31.4%

2 = 2.00.% = 200%

0.07 = 0.07.% = 7%

EXERCISES
Change to decimals.

1. 58%   2. 77%   3. 95%   4. 16%   5. 3%

6. 9%   7. 1%   8. 4.6%   9. 13.7%   10. 46.8%

11. 150%   12. 395%   13. 1000%   14. 186.3%   15. 0.4%

16. 0.6%   17. 3.8%   18. 75%   19. 0.32%   20. 0.51%

Change to percents.

21. 0.82
22. 0.75
23. 0.50
24. 0.4
25. 0.7

26. 3
27. 2
28. 3.6
29. 0.02
30. 0.07

31. 0.251
32. 0.384
33. 0.462
34. 0.8
35. 4

36. 0.001
37. 0.01
38. 0.1
39. 1
40. 0.173

Change to percents. *Hint:* **First change to decimals.**

41. $\frac{1}{2}$
42. $\frac{3}{2}$
43. $\frac{1}{4}$
44. $\frac{3}{4}$
45. $\frac{5}{4}$

46. $\frac{7}{4}$
47. $\frac{1}{5}$
48. $\frac{2}{5}$
49. $\frac{3}{5}$
50. $\frac{4}{5}$

51. $\frac{7}{5}$
52. $\frac{1}{8}$
53. $\frac{3}{8}$
54. $\frac{5}{8}$
55. $\frac{7}{8}$

Change each number to a percent.

56. More than $\frac{1}{2}$ of the babies born are boys.

57. About $\frac{3}{4}$ of the earth is covered by water.

58. About 0.55 of the students in one school are girls.

59. Jim scored 0.35 of the team's points.

60. Karen answered $\frac{3}{5}$ of the questions correctly.

61. Marcia is $\frac{4}{5}$ as tall as Mary.

62. Ken earned 0.7 as much as Carl.

63. Bill spent 0.65 of the money he earned.

64. During a sale the price was reduced by $\frac{1}{4}$.

65. There is a sales tax of $\frac{1}{20}$ of the price of a football.

Fractions and percents

On a mathematics test a student got 18 problems correct out of a total of 22 problems. What percent of the problems did she get correct?

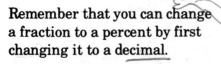

Remember that you can change a fraction to a percent by first changing it to a decimal.

$$\frac{18}{22} = ?\%$$

$$
\begin{array}{r}
0.81\frac{9}{11} \\
22\overline{)18.00} \\
-17\ 6 \\
\hline
40 \\
-22 \\
\hline
18
\end{array}
$$

The student got $81\frac{9}{11}\%$ of the problems correct. The teacher rounded the score to the nearest percent, 82%.

EXERCISES

Change each fraction to a percent.

1. $\frac{1}{3}$　　2. $\frac{1}{8}$　　3. $\frac{1}{6}$　　4. $\frac{2}{3}$　　5. $\frac{1}{9}$　　6. $\frac{5}{8}$

7. $\frac{4}{9}$　　8. $\frac{1}{16}$　　9. $\frac{7}{8}$　　10. $\frac{5}{16}$　　11. $\frac{5}{3}$　　12. $\frac{2}{9}$

13. $\frac{3}{8}$　　14. $\frac{4}{3}$　　15. $\frac{15}{8}$　　16. $\frac{5}{6}$　　17. $\frac{7}{6}$　　18. $\frac{9}{8}$

Solve.

19. $20 = \underline{\ ?\ }\%$ of 40　　20. $7 = \underline{\ ?\ }\%$ of 28　　21. $9 = \underline{\ ?\ }\%$ of 27

22. $11 = \underline{\ ?\ }\%$ of 53　　23. $12 = \underline{\ ?\ }\%$ of 8　　24. $50 = \underline{\ ?\ }\%$ of 86

Solve.

25.

WEAVER JUNIOR HIGH SCHOOL

Starting Line-up	Shots Made	Shots Attempted
Jones	40	96
Casey	36	80
Allen	36	72
Davis	50	112
Garcia	34	64

a. What percent of his shots did Jones make?

b. How many players made less than 50% of their shots?

c. Who made the higher percent of shots, Jones or Davis?

26. A boys' club sold 325 out of 450 boxes of candy. What percent of the candy did they sell?

27. Janice spent $1.60 of her $3.00 allowance for a book. What percent of her allowance did she spend for the book?

28. Stan read 126 pages of a 240-page book. What percent of the book did he read?

29. In a large city there are 567,344 people who are 21 years old or older and 487,398 people who are under 21 years old. What percent of the people are under 21?

30. Ralph wants to buy a car that costs $4576.95. He has saved $2985.64. What percent of the cost of the car has he saved?

Multiply.

1. 58×0.02

2. 26×0.06

3. 74×0.35

4. 93×0.64

5. 52×0.18

6. 45×0.25

7. 381×0.16

8. 253×0.33

9. 56.4×0.81

10. 78.2×0.60

11. 9.11×0.29

12. 60.3×0.75

Finding a percent of a number

Most of the percent problems that you will have to solve involve finding a percent of a number. Here is an example.

What is the sale price of the bicycle?

Equation: 75% of 160 = n

Since you already know how to find a fraction of a number, you can solve the percent equation by solving a fraction equation.

$\frac{75}{100}$

$$75\% \text{ of } 160 = \frac{3}{4} \text{ of } 160$$

$$= \frac{3}{4} \times 160$$

$$= 120$$

So, the sale price is $120.

Here are some other examples of finding a percent of a number.

$\frac{50}{100}$

$$50\% \text{ of } 24 = \frac{1}{2} \text{ of } 24$$

$$= \frac{1}{2} \times 24$$

$$= 12$$

$\frac{125}{100}$

$$125\% \text{ of } 36 = \frac{5}{4} \text{ of } 36$$

$$= \frac{5}{4} \times 36$$

$$= 45$$

EXERCISES

Solve.

1. 75% of 40 = n

2. 25% of 56 = n

3. 50% of 38 = n

4. 40% of 45 = n

5. 80% of 35 = n

6. 10% of 40 = n

7. 60% of 35 = n

8. 150% of 48 = n

9. 100% of 36 = n

10. 175% of 80 = n

11. 5% of 120 = n

12. 30% of 100 = n

13. 90% of 150 = n

14. 125% of 64 = n

15. 20% of 60 = n

To find 125% of a number, I add the number to $\frac{1}{4}$ the number.

25% of 20 = 5

20 + 5 = 25

SHORTCUT II

Use the shortcut to solve these equations.

16. 125% of 20 = n

17. 125% of 48 = n

18. 150% of 18 = n

19. 150% of 30 = n

20. 175% of 24 = n

21. 175% of 36 = n

22. 120% of 50 = n

23. 120% of 80 = n

24. 160% of 45 = n

25. 160% of 75 = n

26. 105% of 80 = n

27. 105% of 100 = n

Solve.

28. A 3-speed bicycle is on sale for 80% of the regular price. The regular price is $96. What is the sale price?

29. In a survey of 120 seventh-grade students it was found that 85% owned a bicycle. How many students was that?

30. The price of a certain lightweight touring bicycle is $189 plus 5% sales tax. What is the total cost?

31. Terry wants to trade in her old bicycle for a new 10-speed bicycle that sells for $169. The dealer will allow her $45 for her old bicycle. How much money will she need if she has to pay a 5% sales tax on the difference?

More about finding a percent of a number

In a survey of 120 seventh-grade students it was found that 20% have stereo sets. How many students have stereos?

Here are 3 ways to solve the problem.

1. Multiply by an equivalent fraction.

$$\frac{20}{100} = \frac{1}{5} \qquad \frac{1}{5} \times \overset{24}{\cancel{120}} = 24$$

20% of 120 = 24

2. Multiply by an equivalent decimal.

$$20\% = 0.20 \qquad \begin{array}{r} 120 \\ \times\ .20 \\ \hline 24.00 \end{array}$$

20% of 120 = 24

3. Solve a proportion.

$$\frac{20}{100} = \frac{n}{120}$$
$$100\,n = 2400$$
$$n = 24$$

20% of 120 = 24

The method you use will probably depend on the problem.

EXERCISES
Solve by multiplying by an equivalent fraction.

1. 25% of 32 = n

2. 75% of 36 = n

3. 50% of 60 = n

4. 40% of 40 = n

5. 80% of 35 = n

6. 60% of 150 = n

7. 150% of 60 = n

8. 10% of 80 = n

9. 120% of 75 = n

Solve by multiplying by an equivalent decimal.

10. 18% of 25 = n   11. 16% of 38 = n

12. 22% of 19 = n   13. 25% of 56 = n

14. 36% of 74 = n   15. 17% of 58 = n

16. 8% of 83 = n   17. 3% of 65 = n

18. 2% of 75 = n   19. 6% of 142 = n

20. 9% of 108 = n   21. 7% of 256 = n

22. 118% of 325 = n   23. 126% of 378 = n

Solve by solving a proportion.

24. 8% of 51 = n   25. 6% of 63 = n

26. 3% of 54 = n   27. 15% of 29 = n

28. 29% of 78 = n   29. 35% of 125 = n

30. $37\frac{1}{2}$% of 77 = n   31. $42\frac{1}{2}$% of 61 = n

32. $18\frac{1}{4}$% of 59 = n   33. $8\frac{1}{3}$% of 63 = n

34. $6\frac{3}{4}$% of 75 = n   35. $9\frac{1}{2}$% of 95 = n

In another survey, 160 students were asked how many minutes each day they spent listening to their favorite radio station. The table shows the results of the survey.

How many students listened

36. between 61 and 90 minutes?

37. more than 3 hours?

38. between half an hour and an hour?

39. more than 30 minutes?

TIME SPENT LISTENING TO FAVORITE STATION	
Time in Minutes	Percent of Students Surveyed
0	$12\frac{1}{2}$
1 — 30	$6\frac{1}{4}$
31 — 60	$37\frac{1}{2}$
61 — 90	10
91 — 120	15
121 — 150	$7\frac{1}{2}$
151 — 180	$6\frac{1}{4}$
181 — 210	5

Finding the number
when a percent is known

We can solve a proportion to find the number when a percent
of the number is known.

That's 75% of my albums!

EXAMPLE.

Percent   Number   Percent
of Number

$$75\% \quad \text{of} \quad n \quad = \quad 15$$

Solution.

$$\text{Part} \longrightarrow \frac{75}{100} \longleftarrow \text{Whole} = \frac{15}{n} \begin{array}{l} \leftarrow \text{Part} \\ \leftarrow \text{Whole} \end{array}$$

$$75 \times n = 1500$$
$$n = 20$$

EXERCISES
Solve by using a proportion.

$$\frac{25}{100} = \frac{8}{n}$$

1. 25% of $n = 8$

2. 20% of $n = 16$

3. 30% of $n = 24$

4. 75% of $n = 36$

5. 60% of $n = 9$

6. 25% of $n = 63$

7. 30% of $n = 42$

8. 75% of $n = 96$

9. 15% of $n = 200$

10. $16\frac{2}{3}$% of $n = 45$

11. $37\frac{1}{2}$% of $n = 12$

12. $62\frac{1}{2}$% of $n = 45$

13. $87\frac{1}{2}$% of $n = 63$

14. $12\frac{1}{2}$% of $n = 15$

15. $6\frac{1}{4}$% of $n = 28$

16. $37\frac{1}{2}$% of $n = 33$

17. 175% of $n = 49$

18. 300% of $n = 81$

Solve by using a proportion.

sale price $13.00

SALE: 75% of regular price

19. What was the regular price?

$9.36 down

Only 12% down payment

20. How much is the full price?

21. There were 72 problems on the math test. Find the percent that each student worked correctly.

Math Test Results		
Name	*Number Correct*	*Percent*
Adams, John	48	
Andrews, Susan	60	
Bartlow, Kevin	64	
Collins, Anne	56	
Cortez, Alex	66	

22. One week Lynn spent 60% of her allowance for a movie ticket. The ticket cost $1.20. How much was her allowance?

★**23.** $62\frac{1}{2}$% of the students in a seventh grade went on a field trip. If 175 students went on the field trip, how many students did not go?

Divide.

1. $1.5\overline{)8.70}$

2. $.42\overline{)1.512}$

3. $2.7\overline{)1.215}$

4. $0.53\overline{)3.498}$

5. $68\overline{)510}$

6. $7.5\overline{)292.5}$

7. $40\overline{)312}$

8. $0.23\overline{)2.139}$

9. $1.9\overline{)5.51}$

10. $2.7\overline{)1.566}$

11. $6.3\overline{)2.142}$

12. $0.34\overline{)2.142}$

Practice exercises

Complete this table.

	1.	2.	3.	4.	5.	6.	7.	8.
Decimal	0.31	0.17	0.89					0.09
Fraction	$\frac{31}{100}$			$\frac{1}{2}$	$\frac{3}{4}$		$\frac{1}{100}$	
Percent	31%					3%		

Solve.

9. 25% of 24 $= n$

10. 50% of 38 $= n$

11. 75% of 60 $= n$

12. 40% of 55 $= n$

13. 60% of 65 $= n$

14. 10% of 150 $= n$

15. 5% of 62 $= n$

16. 125% of 38 $= n$

17. 150% of 82 $= n$

18. $6\frac{1}{4}$% of 96 $= n$

19. $16\frac{2}{3}$% of 72 $= n$

20. $37\frac{1}{2}$% of 45 $= n$

21. $8\frac{1}{3}$% of 72 $= n$

22. $12\frac{1}{2}$% of 112 $= n$

23. $62\frac{1}{2}$% of 270 $= n$

24. 40% of 110 $= n$

25. $66\frac{2}{3}$% of 45 $= n$

26. 75% of 135 $= n$

27. $87\frac{1}{2}$% of 156 $= n$

28. 45% of 90 $= n$

29. $12\frac{1}{2}$% of 124 $= n$

Solve.

30. 30% of $n = 27$

31. 25% of $n = 32$

32. 80% of $n = 41$

33. 75% of $n = 48$

34. 70% of $n = 42$

35. 120% of $n = 96$

36. 8% of $n = 15$

37. 100% of $n = 135$

38. 1% of $n = 6$

39. $66\frac{2}{3}$% of $n = 34$

40. $83\frac{1}{3}$% of $n = 58$

41. $87\frac{1}{2}$% of $n = 135$

42. $37\frac{1}{2}$% of $n = 150$

43. $33\frac{1}{3}$% of $n = 216$

44. $62\frac{1}{2}$% of $n = 352$

45. $33\frac{1}{3}$% of $n = 124$

46. 120% of $n = 36$

47. 43% of $n = 19$

48. $112\frac{1}{2}$% of $n = 54$

49. 110% of $n = 22$

50. 60% of $n = 12$

Mathematics and science

Robert Hooke (1635–1703) found that, for a particular spring, the ratio of the change in length of a spring to the force (weight) that is stretching the spring is always the same.

For example:

When the weight is 3 times as much, the spring is stretched 3 times as much.

The ratio is constant as long as the spring is not stretched "beyond its limit." The ratio is different for different springs.

EXERCISES

In each exercise the same spring is shown with two different weights. Solve a proportion to find the missing number.

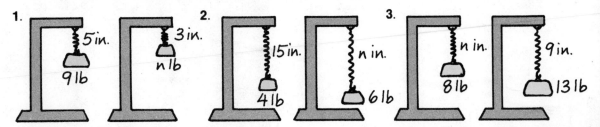

4. A force of 6 pounds stretches a spring 8.5 inches. If the force is increased by 50%, how much will the spring be stretched?

★5. A 4.5-pound weight stretches a spring 12 inches. What weight would increase the stretch by 75%?

Problem solving

1. To raise money for a canoe camping trip, a club decided to have a car wash. During the first 2 hours they washed 5 cars. At that rate, how many cars could they wash in 7 hours?

2. Fourteen boys went on the trip. They were charged $7.35 rent for each canoe. If not more than 3 boys could be in a canoe, what was each boy's share of the canoe rental? Round your answer to the nearest cent.

3. When planning the trip, it was decided that each boy could take 40% of his weight in supplies. Sam weighed 52 kg. How many kg of supplies could he take?

4. It was 17 km to where they decided to camp. They canoed 5 km before taking a break. What percent of the trip had they completed?

5. At the end of 3 hours they had canoed 7 km. At that rate, how long would it take them to canoe 11 km?

6. For their last meal they made chili. The recipe called for 2 cups of tomatoes and 3 cups of beans. They had $7\frac{1}{2}$ cups of tomatoes. How many cups of beans should they have used?

7. The boys took a different return route. After canoeing 6 kilometers they had traveled $37\frac{1}{2}\%$ of the way. How many kilometers long was the return trip?

8. The first 9 kilometers of the return trip took 4 hours. At that rate, how long would it take them to return? [*Hint:* For length of return trip, see exercise 7.]

Excursion

Elaine wanted these five pieces of chain joined together to make one chain.

ⓛⓛ ⓛⓛ ⓛⓛ ⓛⓛ ⓛⓛ

A jeweler would do the job, charging $2 for each link that was cut and rejoined. What is the minimum cost of the job?

CHAPTER CHECKUP

Give the ratio. [pages 240–241]

1. triangles to circles
2. circles to squares
3. squares to circles
4. red figures to green figures
5. blue squares to red circles
6. red triangles to green figures

Solve each proportion. [pages 242–243, 250]

7. $\dfrac{3}{4} = \dfrac{n}{32}$

8. $\dfrac{5}{9} = \dfrac{4}{n}$

9. $\dfrac{n}{6} = \dfrac{3}{10}$

10. $\dfrac{6}{6} = \dfrac{n}{7}$

11. $\dfrac{n}{3} = \dfrac{5}{8}$

12. $\dfrac{5}{n} = \dfrac{3}{7}$

13. $\dfrac{n}{4} = \dfrac{15}{23}$

14. $\dfrac{7}{n} = \dfrac{29}{18}$

Solve by using a proportion. [pages 244–247]

15. What is the price of 20 cookies?

16. A passenger train traveled 215 km in $2\dfrac{1}{4}$ hours. At that rate, how far would it travel in 4 hours?

Change each fraction to a percent. [pages 252–257]

17. $\dfrac{1}{4}$

18. $\dfrac{3}{4}$

19. $\dfrac{5}{2}$

20. $\dfrac{1}{3}$

21. $\dfrac{3}{8}$

22. $\dfrac{5}{16}$

Solve. [pages 258–264]

23. 25% of 72 = n

24. 40% of 60 = n

25. 8% of 75 = n

26. $33\dfrac{1}{3}$% of 50 = n

27. $87\dfrac{1}{2}$% of 94 = n

28. $112\dfrac{1}{2}$% of 150 = n

29. 50% of n = 19

30. 18% of n = 9

31. 72% of n = 45

32. 175% of n = 25

33. $83\dfrac{1}{3}$% of n = 28

34. $16\dfrac{2}{3}$% of n = 20

Solve. [pages 266–267]

35. An ecology club collected a total of 8000 kg of newspaper. One team collected $33\dfrac{1}{3}$% of the total. How many kg did that team collect?

36. Some hiking boots are on sale for 75% of the regular price. What is the regular price if the sale price is $28.35?

Project

1. List the titles of the six songs that you think are the most popular. Order the titles from most popular to least popular.

2. Survey twenty or more students and have them pick their favorite song from your list. Be sure to keep a tally.

3. Compare the way you ordered the titles with your survey. For example, did your number 1 song get the greatest number of votes?

4. Use your survey and make a bar graph.

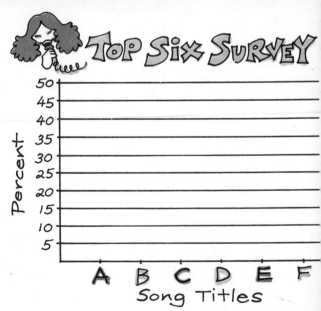

TOP SIX SURVEY

Percent

50
45
40
35
30
25
20
15
10
5

A B C D E F

Song Titles

CHAPTER REVIEW

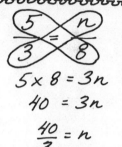

$$\frac{5}{3} = \frac{n}{8}$$

$$5 \times 8 = 3n$$

$$40 = 3n$$

$$\frac{40}{3} = n$$

$$\frac{2}{3} = n\%$$

$$3\overline{)2.00} \quad .66\frac{2}{3}$$
$$\underline{-18}$$
$$20$$
$$\underline{-18}$$
$$2$$

So, $\frac{2}{3} = 66\frac{2}{3}\%$

$$37\frac{1}{2}\% \text{ of } 60 = n$$

$$\frac{37\frac{1}{2}}{100} = \frac{n}{60}$$

$$37\frac{1}{2} \times 60 = 100n$$

$$2250 = 100n$$

$$22\frac{1}{2} = n$$

$$33\frac{1}{3}\% \text{ of } n = 8$$

$$\frac{33\frac{1}{3}}{100} = \frac{8}{n}$$

$$33\frac{1}{3}n = 100 \times 8$$

$$33\frac{1}{3}n = 800$$

$$n = 24$$

Solve each proportion.

1. $\frac{5}{9} = \frac{n}{27}$ 2. $\frac{7}{2} = \frac{n}{5}$ 3. $\frac{3}{11} = \frac{n}{8}$

4. $\frac{6}{5} = \frac{9}{n}$ 5. $\frac{8}{4} = \frac{5}{n}$ 6. $\frac{9}{6} = \frac{12}{n}$

7. $\frac{n}{4} = \frac{12}{5}$ 8. $\frac{n}{9} = \frac{6}{5}$ 9. $\frac{n}{7} = \frac{8}{3}$

10. $\frac{9}{n} = \frac{7}{14}$ 11. $\frac{6}{n} = \frac{15}{3}$ 12. $\frac{6}{n} = \frac{12}{5}$

Change each fraction to a percent.

13. $\frac{1}{3}$ 14. $\frac{3}{8}$ 15. $\frac{7}{4}$ 16. $\frac{2}{9}$ 17. $\frac{5}{6}$ 18. $\frac{9}{8}$

Solve.

19. 20% of 60 $= n$ 20. 25% of 48 $= n$

21. 50% of 38 $= n$ 22. 75% of 36 $= n$

23. 60% of 45 $= n$ 24. 150% of 72 $= n$

25. $33\frac{1}{3}\%$ of 54 $= n$ 26. $37\frac{1}{2}\%$ of 72 $= n$

27. $66\frac{2}{3}\%$ of 96 $= n$ 28. $12\frac{1}{2}\%$ of 18 $= n$

Solve.

29. 25% of $n = 7$ 30. 20% of $n = 12$

31. 40% of $n = 20$ 32. 75% of $n = 36$

33. 125% of $n = 75$ 34. 120% of $n = 72$

35. $37\frac{1}{2}\%$ of $n = 33$ 36. $33\frac{1}{3}\%$ of $n = 23$

37. $62\frac{1}{2}\%$ of $n = 30$ 38. $6\frac{1}{4}\%$ of $n = 15$

The painter wants to mix a special shade of green using this ratio:

$$3 \quad : \quad 5 \quad : \quad 2$$

yellow   blue   white

She has 2 liters of yellow paint. How much of the other colors should she use?

Solution.

yellow

$$\frac{3}{5} = \frac{2}{b}$$

blue

yellow

$$\frac{3}{2} = \frac{2}{w}$$

white

$3b = 10$

$b = 3\frac{1}{3}$

$3w = 4$

$w = 1\frac{1}{3}$

She should mix 2 liters of yellow, $3\frac{1}{3}$ liters of blue, and $1\frac{1}{3}$ liters of white.

Tell how much of each color should be used.

1. Ratio: 2   :   3   :   4
           red   white   green

Use 1 liter of red.

2. Ratio: 3   :   4   :   2
           black   red   yellow

Use 2 liters of black.

3. Ratio: 3   :   4   :   5
           blue   white   green

Use 4 liters of green.

4. Ratio: 2   :   3   :   4
           brown   orange   yellow

Use 4 liters of orange.

Form
14 a b c d   34   14 a b c d   4   30
15 a b c d   a b c   d   31
         a   b   c

MAJOR CHECKUP
Standardized Format

Choose the correct letter.

1. Six billion sixty million is

- **a.** 6,060,000
- **b.** 60,006,000
- **c.** 660,000,000
- **d.** none of these

2. Find the sum.

$5.934 + 26.58$

- **a.** 85.92
- **b.** 8.582
- **c.** 32.514
- **d.** none of these

3. Find the difference.

$62.8 - 3.54$

- **a.** 59.26
- **b.** 2.74
- **c.** 27.4
- **d.** none of these

4. Multiply.

$$\begin{array}{r} 3.26 \\ \times 1.5 \\ \hline \end{array}$$

- **a.** 0.489
- **b.** 4.89
- **c.** 48.9
- **d.** none of these

5. Find the average of 6.8, 3.5, 9.2, 7.45, and 6.05.

- **a.** 6.0
- **b.** 66
- **c.** 6.6
- **d.** none of these

6. $825 \text{ g} = \underline{\quad ? \quad} \text{ kg}$

- **a.** 0.825 kg
- **b.** 8.25 kg
- **c.** 82.5 kg
- **d.** none of these

7. Find the circumference. Use 3.14 as an approximation for π.

1.5 cm

- **a.** 7.0650 cm
- **b.** 9.42 cm
- **c.** 4.71 cm
- **d.** none of these

8. The prime factorization of 24 is

- **a.** 6×4
- **b.** $2 \times 3 \times 4$
- **c.** 1×24
- **d.** none of these

9. Give the sum.

$$\frac{5}{9} + \frac{5}{6}$$

- **a.** $\frac{2}{3}$
- **b.** $\frac{5}{27}$
- **c.** $\frac{25}{18}$
- **d.** none of these

10. Give the difference.

$$\frac{7}{4} - \frac{3}{7}$$

- **a.** $\frac{37}{28}$
- **b.** $\frac{1}{7}$
- **c.** $\frac{3}{4}$
- **d.** none of these

11. Give the product.

$$2\frac{1}{2} \times 4\frac{1}{4}$$

- **a.** $\frac{10}{17}$
- **b.** $10\frac{5}{8}$
- **c.** $1\frac{7}{10}$
- **d.** none of these

12. Give the quotient.

$$5\frac{1}{2} \div 2\frac{1}{3}$$

- **a.** $2\frac{5}{14}$
- **b.** $12\frac{5}{6}$
- **c.** $\frac{6}{77}$
- **d.** none of these

272

9

Consumer Mathematics

Solve.

1. $\frac{3}{4}$ of $80 = n$

2. $\frac{2}{3}$ of $48 = n$

3. $\frac{5}{6}$ of $84 = n$

4. 25% of $16 = n$

5. 60% of $25 = n$

6. $12\frac{1}{2}$% of $36 = n$

Solve.

7. $\frac{1}{3}$ of $n = 13

8. $\frac{3}{8}$ of $n = 24

9. $\frac{4}{5}$ of $n = 56

10. 20% of $n = 64

11. $33\frac{1}{3}$% of $n = 35

12. $137\frac{1}{2}$% of $n = 121

Earning money

The examples show some different ways in which people are paid.

Joan baby-sits to earn money. She is paid $1.25 an hour.

David sells peanuts at a ball park. He is paid a commission of $12\frac{1}{2}$% of his sales.

Debbie is paid 35¢ a week for each sub- scriber on her paper route.

EXERCISES

Suppose that you charge $1.25 for an hour of baby-sitting. Study the example. Then copy and complete this table. Round each charge to the nearest cent.

	From	To	Number of hours	Charge
1.	8:00 P.M.	10:45 P.M.	$2\frac{3}{4}$	$3.44
2.	6:30 P.M.	9:30 P.M.		
3.	7:00 P.M.	9:15 P.M.		
4.	8:30 P.M.	10:00 P.M.		
5.	5:15 P.M.	8:30 P.M.		
6.	11:00 A.M.	2:30 P.M.		

$$2\frac{3}{4} = 2.75$$

$$
\begin{array}{r}
\$1.25 \\
\times 2.75 \\
\hline
625 \\
875 \\
250 \\
\hline
\$3.4375
\end{array}
$$

Pretend that you sell peanuts at a ball park and you are paid $12\frac{1}{2}$% of your total sales.

7. How much would you earn if you sold $120 worth of peanuts?
[*Hint:* $12\frac{1}{2}\% = 12.5\% = 0.125$]

8. If you sold 264 bags of peanuts for 60¢ a bag, how much would you earn?

Suppose that you are paid 35¢ a week for each subscriber on a paper route.

9. How much would you earn per week if you had 88 subscribers?

10. If you had 104 subscribers, how much would you earn in 12 weeks?

Excursion ■●■●■●■●■●■●■●■●■●■●■●■●■●■●■●■●■●■
The price of a $200 bicycle is reduced 10% and later raised 10%. What is the final price? (The answer is not $200.) Answer the same question if the price is first raised 10% and later reduced 10%.

Budgets

A **budget** is a plan for using your money. Here is a student's sample budget.

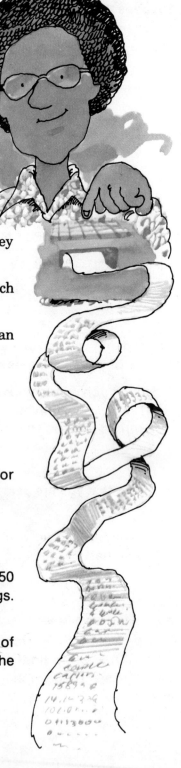

EARNINGS: $15 per week
Budget
Savings: $5.00
Lunches: 2.25
Movie: 3.50
Record: 2.25
Snacks: 2.00

Here are some reasons people use budgets.

(1) To spread out spending so that they don't run out of money between paychecks.

(2) To be sure that they put some money into savings each pay day.

(3) To control "impulsive" spending so that all necessities can be taken care of.

EXERCISES

In exercises 1–6, use the budget shown at the top of the page.

1. What percent of the earnings did the student save?

2. What percent of the earnings did the student spend for lunches?

3. What percent was spent for movies?

4. What percent was spent for food?

5. One week the student saw two movies that cost $3.50 each. The extra money for movies came from savings. What percent was saved that week?

6. One week the student earned an extra $5. Three dollars of that was spent and the rest was saved. What percent of the total earnings was saved?

Remember that you can find a fraction or percent of a quantity by multiplying. For example, to find the amount budgeted for utilities, you might use this method:

8% of $16,000 = ?

equivalent →

$$\begin{array}{r} \$16{,}000 \\ \times\ .08 \\ \hline \$1280.00 \end{array}$$

Family Budget

Utilities 8%
Clothing 10%
Automobile 16%
Housing 20%
Recreation 5%
Life Insurance 6%
Savings 11%
Food 20%
Misc. 4%

Yearly Income of $16,000

Refer to the graph of the family budget to answer the questions below.

7. How many dollars did the family budget for housing?

8. How many dollars did the family budget for savings?

9. What fraction of the total budget is for food and housing? Give answer in lowest terms.

10. How much more money was budgeted for clothing than for life insurance?

11. How much money is budgeted for both recreation and automobile?

12. What is the total percent budgeted for clothing, housing, and food?

13. If life insurance is considered as savings, how much money is budgeted to be saved?

14. The monthly car payment is $84.96. How much budgeted money a month is left for other car expenses?

15. Make a graph to show how you used your money last week.

16. Make a budget to show how you would like to use your money.

277

Spending wisely

Suppose that you are in a store and see this notebook paper. Before buying the paper you should ask yourself such questions as

(1) Is the price within my budget?
(2) Do I really need or want the paper?
(3) Which is the better buy?

If the answers to questions 1 and 2 are *yes*, then you could answer question 3 by computing the **unit price** (price per sheet) for each package.

$$\begin{array}{r} .008 \\ 120\overline{)0.960} \end{array} \qquad \begin{array}{r} .007 \\ 150\overline{)\,1.050} \end{array}$$

Is the $1.05 package a better buy?

What else besides price should you think about when deciding which of two items is the better buy?

EXERCISES

Suppose that both items are of equal quality. Compute the unit price and tell which is the better buy.

1.

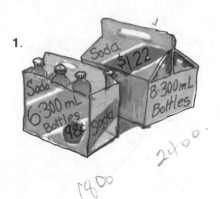

2.

3.

In many supermarkets you don't have to compute unit prices. The store does it for you and posts those prices on their shelves. Here are some ways that unit prices are posted. Give the unit price for each item. What is the unit?

4.

UNIT PRICE	50 G	RETAIL PRICE
1.48		.74
CNTS/GRAM	GROUND ALMONDS	

5.

UNIT PRICE	.475 L	RETAIL PRICE
1.03		.49
DOLS/LITER	CURRANT JELLY	

6.

UNIT PRICE	340 G	RETAIL PRICE
1.68		.57
DOLS/KG	CHILI SAUCE	

7.

UNIT PRICE	260 G	RETAIL PRICE
4.50		1.17
DOLS/KG	TUNA	

8.

UNIT PRICE	450 G	RETAIL PRICE
1.47		.66
DOLS/KG	SPAGHETTI SAUCE	

★9. Why do you think that in some cases the gram is used as a unit, while in other cases the kilogram is used?

Change to a percent.

1. $\frac{3}{4}$ 2. $\frac{5}{2}$

3. $\frac{2}{5}$ 4. $\frac{1}{3}$

5. $\frac{5}{8}$ 6. $\frac{9}{16}$

Solve. (*Hint:* Change the percent to a decimal and multiply.)

7. 20% of 60 = n

8. 35% of 28 = n

9. 42% of 74 = n

10. 85% of 95 = n

11. 62% of 153 = n

12. 34% of 276 = n

Computing prices

Perhaps a student group at your school raises money by selling school supplies. Suppose that you had the job of computing the total amount of each sale. Below are some problems that you might have.

Pencils: 2 for 25¢
What is the price of 1 pencil?

Solution: Compute the exact price of 1 pencil and *round up* to the next cent.

$$2\overline{)25} \quad 12\tfrac{1}{2}$$ The price is 13¢.

Erasers: 3 for 59¢
What is the price of 2 erasers?

Solution: Compute the exact price of 2 erasers and *round up* to the next cent.

$$\frac{3}{59} = \frac{2}{n}$$
$$3n = 118$$
$$n = 39\tfrac{1}{3} \quad \text{The price is 40¢.}$$

Erasers: 3 for 59¢
What is the price of 5 erasers?

Solution: Add the price of 3 erasers and the price of 2 erasers.

$$59¢ + 40¢ = 99¢$$

pencils: 2 for 25¢
erasers: 3 for 59¢
rulers: 45¢ each
pencil erasers: 3 for 20¢
compasses: 93¢ each
notebook paper: 86¢ each
protractors: 54¢ each
pens: 36¢ each

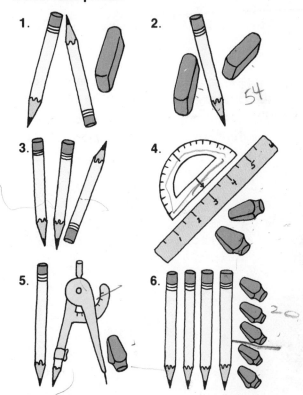

EXERCISES
Refer to the prices on page 280 to compute these total prices.

1.

2.   54

3.

4.

5.

6.   20

Solve.

7. A customer buys 7 pencils and gives you a dollar. How much change should you give?

8. A customer buys 3 packages of notebook paper and 5 pencils. He gives you $5. How much change should you give back?

9. Suppose someone returns a protractor and buys 1 eraser and 2 pencil erasers. How much money should you give back?

10. Another customer returns one compass and 2 pens. He then buys 4 packages of notebook paper and gives you $2. How much change should you give back?

LAURA

Discounts

Have you ever seen a sign like this in a store?

To sell the pack frame, the merchant is discounting (decreasing) the price 20%. The amount a price is decreased is called the **discount**. Here are 3 ways to find the sale price.

TRANS-AMERICA
PACKFRAME
$28.60
NOW
20% OFF!

If the discount is 20%, then the sale price is 80% of the regular price.

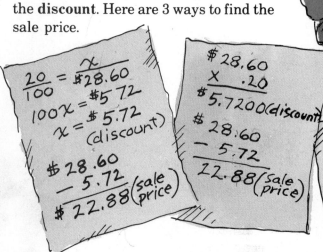

$$\frac{20}{100} = \frac{x}{\$28.60}$$
$$100x = \$572$$
$$x = \$5.72 \text{ (discount)}$$

$$\begin{array}{r} \$28.60 \\ -\ 5.72 \\ \hline \$22.88 \text{ (sale price)} \end{array}$$

$$\begin{array}{r} \$28.60 \\ \times\ \ \ .20 \\ \hline \$5.7200 \text{ (discount)} \end{array}$$

$$\begin{array}{r} \$28.60 \\ -\ 5.72 \\ \hline 22.88 \text{ (sale price)} \end{array}$$

$$\begin{array}{r} \$28.60 \\ \times\ \ \ .80 \\ \hline \$22.8800 \\ \text{(sale price)} \end{array}$$

The percent a price is decreased is sometimes called the **percent of discount**.

This pair of hiking boots was discounted for a sale.

ORIGINAL PRICE
$48.00

SALE PRICE
$42.00

To find the percent of discount, find what percent of the original price the discount is.

amount of discount →
original price →

$$\frac{6}{48} = \frac{n}{100}$$
$$48n = 600$$
$$n = 12\frac{1}{2}$$

The percent of discount was $12\frac{1}{2}\%$.

EXERCISES

The regular price and the percent of discount are given. Compute the discount.

1. tent: $36.50
   discount: 25%

2. mess kit: $12.50
   discount: 10%

3. pack: $27.60
   discount: $33\frac{1}{3}$%

4. sleeping bag: $56.80
   discount: $12\frac{1}{2}$%

The regular price and the percent of discount are given. Find the total cost, including a sales tax of 5%. Refer to the table for the sales tax.

5. flashlight: $8.50
   discount: 10%

6. poncho: $16.60
   discount: 25%

7. pack frame: $29.50
   discount: 12%

8. stove: $24.75
   discount: $33\frac{1}{3}$%

Find the percent of discount.

9.

10.

Sale	Tax	Sale	Tax
6.90 – 7.09	.35	18.90 – 19.09	.95
7.10 – 7.29	.36	19.10 – 19.29	.96
7.30 – 7.49	.37	19.30 – 19.49	.97
7.50 – 7.69	.38	19.50 – 19.69	.98
7.70 – 7.89	.39	19.70 – 19.89	.99
7.90 – 8.09	.40	19.90 – 20.09	1.00
8.10 – 8.29	.41	20.10 – 20.29	1.01
8.30 – 8.49	.42	20.30 – 20.49	1.02
8.50 – 8.69	.43	20.50 – 20.69	1.03
8.70 – 8.89	.44	20.70 – 20.89	1.04
8.90 – 9.09	.45	20.90 – 21.09	1.05
9.10 – 9.29	.46	21.10 – 21.29	1.06
9.30 – 9.49	.47	21.30 – 21.49	1.07
9.50 – 9.69	.48	21.50 – 21.69	1.08
9.70 – 9.89	.49	21.70 – 21.89	1.09
9.90 – 10.09	.50	21.90 – 22.09	1.10
10.10 – 10.29	.51	22.10 – 22.29	1.11
10.30 – 10.49	.52	22.30 – 22.49	1.12
10.50 – 10.69	.53	22.50 – 22.69	1.13
10.70 – 10.89	.54	22.70 – 22.89	1.14
10.90 – 11.09	.55	22.90 – 23.09	1.15
11.10 – 11.29	.56	23.10 – 23.29	1.16
11.30 – 11.49	.57	23.30 – 23.49	1.17
11.50 – 11.69	.58	23.50 – 23.69	1.18
11.70 – 11.89	.59	23.70 – 23.89	1.19
11.90 – 12.09	.60	23.90 – 24.09	1.20
12.10 – 12.29	.61	24.10 – 24.29	1.21
12.30 – 12.49	.62	24.30 – 24.49	1.22
12.50 – 12.69	.63	24.50 – 24.69	1.23
12.70 – 12.89	.64	24.70 – 24.89	1.24
12.90 – 13.09	.65	24.90 – 25.09	1.25
13.10 – 13.29	.66	25.10 – 25.29	1.26
13.30 – 13.49	.67	25.30 – 25.49	1.27
13.50 – 13.69	.68	25.50 – 25.69	1.28
13.70 – 13.89	.69	25.70 – 25.89	1.29
13.90 – 14.09	.70	25.90 – 26.09	1.30
14.10 – 14.29	.71	26.10 – 26.29	1.31
14.30 – 14.49	.72	26.30 – 26.49	1.32
14.50 – 14.69	.73	26.50 – 26.69	1.33
14.70 – 14.89	.74	26.70 – 26.89	1.34
14.90 – 15.09	.75	26.90 – 27.09	1.35
15.10 – 15.29	.76	27.10 – 27.29	1.36
15.30 – 15.49	.77	27.30 – 27.49	1.37
15.50 – 15.69	.78	27.50 – 27.69	1.38
15.70 – 15.89	.79	27.70 – 27.89	1.39
15.90 – 16.09	.80	27.90 – 28.09	1.40
16.10 – 16.29	.81	28.10 – 28.29	1.41
16.30 – 16.49	.82	28.30 – 28.49	1.42
16.50 – 16.69	.83	28.50 – 28.69	1.43
16.70 – 16.89	.84	28.70 – 28.89	1.44
16.90 – 17.09	.85	28.90 – 29.09	1.45
17.10 – 17.29	.86	29.10 – 29.29	1.46
17.30 – 17.49	.87	29.30 – 29.49	1.47
17.50 – 17.69	.88	29.50 – 29.69	1.48
17.70 – 17.89	.89	29.70 – 29.89	1.49
17.90 – 18.09	.90	29.90 – 30.09	1.50
18.10 – 18.29	.91	30.10 – 30.29	1.51
18.30 – 18.49	.92	30.30 – 30.49	1.52
18.50 – 18.69	.93	30.50 – 30.69	1.53
18.70 – 18.89	.94	30.70 – 30.89	1.54

A checking account

It is not usually a wise idea to keep large amounts of cash in your billfold or even in your home. It can be accidentally destroyed, lost, or stolen. Millions of people put their money into **checking accounts** in banks to keep it safe. Whenever they wish to use some of the money they write a **check**. Checks are just notes that tell the bank to give some of the money in an account to a company or a person.

This check tells the First National Bank of Hometown, USA, to pay Mary R. Cooper $18.25 from the checking account of Sarah Smith.

Sarah Smith 564 East 54th Street Hometown, USA	No. 3206

July 21, 19 79

PAY TO THE ORDER OF _Mary R. Cooper_ $18.25

Eighteen and 25/100 _____ DOLLARS

First National Bank
Hometown, USA

Sarah Smith

⑆0 5 ⑈2⑉053⑆ ⑈ 343 123⑈

A checkbook has a section in which a record of the account is kept. Study this part of Sarah Smith's record:

CHECK NO.	DATE	PAY TO	AMOUNT	DEPOSIT	BALANCE	
					26	42
3204	July 11	LP Records	14.20		12	22
	July 15			50.00	62	22
3205	July 18	Allan's Bookstore	8.57		53	.65
3206	July 21	Mary R. Cooper	18.25		35	40

Mary R. Cooper will have to sign her name on the back of the check before she can cash the check. This is called **endorsing** the check. The endorsed check is proof that Sarah Smith paid the money to Mary R. Cooper.

EXERCISES

Refer to the preceding page to answer the following questions.

1. What is the number of the check that was written to Mary Cooper?

2. On what date was a $50 deposit made?

3. Check 3204 was written for what amount?

4. How much was the check written to Allan's Bookstore?

5. What was the balance in the account after check 3206 was written?

6. To whom was a check of $14.20 written?

7. Why do you think that a check should be written in ink?

8. Why do you think the amount is written in both numerals and words?

9. Who can cash this check?

Sarah Smith
564 East 54th Street
Hometown, USA

No. *3214*

July 30 19 *79*

PAY TO THE
ORDER OF *Cash*

$ *50.00*

Fifty and 00/100 _____ DOLLARS

First National Bank
Hometown, USA

Sarah Smith

⑈0 5 1 2⑈0 5 3⑈ ⑈ 3 4 3 1 2 3⑈

Write in words, as you would on a check.

10. $37.50   11. $42.75   12. $60.00   13. $135.45   14. $203.04

Project

1. Find out whether your bank charges a service charge for a checking account. If so, how do they compute the service charge?

2. Find out what "overdrawn account" means.

Borrowing money

Some day you may need to borrow money. If you do, you will probably borrow the money from a bank, credit union, or loan company. You will have to pay **interest** (rent) for using the money. The amount of interest that you will pay depends on the **principal** (the amount you borrow), the **rate** (percent) of interest charged, and the **time** for which you borrow the money.

He will have to sign a note saying he will pay back the $600 plus the interest in 1 year.

The amount of interest can be computed by using this formula:

$$\text{Interest} = \text{principal} \times \text{rate} \times \text{time}$$

$$I = prt$$

principal: $600

rate: 8% per year

time: 1 year

These time units must be the same when using the formula.

$I = prt$

$I = \$600 \times \dfrac{8}{100} \times 1$

$I = \$48$

He will repay $648 at the end of 1 year.

Important: Before you borrow, you should compare the rates of several banks.

286

EXERCISES

Compute the interest to the nearest cent.

	Interest	Principal	Interest rate per year	Time
1.	64	$800	8%	1 year
2.	60	$1000	6%	1 year
3.	70	$2000	7%	6 months
4.	45	$750	8%	9 months
5.	20	$500	6%	8 months
6.	81.25	$1250	$6\frac{1}{2}$%	1 year
7.	21.25	$500	$8\frac{1}{2}$%	6 months
8.	42.50	$850	$7\frac{1}{2}$%	8 months
9.	35.16	$1250	$6\frac{3}{4}$%	5 months
10.		$1875	$9\frac{1}{4}$%	2 months

Solve.

11. Jane borrowed $1800 for 1 year to buy a car. If the yearly rate was 8%, how much interest would she owe at the end of the year?

12. **a.** A motorcycle is on sale for $1350. A bank will loan 80% of the money. How much money will the bank loan on the motorcycle?
    b. If the bank will loan the money at 9% for 1 year, how much interest will be charged?

13. John saved $120 to buy a stereo set. A stereo that generally sells for $379.00 is on sale for 25% off.
    a. How much money will he have to borrow?
    b. If he borrows the money for 6 months at 8%, how much interest will he pay?

Keeping Skills Sharp

Solve.

1. 25% of $n = 32$
2. 50% of $n = 20$
3. $33\frac{1}{3}$% of $n = 18$
4. $66\frac{2}{3}$% of $n = 14$
5. 15% of $n = 7.5$
6. 28% of $n = 42$
7. 16% of $n = 4$
8. $37\frac{1}{2}$% of $n = 27$
9. $62\frac{1}{2}$% of $n = 31$
10. 115% of $n = 69$
11. $112\frac{1}{2}$% of $n = 68.4$
12. 120% of $n = 105$

287

Installment buying

Suppose that you wanted to buy this television set but didn't have $180. You could pay a down payment of $30, sign the agreement to pay $14 a month for 12 payments, and take the television set with you. Until you are older and have "established credit," you will probably have to have someone sign the agreement with you. Such a person is called a **cosigner**.

When you buy an item on an installment plan, you usually have to pay more.

Cash	Installment Plan
$180	$14
	× 12
	28
	14
	$168
	+ 30
	$198

The extra $18 that you are charged on the installment plan is interest that you must pay because you borrowed from the television store.

Before buying on an installment plan, check to see if you could save money by borrowing the money from a bank or credit union.

$180⁰⁰ ONLY $30 DOWN AND $14 MONTHLY FOR 1 YEAR

EXERCISES

How much more does the installment plan cost?

1.

Cash: $68
Installment plan:
$20 down
$4.48 per month
   for 12 months

2.

Cash: $156
Installment plan:
$30 down
$12.06 per month
   for 12 months

3.

Cash: $59
Installment plan:
no down payment
$7.15 per month
   for 9 months

4.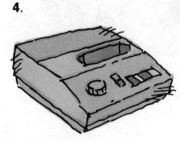

Cash: $72
Installment plan:
$15 down
$4.37 per month
   for 15 months

5.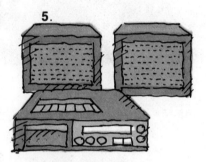

Cash: $248
Installment plan:
$50 down
$14.36 per month
   for 16 months

6.

Cash: $98
Installment plan:
$18 down
$14.13 per month
   for 6 months

Solve.

7. Suppose that it costs $14.88 interest to finance a $120 purchase for 1 year on an installment plan. How much could be saved by borrowing the money at a bank for 8%?

8. Suppose that a merchant offers to finance $460 for 18 months at $30.15 per month. You can also borrow the money for $8\frac{1}{2}\%$ at a bank. Which would cost less? How much less?

Mathematics in careers

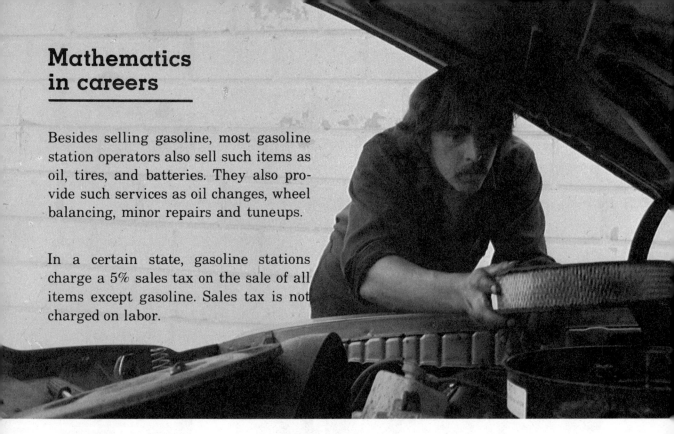

Besides selling gasoline, most gasoline station operators also sell such items as oil, tires, and batteries. They also provide such services as oil changes, wheel balancing, minor repairs and tuneups.

In a certain state, gasoline stations charge a 5% sales tax on the sale of all items except gasoline. Sales tax is not charged on labor.

EXERCISES
Compute the total. For the sales tax, refer to the table on page 283.

1.

CRAIG'S SERVICE STATION

Labor			
minor Tune-up	$17.50	Gasoline	$9.50
Oil Change	1.50	5 L Oil	
Oil Filter	1.00	(89¢/L)	
		Oil Filter	3.75
		Sales Tax	
Labor Total		→	
		Total	

2.

CRAIG'S SERVICE STATION

Labor			
Balance (4 wheels)	$7.00	Gasoline	$6.75
		1 L Oil	.89
		Sales Tax	
Labor Total		→	
		Total	

3.

CRAIG'S SERVICE STATION

Labor			
Oil Change	$1.50	Gasoline	$6.93
Filter (Oil)	1.00	Oil Filter	3.75
Filter (Air)	.75	Air Filter	2.95
Lubrication	2.85	4 L Oil	
		(89¢/L)	
		Sales Tax	
Labor Total		→	
		Total	

Mathematics in careers

Property such as houses, buildings, and land is called *real estate*. Real estate is generally sold by a real-estate agent. For selling the property, the agent receives a commission, which is generally a percentage of the selling price.

Often several real-estate agents in the same area belong to a multiple listing service. When such an agent lists (signs an agreement to try to sell) some real estate, he informs the other agents who belong to the multiple listing service. Any of these agents can then sell the property. If an agent other than the one who listed the property sells it, the commission is divided between the agent who listed the property and the one who sold it.

EXERCISES

During one week, the R. E. Johnson Real Estate Company received commissions from the sale of the properties listed below. The total commission paid was 6% of the selling price. How much commission did the R. E. Johnson Real Estate Company receive during this week?

1. Listed by R. E. Johnson
   Sold by R. E. Johnson

   Well-maintained, professionally landscaped 3-bedroom ranch home, near schools, with living room, kitchen, utility room, and large bath. Attic with pull-down stairs, patio, attached garage. Has central air conditioning, carpet and tile floors, and maintenance-free aluminum siding. This home is a real buy at $59,900.

2. Listed by A. J. Thomas
   Sold by R. E. Johnson

   Large exceptionally nice bi-level in Kenwood School area, with 3 large bedrooms and bath up. Lower level has big "L" shaped family room, 4th bedroom, large bath, utility area. Storm windows, carpet and tile floors, redwood sun deck off kitchen. A beautiful white aluminum-sided home in excellent condition. Will consider trade. $64,900.

3. Listed by R. E. Johnson
   Sold by C. R. Davidson

   Beautifully cared for older air-conditioned brick-on-tile home in established area. 4 bedrooms and lovely bath on 2nd, study and family room on first. Brick fireplace in carpeted and draped living room. Beamed ceiling in magnificent dining room. Recreation room, work room, etc., in basement. Attic, 2-car garage. $69,900.

4. Listed by R. E. Johnson
   Sold by R. E. Johnson

   12-unit brick apartment building in good location. 8 units furnished and 4 unfurnished. Furnishings include washers and dryers, disposals in most. This apartment building has a net income of $42,000 per year. Call for more details. $490,000.

CHAPTER CHECKUP

Solve. [pages 274–275, 284–285]

1. John Roberto worked 3 hours for the amount shown on the check. How much did he earn per hour?

2. The balance of the account before the check was written was $142.13. What was the balance after the check was written?

3. Who wrote the check?

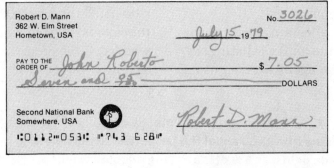

[pages 280–281]

Find the price of

4. 1 record.

5. 2 records.

6. 5 records.

Solve. [pages 282–283]

7. A $112 bicycle was put on sale at a discount of 20%. What was the sale price?

8. A $48 camera was put on sale for $36. What was the percent of discount?

Solve. [pages 286–289]

9. If you borrowed $85 for 1 year and paid 9% interest, how much interest would you pay?

10. A $156 canoe can be bought for $30 down and $11.76 a month for 12 months. Find the amount of interest.

Project

1. From a classified ad in a newspaper, compute the average prices of 1-year-old Chevrolets, 2-year-old Chevrolets, 3-year-old Chevrolets, and 4-year-old Chevrolets.

2. Show your findings on a bar graph like this:

Average Price of Chevrolets

Price (vertical axis):
$5000
$4500
$4000
$3500
$3000
$2500
$2000
$1500
$1000
$500

Years Old (horizontal axis): 1 2 3 4

3. Repeat the project for another make of automobile. Compare your results.

293

CHAPTER REVIEW

Solve.

1. Find the price of 1 bird.
   [*Hint:* Divide by 3 and round up to the next cent.]

2. Find the price of 2 birds.
   [*Hint:* Compute the exact price of 2 birds and round up to the next cent.]

3. Find the price of 5 birds.
   [*Hint:* Add the price of 3 birds and the price of 2 birds.]

Solve.

4. How much is the discount?
   [*Hint:* Take 20% of $18.50.]

5. What is the sale price?
   [*Hint:* Subtract the discount from $18.50.]

Solve.

6. What is the cash price?

7. **a.** What is the down payment?
   b. What is the total of the monthly payments?

8. How much more does the installment plan cost?

CHAPTER CHALLENGE

Perhaps you have a savings account. If you do, you probably know that the interest your account earns is added to your account several times during the year.

Study this example.

On January 1, $100 is deposited in a savings account that pays 6% interest per year.

At the end of 3 months ($\frac{1}{4}$ year) the interest is added to the account.

$$I = p \times r \times t$$
$$I = \$100 \times \frac{6}{100} \times \frac{1}{4}$$
$$I = \$1.50$$

The new balance is $101.50.

At the end of the next 3 months, the interest is figured on $101.50 and added to the account.

$$I = p \times r \times t$$
$$I = \$101.50 \times \frac{6}{100} \times \frac{1}{4}$$
$$I = \$1.52 \text{ rounded to the nearest cent}$$

The new balance is $103.02.

Notice that "interest on interest" is being paid. This is called **compounding** the interest.

Pretend that you deposit $100 in a savings account that pays 6% interest compounded every 3 months. Find how much money you would have in your account after 2 years.

| a | b | c | d | | a | b | c | d | | a | b | c | d | | a | b | c | d | | a | b | c | d |
14
34
14
4
30
| a | b | c | d | | | | | | | | | | | | | | c | d | | a | b | c | d |
15
31
| | | | | | | | | a | b | c | | | | | | | a | b | c | d |

MAJOR CHECKUP
Standardized Format

Choose the correct letter.

1. Round 52.6396 to the nearest thousandth.

- **a.** 52.640
- **b.** 52.639
- **c.** 52.649
- **d.** none of these

2. Multiply.

$$\begin{array}{r} 5.23 \\ \times\, 27.5 \\ \hline \end{array}$$

- **a.** 143.715
- **b.** 143.825
- **c.** 1438.25
- **d.** none of these

3. Divide.

$0.79\overline{)21.646}$

- **a.** 2.74
- **b.** 274.0
- **c.** 27.4
- **d.** none of these

4. Complete.

5.38 kg = _____?_____ g

- **a.** .538
- **b.** 53.8
- **c.** 538
- **d.** none of these

5. Find the area.

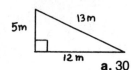

- **a.** 30 sq m
- **b.** 17 sq m
- **c.** 60 sq m
- **d.** none of these

6. Add.

$$\begin{array}{r} 9\frac{2}{3} \\ +\,8\frac{3}{8} \\ \hline \end{array}$$

- **a.** $17\frac{1}{24}$
- **b.** $17\frac{7}{24}$
- **c.** $18\frac{1}{24}$
- **d.** none of these

7. Subtract.

$$\begin{array}{r} 5\frac{1}{3} \\ -\,3\frac{3}{4} \\ \hline \end{array}$$

- **a.** $7\frac{5}{12}$
- **b.** $2\frac{7}{12}$
- **c.** $1\frac{7}{12}$
- **d.** none of these

8. Give the product.

$$\frac{7}{3} \times \frac{3}{5}$$

- **a.** $\frac{7}{5}$
- **b.** $\frac{35}{9}$
- **c.** $\frac{9}{35}$
- **d.** none of these

9. Give the quotient.

$$\frac{9}{5} \div \frac{10}{3}$$

- **a.** 6
- **b.** $\frac{27}{50}$
- **c.** $\frac{57}{20}$
- **d.** none of these

10. Solve.

$$\frac{n}{15} = \frac{13}{8}$$

- **a.** $24\frac{3}{8}$
- **b.** $6\frac{14}{15}$
- **c.** $9\frac{3}{13}$
- **d.** none of these

11. 20% of 50 =

- **a.** 10
- **b.** 250
- **c.** 100
- **d.** none of these

12. $33\frac{1}{3}$% of n = 24

n =

- **a.** 8
- **b.** 72
- **c.** 48
- **d.** none of these

10
Geometry

READY OR NOT !

Match.

1. point   a.

2. segment b.

3. ray   c.

4. line   d. •

5. angle   e.

6. Which line intersects line *l* at point *R*?

7. Which line II (is parallel to) line *m*?

8. Which line ⊥ (is perpendicular to) line *m*?

Constructions

Look around you. What shapes can you find? Perhaps you see square tiles, a rectangular room, and a circular clock. What other shapes are there? In this chapter you will study shapes and their properties.

First let's do some work with the tools of geometry, the **compass** and **straightedge.**

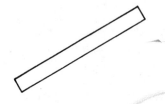

Follow these steps to copy a segment, $\overline{AB}$.

Step 1. Set the compass legs on *A* and *B*.

Step 2. Mark the paper with both the pencil and the point.

Step 3. Draw the segment.

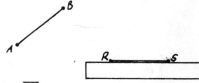

$\overline{AB}$ and $\overline{RS}$ are the same length.

Follow these steps to copy an angle, ∠B.

Step 1. Draw $\overrightarrow{TR}$.

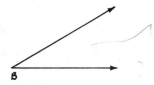

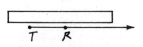

Step 2. Draw an arc that intersects the sides of ∠B.

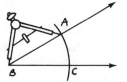

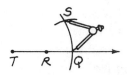

Step 3. Use the same compass setting to draw an arc as shown.

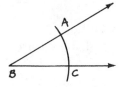

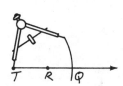

Step 4. Set the compass as shown.

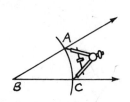

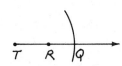

Step 5. Use the same setting to draw an arc as shown.

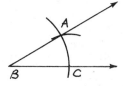

Step 6. Draw $\overrightarrow{TS}$, as shown.

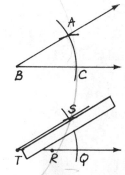

∠B and ∠T are the same size.

EXERCISES

1. First draw some segments. Then use a compass and straightedge to copy each segment.

2. First draw some angles. Then use a compass and straightedge to copy each angle.

3. Draw a circle. Do not change the compass setting. Mark off 6 equal arcs on the circle.

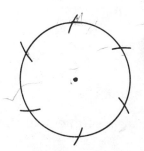

Bisecting segments and angles

Here is how to use a straightedge and compass to bisect (find the midpoint of) a segment.

Step 1. Using point *A* as the center, draw an arc as shown.

Step 2. Using point *B* as the center and the same compass setting, draw another arc.

Step 3. Put the straight-edge on the points where the arcs cross. Mark where the straightedge crosses the segment.

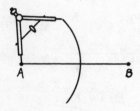

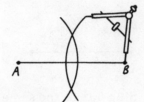

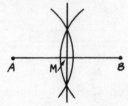

M is the midpoint of $\overline{AB}$.

You can also bisect an angle with a compass and straightedge.

Step 1. Using the vertex as the center, draw an arc as shown.

Step 2. Use points *X* and *Y* as centers. Draw two crossing arcs, using the same compass setting for both.

Step 3. Draw the ray from the vertex to the point where the arcs cross.

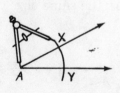

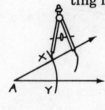

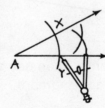

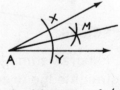

$\overrightarrow{AM}$ is the bisector of $\angle A$.

EXERCISES

1. Draw a segment and bisect it.

2. Draw an angle and bisect it.

3. Draw a triangle. Draw the bisector of each angle. If you are very careful, the three bisectors will all cross at the same point.

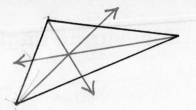

4. Draw a triangle. Bisect each side. Draw segments from a vertex to the midpoint of the opposite side. These segments are called **medians** of the triangle. If you are very careful, the three medians will all cross at the same point.

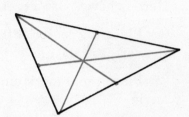

5. Draw a long segment. Bisect the segment. Bisect each half of the segment. You have divided the segment into 4 equal parts.

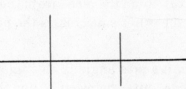

6. Draw a segment and divide it into 8 equal parts.

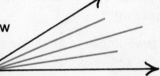

7. Draw an angle and bisect it. Bisect each of the new angles.

Excursion ■□■

1. Get a strip of paper that is about 40 centimeters long.

2. Give the paper a half-twist and tape the ends together.

 This is called a Moebius strip.

3. Cut around the strip at the middle.

What happened?

Measuring angles

A **protractor** is used for measuring angles.

Here is how to use a protractor:

(1) Place the center of the protractor at the vertex of the angle.

(2) Place the 0 mark on one side of the angle.

(3) Read the measure of the angle where the other side crosses the protractor.

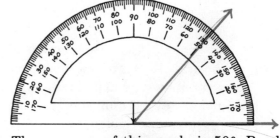

The measure of this angle is 50°. Read "50°" as "fifty degrees."

An **acute angle** is an angle that measures between 0° and 90°.

A **right angle** is an angle that measures 90°.

An **obtuse angle** is an angle that measures between 90° and 180°.

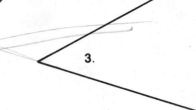

This means that the angle is a right angle.

EXERCISES
Measure each angle.

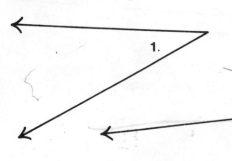

1.

2.

3.

Draw angles having these measures.

4. 35°   **5.** 135°   **6.** 90°   **7.** 75°   **8.** 175°

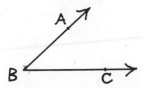

A
B C

Point *B* is called the **vertex** of the angle. Here are 3 ways to name the angle.

∠B   "angle *B*"

∠ABC   "angle *ABC*"

∠CBA   "angle *CBA*"

Acute, right, or obtuse?

S
R
Q P T

9. ∠QPT

10. ∠SPT

11. ∠SPQ

12. ∠RPT

Some angles have been drawn on grid paper. Estimate the measure of each angle.

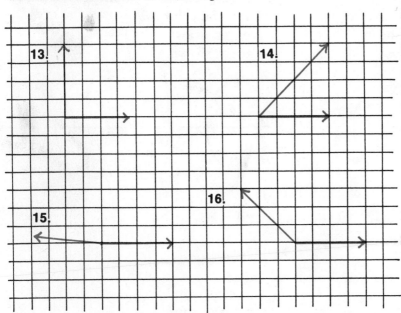

13.

14.

15.

16.

Give each difference.

1. 7.92 – 3.06

2. 4.283 – 1.096

3. 5.80 – 2.39

4. 9.036 – 4.958

5. 6.9 – 0.28

6. 5.93 – 4.6

7. 7 – 2.8

8. 9 – 3.64

9. 2.8 – 1.99

10. 6.3 – 1.05

17. Draw a large triangle. Add the measures of the angles. Repeat for several other triangles. Did you always get the same sum?

18. Repeat exercise 17 using quadrilaterals (four-sided figures).

Perpendicular lines and parallel lines

Two lines that intersect to form right angles are called **perpendicular lines.**

We say:

line l is perpendicular to line m

we write:

$l \perp m$

Here is how to use your straightedge and compass to construct two perpendicular lines.

Step 1.
Draw a line.

Step 2.
Using point A as center, draw an arc as shown.

Step 3.
Using the same setting and point B as center, draw an arc as shown.

Step 4.
Connect the points where the arcs cross.

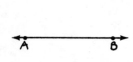 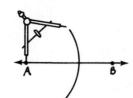 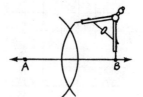 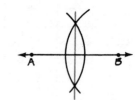

Notice that the red line in step 4 also bisects $\overline{AB}$. It is called the **perpendicular bisector** of $\overline{AB}$.

Two lines in a plane that do not intersect are called **parallel lines.**

We say:

line r is parallel to line s

we write:

$r \parallel s$

EXERCISES

1. Use a compass and straightedge to construct two perpendicular lines.

2. Follow these steps to construct two parallel lines.

   a. Draw a line *l* and construct a perpendicular line to line *l*.

   b. Construct a second perpendicular line to line *l*.

   c. What can you say about the two lines that are perpendicular to line *l*?

   d. Can you now construct a line that is parallel to line *l*?

   e. How many lines do you think there are that are parallel to line *l*? Perpendicular to line *l*?

3. Draw a triangle. Construct the perpendicular bisector to each side.
   If you are very careful, the three lines will all cross at the same point.

4. Draw a large triangle with sides of different lengths. Construct the three angle bisectors, the three perpendicular bisectors, and the three medians (see exercise 4 on page 301).

Excursion ■○■○■○■○■○■○■○■○■○■
Make a Moebius strip. (See page 301.)

Cut around the strip, always staying nearer one edge than the other. Guess what will happen. What did happen?

Congruent figures

You have seen pairs of figures that have the same size and
shape. Such figures are called **congruent figures**. For example, the two trianges below are congruent because a tracing of
$\triangle ABC$ ("triangle ABC") fits $\triangle QPR$.

We write: $\triangle \textbf{ABC} \cong \triangle \textbf{QPR}$

We say: $\triangle \textbf{ABC}$ is congruent to $\triangle \textbf{QPR}$

Notice that for this fitting, we have this
matching of the vertices:

$$A \longleftrightarrow Q$$
$$B \longleftrightarrow P$$
$$C \longleftrightarrow R$$

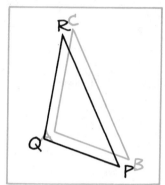

The sides and angles that match are called
corresponding parts.

Corresponding sides	Corresponding angles
$\overline{AB} \longleftrightarrow \overline{QP}$	$\angle A \longleftrightarrow \angle Q$
$\overline{AC} \longleftrightarrow \overline{QR}$	$\angle B \longleftrightarrow \angle P$
$\overline{BC} \longleftrightarrow \overline{PR}$	$\angle C \longleftrightarrow \angle R$

EXERCISES
In each exercise the two figures are congruent. Name all pairs of
corresponding parts for the congruent fitting.

1.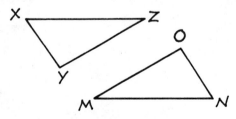

2.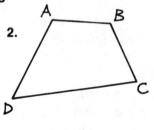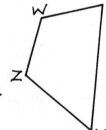

For exercises 3–6, use the figures below. The triangles are congruent.

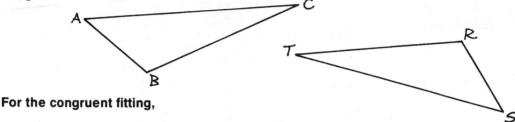

For the congruent fitting,

3. which side of △RST corresponds to $\overline{AB}$?

4. is $\overline{RT}$ congruent to $\overline{AB}$? Why?

5. which angle of △RST is congruent to ∠C? How do you know?

6. which side of △ABC is congruent to $\overline{ST}$? How do you know?

7. True or false? For a congruent fitting, the corresponding parts are congruent.

Some information about a pair of triangles is given. If you completed the triangles, would they be congruent?

8. The red straws are congruent.
   The green straws are congruent.
   The angles formed by the
      pipe cleaners are congruent.

9. The angles formed by the red
      pipe cleaners are congruent.
   The angles formed by the green
      pipe cleaners are congruent.
   The straws are congruent.

10. If two triangles have three pairs of congruent sides, will the triangles be congruent?

 Project

1. Use a straightedge and draw a triangle.

2. Use a compass and straightedge to construct a congruent triangle.

A line of symmetry

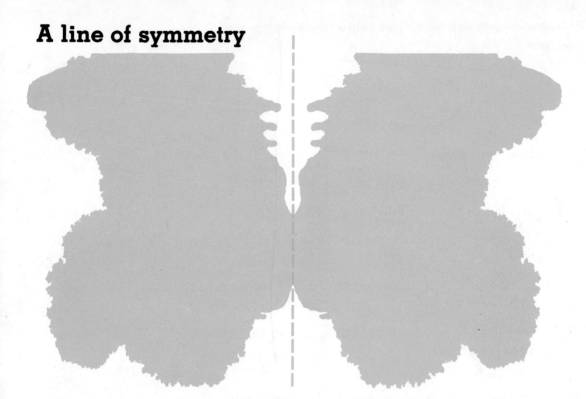

Notice that the two halves on each side of the fold line match.
The fold line is a **line of symmetry**.

EXERCISES

Is the dotted line a line of symmetry? *Hint:* **If you fold along the
dotted line, will the two parts match?**

1.

2.

3.

4.
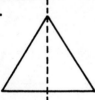

5.
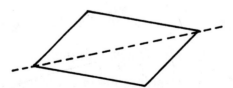

6.
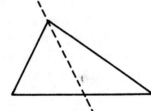

Trace each figure and draw all lines of symmetry.

7.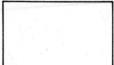

8.

9.

Only half of the figure is pictured. The red line is a line of symmetry. First trace the given half. Then draw the missing half.

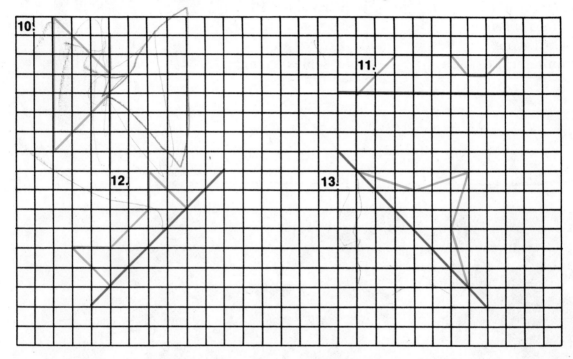

10.

11.

12.

13.

14. a. Construct a triangle having just two congruent sides.

    b. Draw all lines of symmetry.

15. a. Construct a triangle having three congruent sides.

    b. Draw all lines of symmetry.

16. Do you think it's possible for a triangle to have exactly two lines of symmetry?

309

Triangles

Now let's use the idea of a line of symmetry to study the properties of triangles. Any triangle can be classified according to its number of lines of symmetry.

A triangle with 3 lines of symmetry is called an **equilateral triangle**.

A triangle with 1 line of symmetry is called an **isosceles triangle**.

A triangle with 0 lines of symmetry is called a **scalene triangle**.

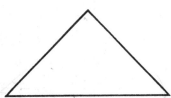

EXERCISES

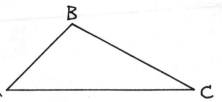

Trace this scalene triangle.

1. Does your tracing of $\overline{AB}$ fit $\overline{BC}$ or $\overline{AC}$? Does a scalene triangle have any congruent sides?

2. Does your tracing of $\angle B$ fit $\angle C$ or $\angle A$? Does a scalene triangle have any congruent angles?

> A scalene triangle has no congruent sides.

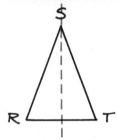

Trace this isosceles triangle.

3. Flip your drawing face-down about the line of symmetry. Does $\overline{RS}$ fit $\overline{TS}$? Does $\angle R$ fit $\angle T$?

4. What can you say about 2 sides of an isosceles triangle? About 2 angles of an isosceles triangle?

> An isosceles triangle has 2 congruent sides.

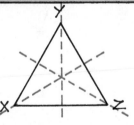

Trace this equilateral triangle.

5. If you flip your tracing face-down, does $\overline{XY}$ fit $\overline{YZ}$ and $\overline{XZ}$? Does $\angle X$ fit $\angle Y$ and $\angle Z$?

6. What can you say about the 3 sides of an equilateral triangle? About the 3 angles?

> An equilateral triangle has 3 congruent sides.

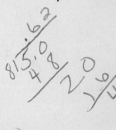

311

A point of symmetry

Think about taking the lid off each box and turning it halfway around.

Which lid would fit back on the box?

If a figure fits itself after a *half-turn* about a point, the point is a **point of symmetry** of the figure.

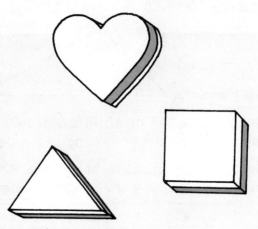

EXAMPLES.

Trace.

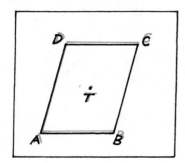

Half-turn. It fits.

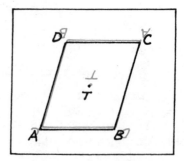

T is a point of symmetry.

Trace.

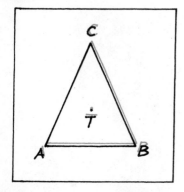

Half-turn. It does not fit.

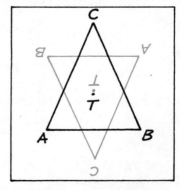

T is *not* a point of symmetry.

EXERCISES

Is the red point a point of symmetry of the figure? *Hint:* Trace the
figure and see if the tracing fits after a *half-turn* about the red point.

1.

2.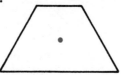

3.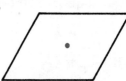

4.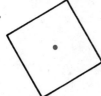

5.

6.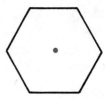

**The red point is a
point of symmetry.**

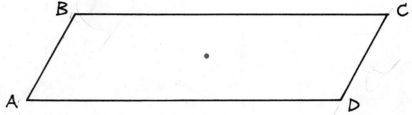

7. **a.** Under a half-turn about the red point, does $\overline{AB}$ fit $\overline{CD}$?

   b. Is $\overline{AB} \cong \overline{CD}$?

   c. $\overline{AB}$ and $\overline{CD}$ are called **opposite sides**.
   Give the other pair of opposite sides.

   d. Are the opposite sides congruent?

8. **a.** Under a half-turn about the red point, does $\angle A$ fit $\angle C$?

   b. Is $\angle A \cong \angle C$?

   c. $\angle A$ and $\angle C$ are called **opposite angles**.
   Give the other pair of opposite angles.

   d. Are the opposite angles congruent?

9. Since the figure above has a point of symmetry, its opposite sides are parallel. Give the two pairs of parallel
   sides.

Quadrilaterals

We can use points and lines of symmetry to study properties of some special quadrilaterals (4-sided figures).

A quadrilateral with:

a point of symmetry is a **parallelogram**.

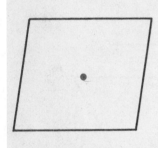

a point of symmetry and two lines of symmetry through opposite vertices is a **rhombus**.

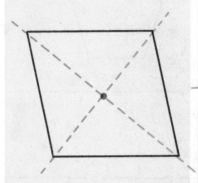

a point of symmetry and two lines of symmetry through opposite sides is a **rectangle**.

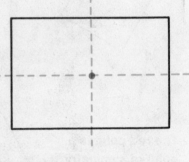

a point of symmetry and four lines of symmetry is a **square**.

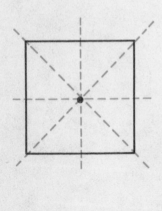

one line of symmetry through opposite sides is an **isosceles trapezoid**.

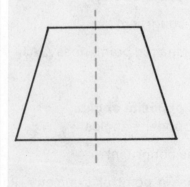

one line of symmetry through opposite vertices is a **kite**.

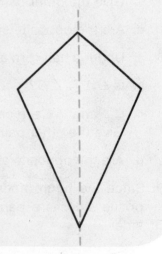

EXERCISES
Which quadrilaterals on page 314 have

1. both pairs of opposite sides parallel?
   Hint: Which have a point of symmetry?

2. both pairs of opposite sides congruent?

3. both pairs of opposite angles congruent?

4. all four angles congruent?

5. exactly one pair of parallel sides and exactly one pair of congruent sides?

6. exactly one pair of opposite angles that are congruent?

A trapezoid is a quadrilateral having just one pair of parallel sides.

7. Draw a trapezoid.

Project   See which quadrilaterals you can construct with a compass and straightedge.

Polygons

These figures are all **polygons**. Their special names are given.

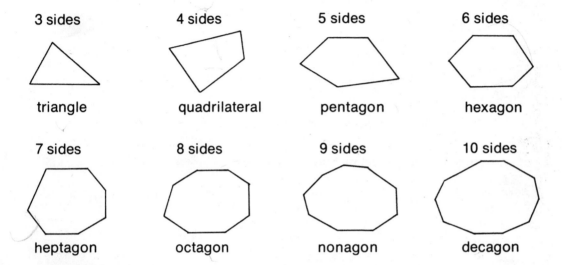

3 sides	4 sides	5 sides	6 sides
triangle	quadrilateral	pentagon	hexagon

7 sides	8 sides	9 sides	10 sides
heptagon	octagon	nonagon	decagon

A **regular polygon** has all its sides congruent and all its angles congruent.

EXERCISES

Can you think of some real object that is shaped like

1. a pentagon? **2.** a hexagon?

3. an octagon?

4. What is a regular triangle called?

5. What is a regular quadrilateral called?

6. Is a rhombus a regular polygon?

7. Exercise 3 on page 299 gives directions for beginning the construction of a regular hexagon. Try to construct a regular hexagon.

Excursion

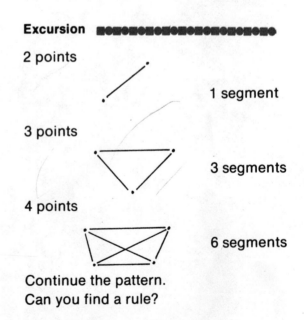

2 points — 1 segment

3 points — 3 segments

4 points — 6 segments

Continue the pattern. Can you find a rule?

Mathematics in careers

A land surveyor determines the shape and size of a part of the earth's surface. He also sets boundaries for property.

The main instrument used by a surveyor is a *transit.* It is used for sighting in a "straight line" and for determining horizontal and vertical angles. Distances are found by measuring with a steel tape. While a survey is being made, the surveyor generally records the data in a field book.

Here are two plots from a field book. Make a scale drawing of each plot. Use a protractor to draw the "corner" angles.

1.

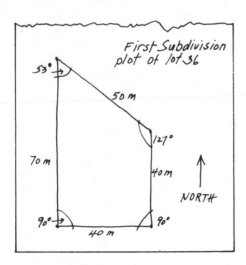

First Subdivision plot of lot 36

53°
50 m
127°
70 m
40 m
90° 90°
40 m
NORTH

2.

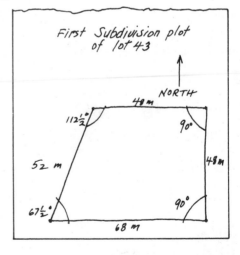

First Subdivision plot of lot 43

48 m
112½° 90°
52 m 48 m
67½° 90°
68 m
NORTH

CHAPTER CHECKUP

Acute, right, or obtuse?
Complete. [pages 302–303]

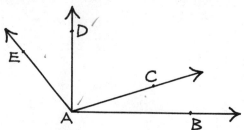

1. ∠ EAB is __?__ .

2. ∠ BAD is __?__ .

3. ∠ DAE is __?__ .

4. An angle that has a measure of 90° is __?__ .

Draw angles with these measures. [pages 302–303]

5. 20°   6. 38°   7. 45°   8. 105°   9. 90°   10. 135°

Which line is [pages 304–305]

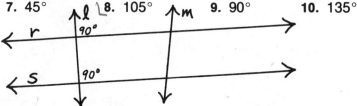

11. perpendicular to line s?

12. parallel to line s?

These two triangles are congruent. Complete these pairs of corresponding parts for the congruent fitting. [pages 306–307]

13. $\overline{AB}$ ⟷ __?__   14. $\overline{BC}$ ⟷ __?__

15. $\overline{CA}$ ⟷ __?__   16. ∠A ⟷ __?__

17. ∠ B ⟷ __?__   18. ∠ C ⟷ __?__

19. Are these corresponding parts congruent?

True or false? [pages 308–311]

20. A scalene triangle has 1 line of symmetry.   *yes*

21. An isosceles triangle has 2 lines of symmetry.   *yes*

22. An equilateral triangle has 3 lines of symmetry.   *yes*

Name the quadrilaterals that have [pages 312–315]

23. a point of symmetry and no lines of symmetry.

24. opposite sides parallel.   25. 4 congruent sides.

26. 4 right angles.   27. 4 congruent sides and 4 right angles.

1. **a.** Draw a triangle like this one using a straightedge. Cut it out.
   b. Fold the triangle so that points *A* and *B* are together. Crease the paper. The line you have folded is the perpendicular bisector of $\overline{AB}$.
   c. Fold the perpendicular bisectors of $\overline{AC}$ and $\overline{BC}$.
   d. What do you notice about the three perpendicular bisectors?

2. **a.** Draw another triangle like △*ABC*. Cut it out.
   b. Fold the triangle so that $\overline{AC}$ falls on $\overline{AB}$. Crease. You have folded the bisector of ∠*A*.
   c. Fold the bisectors of ∠*B* and ∠*C*.
   d. What do you notice about the three bisectors?

3. **a.** Draw a triangle like △*ABC*. Cut it out.
   b. Fold point *A* over to point *B*. Make a small crease where the fold crosses $\overline{AB}$. This is the midpoint of $\overline{AB}$. Do not crease the whole line.
   c. Fold and crease the triangle so that the fold line goes from *C* to the midpoint of $\overline{AB}$. This is a median of the triangle.
   d. Fold the median that goes from *A* to the midpoint of $\overline{BC}$ and the median from *B* to the midpoint of $\overline{AC}$. What do you notice about the three medians?

4. Compare your results in this project with your work on pages 301 and 305.

CHAPTER REVIEW

Complete.

1. The vertex of ∠BAC is point __?__.

2. The measure of ∠A is __?__ 90°.
   (less than, equal to, greater than)

3. An acute angle measures between 0° and __?__.

4. A right angle measures __?__.

5. An obtuse angle measures between 90° and __?__.

Two lines in a plane that intersect to form right angles are called **perpendicular (⊥) lines.**
  Two lines in a plane that do not intersect are called **parallel (‖) lines.**

Complete.

6. l ⊥ __?__

7. l ‖ __?__

Figures that are the same size and shape are called **congruent figures.**

Match congruent figures.

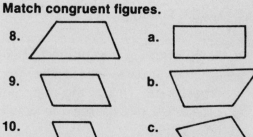

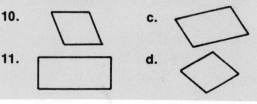

8.

9.

10.

11.

a.

b.

c.

d.

Scalene, isosceles, or equilateral?

12.

13.

14.

Tell how many lines of symmetry.

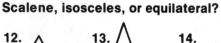

15.

16.

17.

18.

Match.

19. rectangle   20. square   21. parallelogram   22. isosceles trapezoid

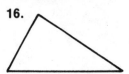

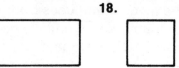

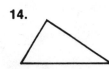

a.

b.

c.

d.

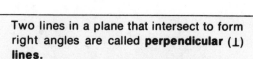

CHAPTER CHALLENGE

A 4-sided figure has 2 diagonals.

How many diagonals does a 5-sided figure have?

1. Draw a 6-sided figure. How many diagonals does it have?

2. Copy and complete this table. If you need to, draw each figure and its diagonals.

3. Study your completed table. Can you give a rule for finding the number of diagonals if you know the number of sides?

Number of sides	Number of diagonals
4	
5	
6	
7	
8	

13
a b c d
14
a b c d
15
a b c
33
a b c d
34
13
a b c d
14
3
a b c d
4
29
a b c d
30
31
a b c d
a b c d
a b c

MAJOR CHECKUP
Standardized Format

Choose the correct letter.

1. Which number is greatest?

    a. 38.2906
    b. 382.145
    c. 382.735
    d. 382.905

2. Multiply.

$$8.76 \times 2.43$$

    a. 20.9458
    b. 2094.58
    c. 21.2868
    d. none of these

3. Divide.

$$0.235 \overline{)14.2645}$$

    a. 6.7
    b. 60.7
    c. 607
    d. none of these

4. Find the area.

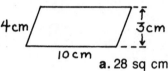

    a. 28 sq cm
    b. 30 sq cm
    c. 40 sq cm
    d. none of these

5. The greatest common factor of 18 and 24 is

    a. 3
    b. 6
    c. 72
    d. none of these

6. Add.

$$8\frac{1}{3} + 3\frac{5}{6}$$

    a. $11\frac{1}{6}$
    b. $10\frac{1}{6}$
    c. $12\frac{1}{6}$
    d. none of these

7. Subtract.

$$5 - 2\frac{3}{4}$$

    a. $3\frac{3}{4}$
    b. $2\frac{1}{4}$
    c. $2\frac{3}{4}$
    d. none of these

8. Give the product.

$$2\frac{2}{3} \times 1\frac{3}{4}$$

    a. $4\frac{2}{3}$
    b. $\frac{3}{14}$
    c. $\frac{21}{32}$
    d. none of these

9. $\dfrac{\frac{3}{4}}{\frac{4}{3}} = \underline{\quad ? \quad}$

    a. 1
    b. $\frac{16}{9}$
    c. $\frac{9}{16}$
    d. none of these

10. $33\frac{1}{3}\%$ of $48 = n$

$$n = \underline{\quad ? \quad}$$

    a. 64
    b. 16
    c. 32
    d. none of these

11. An item that regularly sells for $30 was put on sale for $25. The percent of discount was

    a. 25%
    b. 20%
    c. $16\frac{2}{3}\%$
    d. none of these

12. The interest at 8% for borrowing $600 for 6 months is

    a. $48
    b. $288
    c. $24
    d. none of these

11
Probability and Statistics

Equally likely outcomes

If you toss this coin it can land in one of these two ways.

There are 2 **possible outcomes**.

Since the chance of getting heads or tails is the same, we say that the outcomes are **equally likely**.

If you toss this die it can land in one of these six ways.

1 up 2 up 3 up

4 up  5 up 6 up

There are 6 **possible outcomes**. When a die is tossed, the outcomes are **equally likely**.

If you spin this spinner, there are 4 possible outcomes. The outcomes are *not* equally likely. Why?

EXERCISES

First tell how many possible outcomes there are for tossing each block. Then tell whether or not the outcomes are equally likely.

1.
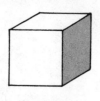
Cube

2.
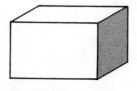
Rectangular prism

3.

Pyramid

First tell how many outcomes. Then tell whether or not the outcomes are equally likely.

4.

5.

6.

7. Think about the possible outcomes of spinning the spinner shown in exercise 5. Which color do you think you would get most often?

8. Think about tossing a paper cup.

   a. How many ways can it land?
   b. Do you think the outcomes are equally likely?

9. Imagine tossing a coin and die at the same time. List all possible outcomes. You could list the outcome shown as (H, 1). Are the outcomes equally likely?

10. List all possible outcomes of spinning this spinner and tossing this die.

    Faces have from 1 through 6 dots.

Project

1. Toss a coin 100 times and record each outcome. How many heads and how many tails did you get? Compare your results with your classmates' results.

2. When a thumbtack is tossed, there are two possible outcomes:

   point up   point down

   Try to decide whether or not the outcomes are equally likely by tossing a thumbtack at least 50 times. Be sure to keep a tally of the outcomes.

A basic counting principle

A tree diagram may be used to show
the possible outcomes of an event.
Here is an example.

Event

First tossing a coin
and then
tossing a die.

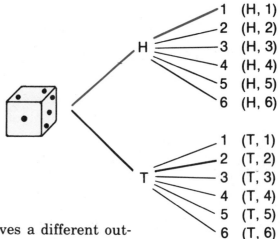

Notice that each "branch" of the tree gives a different outcome. The red branch stands for first tossing heads and then
tossing a 1. The tree diagram shows that there are 2 outcomes
when tossing a coin, and 6 outcomes when tossing a cube. It
also shows that if a coin is tossed and then a cube is tossed,
there are 2 × 6 (or 12) outcomes. This is an example of a basic
counting principle.

> If a first event has *m* outcomes, and if a second event has
> *n* outcomes, then the first event followed by the second
> event has *m* × *n* outcomes.

EXERCISES
**Copy and complete the tree diagram. Then tell how many
outcomes.**

1. *Event*
Toss a coin
and then spin this spinner.

Tree Diagram of Outcomes

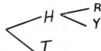

2. *Event*
Spin this spinner
and then spin this spinner.

Tree Diagram of Outcomes

How many outcomes?

3. *Event*
Toss a dime
and then toss a nickel.

4. *Event*
Toss this die

and then toss this die.

5. Think about building a 2-digit number by picking one of these cards and then another.

| 4 | 8 | 3 | 5 | 2 |

  a. How many choices would you have for the first digit?
  b. How many choices would you have for the second digit?
  c. How many 2-digit numbers could you build?

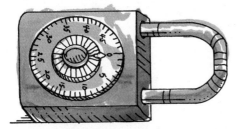

6. Here is a combination lock. If the combination were 35-42-8, you would open the lock by (1) turning the dial clockwise to 35, (2) turning the dial counterclockwise to 42, (3) turning the dial clockwise to 8. How many locks like this could be made without having any two combinations the same?

7. Suppose that you forgot a 3-number combination for a lock having 50 numbers. (See exercise 6.) If it took 10 seconds to try each combination, how long would it take to try them all?

Solve each proportion.

1. $\frac{n}{9} = \frac{3}{8}$

2. $\frac{8}{n} = \frac{5}{2}$

3. $\frac{n}{7} = \frac{1}{5}$

4. $\frac{3}{n} = \frac{4}{9}$

5. $\frac{n}{15} = \frac{6}{5}$

6. $\frac{7}{8} = \frac{n}{16}$

7. $\frac{9}{5} = \frac{n}{19}$

8. $\frac{n}{7} = \frac{3}{5}$

9. $\frac{12}{n} = \frac{2}{9}$

10. $\frac{11}{n} = \frac{1}{6}$

11. $\frac{n}{7} = \frac{0}{3}$

12. $\frac{8}{3} = \frac{11}{n}$

327

Probability

When a die is tossed, there are these 6 equally likely outcomes.

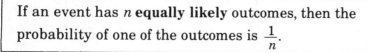

The **probability** of each outcome is $\frac{1}{6}$.

For example, when the die is tossed, the probability of its landing "1 up" is $\frac{1}{6}$. We write

$P(1) = \frac{1}{6}$ (Read as "The probability of 1 equals $\frac{1}{6}$.")

What are $P(2)$, $P(3)$, and $P(6)$? What is $P(\textit{not } 6)$?

> If an event has n **equally likely** outcomes, then the
> probability of one of the outcomes is $\frac{1}{n}$.

Notice the words *equally likely* in the sentence above. The outcomes of spinning this spinner are **not equally likely**. Study these probabilities:

$$P(\text{red}) = \frac{1}{2}$$
$$P(\text{green}) = \frac{1}{4}$$
$$P(\text{yellow}) = \frac{1}{4}$$

The probability of an impossible outcome is 0.
For example, $P(\text{blue}) = 0$.

EXERCISES
Complete.

1. *Event*
Spin this spinner

  a. $P(\text{red}) = ?$
  b. $P(\text{yellow}) = ?$
  c. $P(\text{green}) = ?$
  d. $P(\text{blue}) = ?$
  e. $P(\text{not blue}) = ?$

2. *Event*
Spin this spinner

  a. $P(\text{red}) = ?$
  b. $P(\text{yellow}) = ?$
  c. $P(\text{blue}) = ?$
  d. $P(\text{green}) = ?$
  e. $P(\text{purple}) = ?$

3. *Event*

Reach in a bag without looking and pick one of these marbles.

$P(\text{green}) = \frac{2}{7}$

a. $P(\text{yellow}) = ?$ **b.** $P(\text{blue}) = ?$

c. $P(\text{red}) = ?$ **d.** $P(\text{not red}) = ?$

4. *Event*

Reach in a bag and pick one of these marbles.

a. $P(\text{red}) = ?$ **b.** $P(\text{blue}) = ?$

c. $P(\text{yellow}) = ?$ **d.** $P(\text{green}) = ?$

e. $P(\text{not green}) = ?$ **f.** $P(\text{purple}) = ?$

5. If you toss a die, what is the probability of getting

    a. 6?   **b.** an even number?   **c.** a number less than 5?

6. Suppose that these cards were thoroughly shuffled and that you picked a card without looking.

What is the probability of picking

    a. 4?   **b.** an odd number?   **c.** a prime number?

    d. a multiple of 5?   **e.** a composite number?   **f.** a number less than 16?

Project

1. Toss two different-colored dice at least 50 times and record each outcome with a number pair. For example, the outcome shown can be recorded by using the ordered pair (1, 5).

2. List all possible outcomes of tossing two dice as shown in step 1.

3. How many times did you get a sum of 7? of 5? of 12? What other sums did you get and how many times?

4. Give the probability of tossing a sum of 7; of 5; of 12.

Probability (independent events)

The tree diagram shows all the possible outcomes of first tossing a die and then tossing a coin.

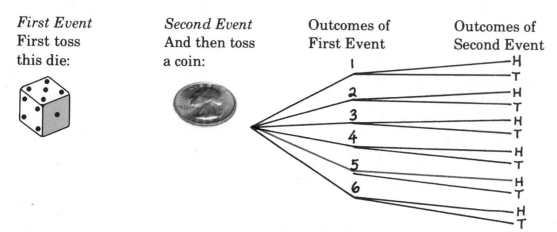

First Event
First toss
this die:

Second Event
And then toss
a coin:

Outcomes of
First Event

Outcomes of
Second Event

The red branch shows the outcome of first tossing a 5 with the die and then tossing a head with the coin. Notice that the probability of tossing a 5 is $\frac{1}{6}$, the probability of tossing heads is $\frac{1}{2}$, and the probability of first tossing a 5 **and then** tossing heads is $\frac{1}{6} \times \frac{1}{2}$, or $\frac{1}{12}$. $P(5$ and then H$) = \frac{1}{12}$. This is an example of the following probability principle:

> If the probability of an outcome of a first event is $\frac{a}{m}$, and if the probability of an outcome of a second event is $\frac{b}{n}$, then the probability of the first outcome followed by the second outcome is $\frac{a}{m} \cdot \frac{b}{n}$.

EXERCISES
Give each probability in lowest terms.

1. *First Event*
   Spin this
   spinner:

   Second Event
   Toss a coin.

   a. P(red and then heads) = ?

   b. P(yellow and then tails) = ?

   c. P(blue and then heads) = ?

2. *First Event*

Spin this spinner:

Second Event

Toss this die:

a. P(red and then 1) = ?

b. P(green and then 4) = ?

c. P(blue and then 6) = ?

d. P(blue and then an even number) = ?

3. *First Event*

Toss this die:

Second Event

Toss the die again.

4 and then 3

a. $P(4, 3)$ = ?

b. $P(5, 1)$ = ?

c. P(6, even number) = ?

d. P(odd number, even number) = ?

4. *First Event*

Toss a coin.

Second Event

Toss the coin again.

Possible outcomes

(H, H), (T, H)
(H, T), (T, T)

a. What is the probability of getting both heads?

b. What is the probability of getting one head and one tail?

5. Imagine tossing a penny 10 times. What is the probability that you would toss heads all 10 times?

Project

1. Make a spinner like this:

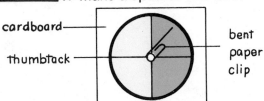

cardboard

thumbtack

bent paper clip

2. Spin the spinner twice and record the outcome by using notation like this:

yellow and then green

(Y, G)

Repeat 50 times.

3. Which outcome did you get the most? Which outcome did you get the least? Did this turn out as you expected?

4. Give the probability of each possible outcome.

Sampling

Suppose that you want to find out how many people in your city can swim. Instead of asking each person, you could ask only some of the people (a **sample**) and then use what you found in your sample to predict how many people in your city can swim. When taking a sample, you should be sure that the sample is not too small and that the sample is not **biased**.

Notice that the second sample is biased. It is biased because most of the people who are in a swimming pool know how to swim.

Suppose that, using an unbiased sample, you found that 140 out of 200 people can swim. You could then use your sample to predict how many people in your city can swim. To do this, you could solve a proportion.

number of swimmers in sample $\longrightarrow \dfrac{140}{200}$ $= \dfrac{n}{12{,}240}$ $\longleftarrow$ number of swimmers in city
number of people in sample $\longrightarrow$ $\phantom{\dfrac{140}{200}}$ $\longleftarrow$ number of people in city

$$\frac{7}{10} = \frac{n}{12{,}240}$$

$$10n = 7 \times 12{,}240$$

$$10n = 85{,}680$$

$$n = 8568$$

From your sample of 200, you would predict that in this city 8568 people can swim.

EXERCISES

1. Suppose that you want to determine the average height of the seventh graders in your school. Tell why one of the following samples would probably be better than the other.

2. Suppose that you wanted to find out the average distance that students travel to get to school. Which of the following samples is more likely to be biased?

Each bag contains some red marbles and some black marbles. The total number of marbles is shown on the bag. Use the sample to predict how many marbles of each color there are. (Assume that the marbles were mixed well before the sample was taken.)

3. 80 marbles

4. 64 marbles

5. 48 marbles

6. 96 marbles

7. 144 marbles

8. 240 marbles

In exercises 3–8, which sample do you consider the best? Why? Which sample do you consider the worst? Why?

Reporting data

Baby-sitting service
Call 352-6782

Willowsprings School	
Day	Money Received
Monday	$ 6.50
Tuesday	$ 8.00
Wednesday	$ 7.75
Thursday	$ 5.50
Friday	$10.25
Saturday	$12.00
Sunday	$ 9.50

The seventh-grade students started a baby-sitting service to raise money for a summer camp. Jan kept this record of the money received during the first week.

To report the money received (the data), she made these graphs:

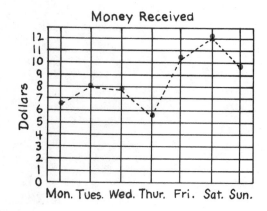

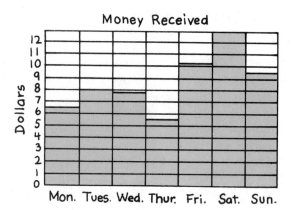

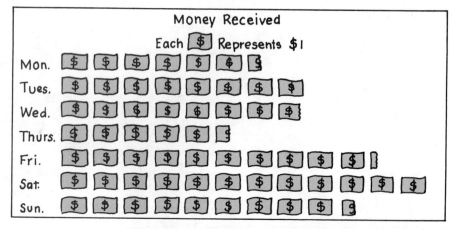

What are some things that each graph tells you?

EXERCISES

Look at the graph to answer the questions.

1.

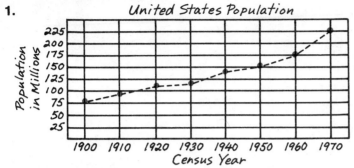

United States Population

a. Did the population increase each 10 years?

b. During which year was the population about 75 million?

c. About what was the population in 1950?

d. During which 10-year period did the population increase about 25 million?

2.

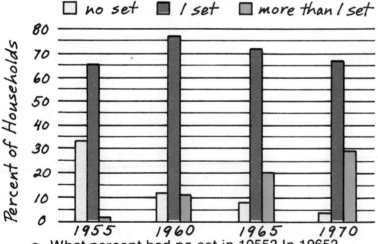

Television Sets In United States Households

□ no set ■ 1 set ▨ more than 1 set

a. What percent had no set in 1955? In 1965?

b. What percent had 1 set in 1960? In 1970?

c. In which year did 20% of the households have more than 1 set?

d. What percent of the households had at least 1 television set in 1970?

Keeping Skills Sharp

Solve.

1. 12% of 25 = n

2. 175% of 12 = n

3. 8% of 50 = n

4. 75% of 35 = n

5. $62\frac{1}{2}$% of 52 = n

6. $112\frac{1}{2}$% of 22 = n

Solve.

7. 4% of n = 2

8. 75% of n = 12

9. 9% of n = 9

10. $33\frac{1}{3}$% of n = 23

11. $12\frac{1}{2}$% of n = 19

12. 150% of n = 36

335

Range, mean, and median

Once data have been collected, we can determine some numbers that tell us something about the data. For example, here are the heights of the members of a certain seventh-grade basketball team:

Player	Height (m)	
Peterson	**1.48** ←	
Jones	1.55	
Campbell	1.59	
Davis	1.63	
Roberts	1.63	
Garcia	1.69	
Allison	1.71	range
Krantz median	**1.72**	
Moore	1.74	0.34
Steinburg	1.75	
Mendez	1.78	
Richards	1.78	
Washington	1.78	
Hargrove	1.80	
Cowan	**1.82** ←	

The **range** is the difference between the least and greatest numbers. The range, from **1.48** to **1.82**, is **0.34**.

The **mean**, or **average**, is found by adding all the numbers and then dividing the sum by the number of numbers.

The mean, rounded to the nearest hundredth, is **1.70 m**.

The **median** is the middle number if you are working with an odd number of numbers. If you are working with an even number of numbers, the median is the average of the two middle numbers.

The median height is **1.72 m**.

Number of players — sum of heights

$$
\begin{array}{r}
1.69 \\
15\overline{)25.45} \\
15 \\
\hline
104 \\
90 \\
\hline
145 \\
135 \\
\hline
10
\end{array}
$$

EXERCISES

1. In seven games, Krantz scored 21, 23, 19, 21, 26, 18, and 22 points. Find the range, the mean, and the median.

2. During the first 5 games, the opposing teams scored 54, 48, 49, 56, and 50 points. Find the range, the mean, and the median.

3. One semester Jane got the following scores on her mathematics tests: 82, 75, 93, 87, 69, 81, 83, and 84. Find the range, the mean, and the median.

4. During the first 8 weeks of school, Alan averaged $3.40 per week for lunches. How much did he spend for lunches during the 8 weeks?

5. Hank Aaron holds the major-league home-run record. The table shows how many home runs he hit during each year that he was in the major leagues. Find the range, the mean and the median.

Home Runs During Regular Season			
Year	Number	Year	Number
1954	13	1965	32
1955	27	1966	44
1956	26	1967	39
1957	44	1968	29
1958	30	1969	44
1959	39	1970	38
1960	40	1971	47
1961	34	1972	34
1962	45	1973	40
1963	44	1974	20
1964	24	1975	12
		1976	10

Project

1. Take your pulse to find out how many times your heart beats in one minute.

2. Determine the range, the mean, and the median of the heart rates of your class.

Mathematics in careers

Demographers study human population. They collect data to study such things as birth rates and death rates. They also study the population density (population per square kilometer) of a region and how population shifts from one region to another.

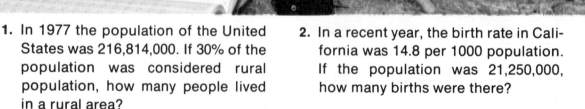

1. In 1977 the population of the United States was 216,814,000. If 30% of the population was considered rural population, how many people lived in a rural area?

2. In a recent year, the birth rate in California was 14.8 per 1000 population. If the population was 21,250,000, how many births were there?

3. In 1900 the population of the United States was 75,994,575. The land area was 7,693,870 square kilometers. What was the population density? Give your answer to the nearest tenth.

4. In 1970 the population was 203,235,298 and the area was 9,173,345 square kilometers. What was the density then?

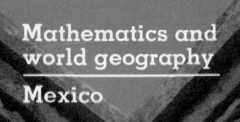

Number of Students for Each Teacher

Student ages

6-12	46.8
12-18	14.2
18 and over	9.4

1. There are about 8,948,000 students in the 6–12 age group. About how many teachers are there for this age group?

2. There are about 102,000 teachers of secondary students (12–18 age group). About how many secondary students are there?

3. Recently the total population of Mexico was about 51 million, with about 47% of the people under 15 years of age. How many of these young people are there in Mexico?

4. Only about 1.2% of the Mexican people are over 75 years of age. About how many people over 75 are there in Mexico?

CHAPTER CHECKUP

First tell how many outcomes. Then tell whether or not the outcomes are equally likely. [pages 324–325]

1. Toss a coin. **2.** Toss a paper cup. **3.** Spin this spinner:

Draw a tree diagram that shows the possible outcomes for these events. [pages 326–327]

4. Spin this spinner and then toss this die.

5. Think about placing these marbles in a bag, mixing them well, and then (without looking) picking one. Give each probability in lowest terms. [pages 328–329]

   a. $P(\text{green}) = ?$ **b.** $P(\text{blue}) = ?$ **c.** $P(\text{yellow}) = ?$

   d. $P(\text{red}) = ?$ **e.** $P(\text{not red}) = ?$ **f.** $P(\text{black}) = ?$

6. Suppose that the first event is followed by the second event. Give each probability in lowest terms. [pages 330–331]

First Event

Spin this spinner

Second Event

then (without looking) pick a marble.

   a. $P(1, \text{blue}) = ?$

   b. $P(3, \text{green}) = ?$

   c. $P(2, \text{red}) = ?$

   d. $P(4, \text{not blue}) = ?$

7. Here are the scores of a mathematics test. Give the range, the mean, and the median. [pages 336–337]

Test Scores							
100	94	88	85	83	76	72	68
100	92	86	85	80	75	70	66
96	91	86	85	78	73	70	62

Project

How far from school do you live?

Take a sample.

1. Ask some of your classmates how far from school they live. Make sure that your sample is reasonably large. Try to include classmates from all parts of your school district.

2. Find the range, the mean, and the median of your sample.

3. Complete a bar graph like the one shown.

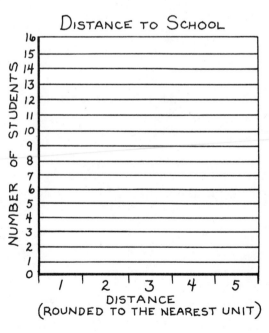

DISTANCE TO SCHOOL

NUMBER OF STUDENTS

16
15
14
13
12
11
10
9
8
7
6
5
4
3
2
1
0

1   2   3   4   5

DISTANCE
(ROUNDED TO THE NEAREST UNIT)

CHAPTER REVIEW

If a first event has *m* outcomes, and if a second event has *n* outcomes, then the first event followed by the second event has $m \times n$ outcomes.

First Event	*Second Event*
Toss this die:	Toss a coin:

Tell how many outcomes there are for the

1. first event.

2. second event.

3. first event and then the second event.

If the probability of a first outcome is $\frac{a}{m}$ and if the probability of a second outcome is $\frac{b}{n}$, then the probability of the first outcome followed by the second outcome is $\frac{a}{m} \cdot \frac{b}{n}$.

Give the probability of

4. tossing a 6.

5. tossing heads.

6. tossing a 6 and then tossing heads.

The range is the difference between the least and greatest numbers.

The mean is the average.

The median is the middle number.

One week Sarah kept this record of the number of calories in her diet.
Give the

7. range.

8. mean.

9. median.

Daily Calories	
Sun.	1275
Mon.	1550
Tues.	1300
Wed.	1150
Thurs.	1260
Fri.	1320
Sat.	1560

CHAPTER CHALLENGE

When we wish to talk about the chances of picking a green button from the box, we can use probability. The probability of picking green is the ratio of the number of green buttons to the total number of buttons.

$$\text{probability of green} = \frac{\text{number of green}}{\text{total number}} = \frac{4}{12} = \frac{1}{3}$$

Another way of talking about the chance of getting a green button is to use **odds**. The odds in favor of picking green is the ratio of green buttons to not-green buttons.

$$\text{odds in favor of green} = \frac{\text{number of green}}{\text{number of not green}} = \frac{4}{8} = \frac{1}{2}$$

The odds against getting green is the reciprocal of the odds in favor of getting green.

$$\text{odds against green} = \frac{\text{number of not green}}{\text{number of green}} = \frac{8}{4} = \frac{2}{1}$$

Give the odds in favor of picking a

1. red button.

2. blue button.

3. yellow button.

Give the odds against picking a

4. yellow button.

5. blue button.

6. red button.

Give the odds

7. in favor of spinning yellow.

8. in favor of spinning blue.

9. against spinning red.

10. against spinning green.

Form W

13 a b c d
14 a b c d
15

33 a b c d
34

13 a b c d
14

3 a b c d
4

29 a b c
30 a b c
31 a b c
a b c

MAJOR CHECKUP
Standardized Format

Choose the correct letter.

1. Complete.

$2.3L = \underline{\quad ? \quad}$

    a. .023 mL
    b. 2300 mL
    c. 230 mL
    d. none of these

2. Give the perimeter.

4 cm
7 cm

    a. 11 cm
    b. 22 cm
    c. 28 cm
    d. none of these

3. The prime factorization of 48 is

    a. 6×8
    b. $2 \times 2 \times 3 \times 3$
    c. $2 \times 2 \times 3 \times 4$
    d. none of these

4. Add.

$7\frac{5}{6}$
$+5\frac{1}{4}$

    a. $13\frac{1}{12}$
    b. $12\frac{7}{12}$
    c. $12\frac{1}{12}$
    d. none of these

5. Subtract.

$8\frac{1}{4}$
$-2\frac{1}{2}$

    a. $6\frac{1}{4}$
    b. $5\frac{3}{4}$
    c. $5\frac{1}{4}$
    d. none of these

6. Find the product.

$6\frac{2}{3} \times 2\frac{5}{8}$

    a. $17\frac{1}{2}$
    b. $\frac{2}{35}$
    c. $2\frac{35}{63}$
    d. none of these

7. Find the quotient.

$8\frac{2}{3} \div 2\frac{3}{4}$

    a. $\frac{11}{34}$
    b. $23\frac{3}{8}$
    c. $3\frac{1}{11}$
    d. none of these

8. 25% of 192 = $\underline{\quad ? \quad}$

    a. 48
    b. 768
    c. $30\frac{2}{5}$
    d. none of these

9. $37\frac{1}{2}\%$ of $\underline{\quad ? \quad} = 21$

    a. $7\frac{7}{8}$
    b. 56
    c. $\frac{8}{63}$
    d. none of these

10. Compute the interest.

principal: $240
rate: 8% per year
time: 6 months

    a. $192
    b. $9.60
    c. $19.20
    d. none of these

11. The measure of an acute angle is

    a. greater than 90°.
    b. 90°.
    c. less than 90°.
    d. none of these

12. If $\overline{AB} \cong \overline{CB}$, then $\triangle ABC$ is

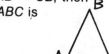

    a. isosceles
    b. scalene
    c. equilateral
    d. none of these

344

12
Computing
with
Integers

Integers

When the temperature is 8° below 0°, the weather report might say that the temperature is ⁻8° ("negative eight degrees"). When the temperature is 15° above 0°, the report might say that the temperature is ⁺15° ("positive fifteen degrees").

Positive numbers and negative numbers like these (and 0) are called **integers**.

Integers	Not Integers
0 ⁻6 ⁺45 ⁻876 ⁻17,358	⁻$\frac{1}{2}$ ⁺$\frac{7}{8}$ ⁻3.97 ⁺17.3

The integers can be shown on the number line like this:

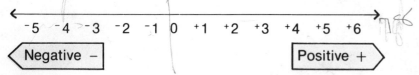

You can use a number line to compare two integers. Notice that the greater of two integers is always to the right. The number line above shows that

⁻4 < ⁻3   ⁺2 < ⁺3   0 < ⁺1   ⁺4 > ⁺3   ⁺1 > ⁻5

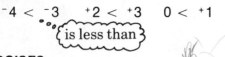

is less than   is greater than

EXERCISES

< or > ?

1. ⁻8 ● ⁻4
2. ⁺8 ● ⁻4
3. ⁻8 ● ⁺4
4. ⁺8 ● ⁺4

5. ⁺6 ● ⁺3
6. ⁺6 ● ⁻3
7. ⁻6 ● ⁺3
8. ⁻6 ● ⁻3

9. ⁻5 ● ⁻4
10. ⁺5 ● ⁺4
11. ⁻9 ● ⁻11
12. ⁺7 ● ⁻9

13. ⁻11 ● ⁻12
14. ⁻11 ● ⁺12
15. ⁺11 ● ⁻12
16. ⁻12 ● ⁺10

17. ⁻18 ● ⁺17
18. ⁺23 ● ⁺22
19. ⁻23 ● ⁺22
20. ⁻23 ● ⁻22

Complete.

21. ___?___ is neither positive nor negative.

22. All ___?___ integers are greater than 0.

23. All ___?___ integers are less than 0.

24. Zero is __○?__ than any negative integer.

25. A negative integer is ___?___ than any positive integer.

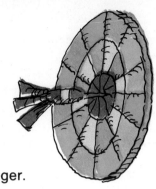

Solve.

26. If ⁺8 stands for a gain of 8 meters, what does ⁻4 stand for?

27. If ⁻10 stands for 10° below zero, what does ⁺16 stand for?

28. If ⁺50 stands for $50 profit, then what stands for a loss of $28?

29. If ⁻40 stands for 40 meters below sea level, then what stands for 220 meters above sea level?

Solve.

30. If ⁺3 stands for 3 centimeters above the average height, then what stands for 2 centimeters below the average height?

31. Gerry used integers to keep a record of how much she earned or spent each day. The table shows that she earned 75¢ on Monday. Did Gerry have more or less money at the end of the week than at the beginning? How much more or less?

Monday	⁺75¢
Tuesday	⁺60¢
Wednesday	⁻50¢
Thursday	⁺75¢
Friday	⁻80¢
Saturday	⁺80¢
Sunday	⁺50¢

Adding integers

Think about some small objects that have either a positive electrical charge or a negative electrical charge. Positive charges and negative charges are opposites. This means that when one positive charge and one negative charge are put together, the result is no charge, or a charge of 0.

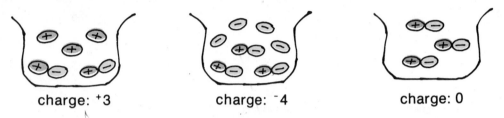

charge: ⁺3   charge: ⁻4   charge: 0

When you wish to add integers, you can think about putting charges together. Study these examples.

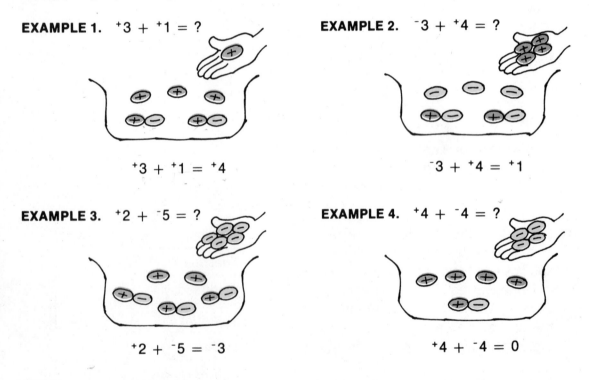

EXAMPLE 1. ⁺3 + ⁺1 = ?

⁺3 + ⁺1 = ⁺4

EXAMPLE 2. ⁻3 + ⁺4 = ?

⁻3 + ⁺4 = ⁺1

EXAMPLE 3. ⁺2 + ⁻5 = ?

⁺2 + ⁻5 = ⁻3

EXAMPLE 4. ⁺4 + ⁻4 = ?

⁺4 + ⁻4 = 0

In Example 4, the sum of the two numbers is 0. Therefore, we say that ⁺4 and ⁻4 are **opposites**.

EXERCISES

Give each sum.

1. $^+8 + {}^+3$ 2. $^+8 + {}^-3$ 3. $^-8 + {}^+3$ 4. $^-8 + {}^-3$

5. $^+6 + {}^+9$ 6. $^+6 + {}^-9$ 7. $^-6 + {}^+9$ 8. $^-6 + {}^-9$

9. $^+7 + {}^+5$ 10. $^+7 + {}^-5$ 11. $^-\frac{1}{7} + {}^-\frac{2}{7}$ 12. $^-7 + {}^-5$

13. $^+9 + {}^-9$ 14. $^+4 + {}^-10$ 15. $^-4 + {}^+10$ 16. $^-6 + {}^+11$

17. $^+2 + {}^-4$ 18. $^-6 + {}^-8$ 19. $^+5 + 0$ 20. $0 + {}^-6$

21. $^-9 + {}^-2$ 22. $^+6 + {}^+9$ 23. $^+10 + {}^-4$ 24. $^+12 + {}^-3$

25. $^-6 + {}^-7$ 26. $^-6 + {}^+7$ 27. $^+6 + {}^-7$ 28. $^+6 + {}^+7$

29. $^-24 + {}^+39$ 30. $^+23 + {}^+36$ 31. $^-53 + {}^-26$ 32. $^+74 + {}^-60$

Solve.

33. Central High had a metric football game. The football coach used integers to record meters gained or lost each time the ball was carried. For example, he used $^+6$ for a gain of 6 meters.

    a. What was Berry's net gain?
    b. Who netted the most meters?
    c. How many meters did Martinez and Phillips net together?

Player			
Berry	Allan	Martinez	Phillips
$^+6$	$^-4$	$^-6$	$^+3$
$^-2$	$^+8$	$^+5$	0
$^+4$	$^+3$	$^+9$	$^-4$
0	$^+2$	$^+1$	$^+6$
$^-3$	$^-5$	$^-2$	$^+2$
$^+5$		$^+1$	$^+1$
$^+11$			$^-1$

Copy and complete these addition boxes. Add across and add down.

34.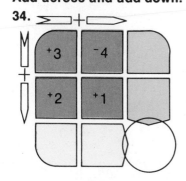

35.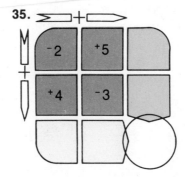

36.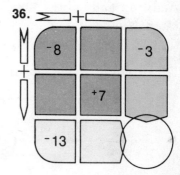

Subtracting integers

You can also think about electrical charges when you wish to subtract integers.

EXAMPLE 1. $^+1 - {}^+3 = ?$

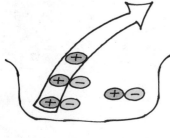

$$^+1 - {}^+3 = {}^-2$$

EXAMPLE 2. $^-4 - {}^-1 = ?$

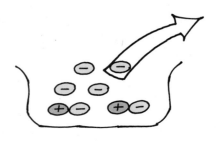

$$^-4 - {}^-1 = {}^-3$$

EXAMPLE 3. $^-2 - {}^-3 = ?$

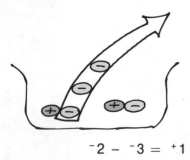

$$^-2 - {}^-3 = {}^+1$$

EXAMPLE 4. $^+2 - {}^-3 = ?$

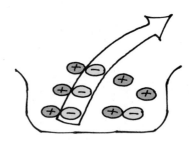

$$^+2 - {}^-3 = {}^+5$$

Addition and subtraction are closely related. Notice that adding $^+2$ and subtracting $^-2$ give the same result.

This gives us a way to subtract.

> To subtract an integer,
> add its opposite.

$$^-3 - {}^+2 = {}^-3 + {}^-2 = {}^-5$$

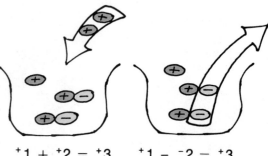

$$^+1 + {}^+2 = {}^+3 \qquad {}^+1 - {}^-2 = {}^+3$$

EXERCISES

Complete.

1. To subtract $^+2$, add ___?___.

2. To subtract $^-5$, add ___?___.

3. To subtract an integer, add the ___?___ of the integer.

Give each difference.

$$(^+8 + {}^-3 = {}^+5)$$ $$(^-5 + {}^+2 = {}^-3)$$

4. $^+8 - {}^+3$ 5. $^-5 - {}^-2$

6. $^-3 - {}^+9$ 7. $^+12 - {}^-3$ 8. $^-5 - {}^-7$

9. $^+7 - 0$ 10. $^-8 - {}^+3$ 11. $^-2 - {}^-3$

12. $^+3 - {}^-8$ 13. $^-5 - {}^-6$ 14. $^-10 - {}^+8$

15. $^-3 - {}^-8$ 16. $^+3 - {}^+6$ 17. $^-9 - {}^+7$

18. $0 - {}^-5$ 19. $^+15 - {}^-4$ 20. $^-4 - {}^+6$

21. $^-8 - {}^-7$ 22. $^+12 - 0$ 23. $^+8 - {}^-12$

24. $^-3 - {}^+13$ 25. $^+15 - {}^-6$ 26. $0 - {}^-4$

27. $^+13 - {}^-3$ 28. $^-10 - {}^-12$ 29. $^+18 - {}^+13$

30. $^-35 - {}^-35$ 31. $^+35 - {}^-35$ 32. $^-19 - {}^+6$

33. $0 - {}^-6$ 34. $0 - {}^+19$ 35. $^+23 - {}^-17$

36. $^-26 - {}^-35$ 37. $^+38 - {}^-59$ 38. $0 - 0$

39. $^+16 - {}^+4$ 40. $^+13 - {}^-14$ 41. $^-8 - {}^+3$

42. $^-18 - {}^+13$ 43. $^+18 - {}^-13$ 44. $^-18 - {}^-13$

Keeping Skills Sharp

Change to a percent.

1. $\dfrac{1}{2}$

2. $\dfrac{1}{4}$

3. $\dfrac{3}{4}$

4. $\dfrac{3}{5}$

5. $\dfrac{1}{3}$

6. $\dfrac{2}{3}$

7. $\dfrac{5}{8}$

8. $\dfrac{9}{8}$

9. $\dfrac{5}{6}$

10. $\dfrac{11}{6}$

11. $\dfrac{5}{9}$

12. $\dfrac{9}{16}$

$$1 - 2 + 3 - 4 + 5 - 6 + 7 - \ldots + 1001 = ?$$

Practice exercises

Give each sum.

1. $^+2 + {}^+6$
2. $^-5 + {}^-9$
3. $^+3 + {}^-7$
4. $0 + {}^-9$

5. $^-7 + {}^+8$
6. $^+3 + {}^+5$
7. $^+4 + {}^-5$
8. $^-9 + {}^-5$

9. $^-5 + {}^-8$
10. $^-7 + {}^-9$
11. $^-2 + {}^+8$
12. $^+6 + {}^+4$

13. $0 + {}^+8$
14. $^-8 + {}^+5$
15. $^-6 + {}^-9$
16. $^-8 + {}^+8$

17. $^+8 + {}^+9$
18. $^+3 + {}^-9$
19. $^+7 + {}^+4$
20. $0 + 0$

21. $^+9 + {}^-9$
22. $^-6 + {}^+8$
23. $^-9 + {}^-8$
24. $^+8 + {}^+8$

25. $^+10 + {}^+7$
26. $^+15 + {}^-9$
27. $^+13 + {}^-10$
28. $^-9 + {}^-15$

29. $^-23 + 0$
30. $^+28 + {}^+19$
31. $^+21 + {}^-21$
32. $^-24 + {}^-16$

Give each difference.

33. $^+9 - {}^+2$
34. $^-5 - 0$
35. $^+8 - {}^+5$
36. $^-6 - {}^+6$

37. $^-6 - {}^-7$
38. $^+6 - {}^-5$
39. $^-8 - {}^-7$
40. $^-5 - {}^+6$

41. $^-9 - {}^+9$
42. $^+3 - {}^+9$
43. $^-4 - {}^-9$
44. $^+8 - {}^+4$

45. $^+8 - {}^-3$
46. $^-9 - {}^-8$
47. $^+2 - {}^-9$
48. $0 - {}^+9$

49. $^-9 - {}^+6$
50. $^+3 - {}^-8$
51. $^+8 - {}^+8$
52. $^-6 - {}^-6$

53. $^+5 - {}^-7$
54. $^+6 - {}^+8$
55. $^+7 - {}^-6$
56. $^-5 - {}^+9$

57. $^+15 - {}^-6$
58. $^+18 - {}^-9$
59. $^-17 - {}^-9$
60. $^+15 - {}^+6$

61. $^+23 - {}^+5$
62. $^-26 - {}^+24$
63. $^-25 - {}^+28$
64. $^+28 - {}^-21$

Mathematics and science

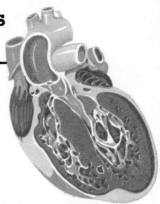

1. The heart is a muscular organ that pumps blood through the body. Take your pulse and compute about how many times a day your heart beats.

2. A man's heart weighs about 312 grams. A woman's heart weighs about $\frac{5}{6}$ as much. How much does a woman's heart weigh?

3. **a.** An adult weighing 75 kilograms has about 4.7 liters of blood. At that ratio, how many liters of blood do you have?
   b. Blood is made up of plasma, white cells, and platelets. About 55% of the volume of blood is plasma. About how many liters of plasma do you have?

4. In an adult the heart pumps about 4.7 liters of blood through the body every minute. How many liters of blood does it pump through the body in a day?

5. A 75-kilogram adult has about 160,000 kilometers of blood vessels. At that ratio, how many kilometers of blood vessels do you have?

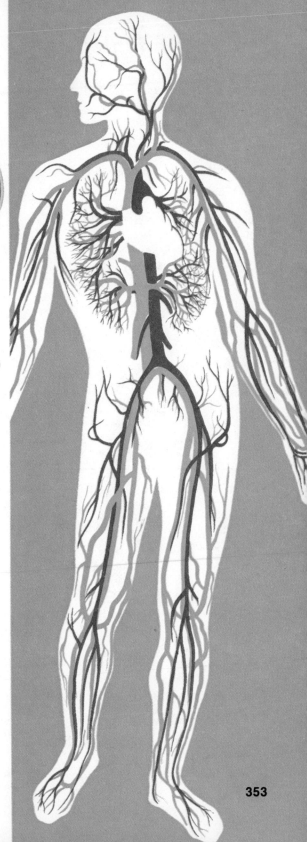

Multiplying integers

To multiply integers we will think of "putting charges in" as positive and "taking charges out" as negative.

EXAMPLE 1. $^{+}3 \times {}^{+}2 = ?$

Start with a 0 charge.

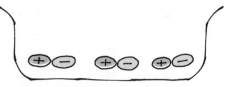

Put in 3 sets of $^{+}2$ charges.

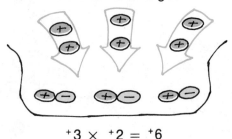

$$^{+}3 \times {}^{+}2 = {}^{+}6$$

EXAMPLE 2. $^{-}3 \times {}^{-}2 = ?$

Start with a 0 charge.

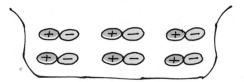

Take out 3 sets of $^{-}2$ charges.

$$^{-}3 \times {}^{-}2 = {}^{+}6$$

EXAMPLE 3. $^{+}3 \times {}^{-}2 = ?$

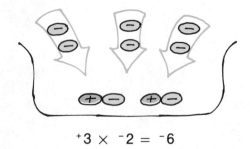

$$^{+}3 \times {}^{-}2 = {}^{-}6$$

EXAMPLE 4. $^{-}3 \times {}^{+}2 = ?$

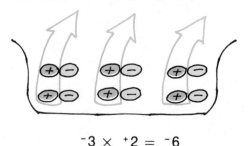

$$^{-}3 \times {}^{+}2 = {}^{-}6$$

The product of two integers with the *same* sign is *positive*.

The product of two integers with *different* signs is *negative*.

The product of any integer and 0 is 0.

Complete.
Positive, negative, or zero?

1. The product of two positive integers is a __?__ integer.

2. The product of two negative integers is a __?__ integer.

3. The product of a positive integer and a negative integer is a __?__ integer.

4. The product of an integer and 0 is __?__.

Give each product.

5. $^+3 \times {}^+4$

6. $^+3 \times {}^-4$

7. $^-3 \times {}^+4$

8. $^-3 \times {}^-4$

9. $^+5 \times {}^+6$

10. $^+5 \times {}^-6$

11. $^-5 \times {}^+6$

12. $^-5 \times {}^-6$

13. $^+7 \times {}^+5$

14. $^+7 \times {}^-5$

15. $^-7 \times {}^+5$

16. $^-7 \times {}^-5$

17. $^+8 \times {}^+6$

18. $^+8 \times {}^-6$

19. $^-8 \times {}^+6$

20. $^-8 \times {}^-6$

21. $^+9 \times {}^+6$

22. $^+9 \times {}^-6$

23. $^-9 \times {}^+6$

24. $^-9 \times {}^-6$

25. $^+9 \times {}^+9$

26. $^-7 \times {}^+7$

27. $^-6 \times 0$

28. $^-7 \times {}^-8$

29. 0×0

30. $0 \times {}^+5$

31. $^-8 \times {}^+8$

32. $^+8 \times {}^-9$

33. $^-7 \times {}^-9$

34. $^+9 \times {}^+8$

35. $^-6 \times {}^-7$

36. $^+3 \times {}^-9$

37. $^-12 \times {}^+5$

38. $^-16 \times {}^+3$

39. $^+9 \times {}^+15$

40. $^-16 \times {}^+4$

41. $^+24 \times {}^-3$

42. $^+12 \times {}^+18$

43. $^+15 \times {}^-15$

44. $^-19 \times 0$

Give the missing factor.

45. $? \times {}^-3 = {}^-24$

46. $^+6 \times ? = {}^+18$

47. $? \times {}^-8 = {}^-72$

48. $? \times {}^+7 = {}^+35$

49. $^-3 \times ? = {}^+3$

50. $? \times {}^+3 = 0$

51. $^+12 \times ? = 0$

52. $^-11 \times ? = {}^-55$

53. $? \times {}^-5 = {}^-5$

54. $^+8 \times ? = {}^-72$

55. $? \times {}^-10 = {}^+100$

56. $? \times {}^+3 = {}^-27$

Dividing integers

Division is finding a missing factor.
Notice that you can find the quotient of two integers by finding a missing factor.

$$^+8 \times {}^+3 = {}^+24$$
$$^+24 \div {}^+8 = {}^+3$$

$$^+8 \times {}^-3 = {}^-24$$
$$^-24 \div {}^+8 = {}^-3$$

$$^-8 \times {}^+3 = {}^-24$$
$$^-24 \div {}^-8 = {}^+3$$

$$^-8 \times {}^-3 = {}^+24$$
$$^+24 \div {}^-8 = {}^-3$$

The quotient of two integers with the *same* sign is *positive*.
The quotient of two integers with *different* signs is *negative*.
The quotient of 0 divided by any nonzero integer is 0.

EXERCISES

Positive, negative, or zero?

1. If you divide a positive integer by a positive integer the quotient is __?__.

2. If you divide a negative integer by a negative integer the quotient is __?__.

3. The quotient of a positive integer divided by a negative integer is __?__.

4. The quotient of a negative integer divided by a positive integer is __?__.

5. The quotient of 0 divided by any integer is __?__.

Give each quotient.

6. $^{+}12 \div {}^{+}6$ 7. $^{-}16 \div {}^{-}2$ 8. $^{-}18 \div {}^{+}9$

9. $^{+}12 \div {}^{-}4$ 10. $^{-}20 \div {}^{-}4$ 11. $^{+}21 \div {}^{+}7$

12. $^{-}40 \div {}^{-}8$ 13. $^{+}24 \div {}^{-}3$ 14. $^{-}18 \div {}^{+}3$

15. $^{-}28 \div {}^{+}7$ 16. $^{+}64 \div {}^{+}8$ 17. $^{+}42 \div {}^{-}7$

18. $^{-}36 \div {}^{-}9$ 19. $^{+}48 \div {}^{-}6$ 20. $0 \div {}^{-}6$

21. $^{-}63 \div {}^{-}9$ 22. $^{+}36 \div {}^{+}4$ 23. $^{-}54 \div {}^{-}9$

24. $0 \div {}^{-}8$ 25. $^{+}72 \div {}^{-}8$ 26. $^{-}45 \div {}^{+}5$

27. $^{+}81 \div {}^{+}9$ 28. $^{-}49 \div {}^{+}7$ 29. $^{+}56 \div {}^{-}7$

30. $^{-}32 \div {}^{+}2$ 31. $^{+}45 \div {}^{-}3$ 32. $^{+}84 \div {}^{+}4$

33. $^{-}52 \div {}^{-}4$ 34. $^{+}95 \div {}^{+}5$ 35. $^{-}72 \div {}^{-}6$

36. $^{-}96 \div {}^{+}24$ 37. $^{-}98 \div {}^{-}14$ 38. $^{+}65 \div {}^{-}13$

Find the end number.

39.

Find the starting number.

40.

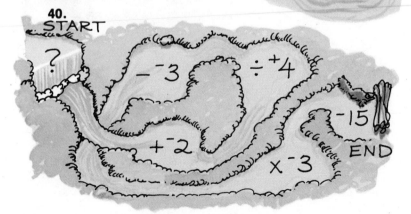

Solve.

1. 18% of 50 $= n$

2. 46% of 150 $= n$

3. 36% of 25 $= n$

4. $37\frac{1}{2}$% of 96 $= n$

5. $66\frac{2}{3}$% of 81 $= n$

6. 110% of 80 $= n$

7. 15% of $n = 15$

8. 23% of $n = 46$

9. 20% of $n = 16$

10. $33\frac{1}{3}$% of $n = 18$

11. $62\frac{1}{2}$% of $n = 55$

12. $83\frac{1}{3}$% of $n = 95$

Practice exercises

Give each product.

1. $^+9 \times {}^+5$ 2. $^-9 \times {}^+6$ 3. $^-7 \times {}^-6$ 4. $^+6 \times {}^-5$

5. $^-7 \times {}^-8$ 6. $^+4 \times {}^-8$ 7. $^+7 \times {}^-7$ 8. $^-8 \times {}^-9$

9. $^+9 \times {}^-4$ 10. $^+8 \times {}^+8$ 11. $^-3 \times {}^+9$ 12. $0 \times {}^-7$

13. $^-6 \times {}^-8$ 14. 0×0 15. $^-9 \times {}^+8$ 16. $^+4 \times {}^+7$

17. $^-9 \times {}^+9$ 18. $^+5 \times {}^+5$ 19. $^-6 \times 0$ 20. $^-8 \times {}^+4$

21. $^+10 \times {}^-5$ 22. $^-11 \times {}^-3$ 23. $^-12 \times {}^-2$ 24. $^+5 \times {}^-11$

25. $^-13 \times {}^+4$ 26. $^+6 \times {}^+15$ 27. $^+19 \times 0$ 28. $^-15 \times {}^+12$

29. $^+16 \times {}^-16$ 30. $^-18 \times {}^+20$ 31. $^+23 \times {}^+13$ 32. $0 \times {}^-22$

Give each quotient.

33. $^+21 \div {}^+7$ 34. $^+24 \div {}^-3$ 35. $^-45 \div {}^+5$ 36. $^-25 \div {}^-5$

37. $^-72 \div {}^-9$ 38. $^+54 \div {}^+6$ 39. $^-28 \div {}^+4$ 40. $^+48 \div {}^-6$

41. $^+30 \div {}^-5$ 42. $^-36 \div {}^+6$ 43. $^-72 \div {}^-8$ 44. $^+32 \div {}^+8$

45. $^-63 \div {}^+7$ 46. $^+35 \div {}^+7$ 47. $^-36 \div {}^-9$ 48. $^+56 \div {}^-8$

49. $^+42 \div {}^-6$ 50. $^-81 \div {}^+9$ 51. $^+49 \div {}^+7$ 52. $^-42 \div {}^-7$

53. $^-24 \div {}^+2$ 54. $0 \div {}^-8$ 55. $^+45 \div {}^+5$ 56. $^+42 \div {}^-21$

57. $0 \div {}^+25$ 58. $^+36 \div {}^+3$ 59. $^+72 \div {}^-18$ 60. $^-75 \div {}^+25$

61. $^+45 \div {}^-15$ 62. $^-60 \div {}^-20$ 63. $^-96 \div {}^+24$ 64. $^+96 \div {}^+12$

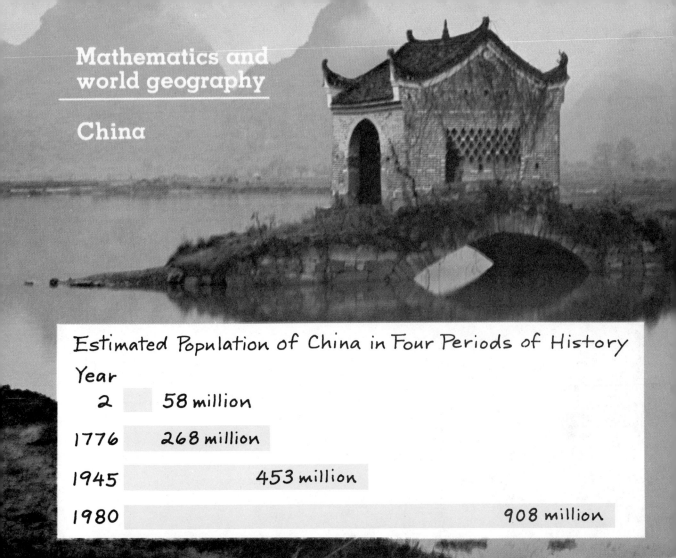

Mathematics and world geography

China

Estimated Population of China in Four Periods of History

Year	
2	58 million
1776	268 million
1945	453 million
1980	908 million

1. How many times greater is the estimated population in 1980 than the estimated population in the year 2?

2. The population of the United States of America is about 24% of the population of China. About how many people lived in the U.S.A. in 1945?

3. China has the highest population of any country in the world. About 21% of all people live in China. What is the estimated population of the world in 1980?

4. The Chinese population doubled between 1945 and 1980. If the population continues to grow at the same rate, when will it be double the 1980 population?

Graphing ordered pairs

Here is a **coordinate plane**. The red horizontal number line is the **first coordinate axis**. The red vertical number line is the **second coordinate axis**. The point where the axes intersect is called the **origin**.

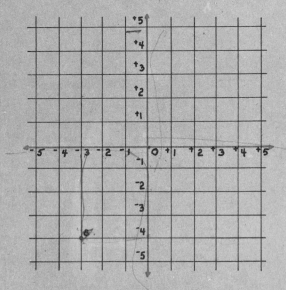

Ordered pairs of numbers may be graphed on a coordinate plane. Here is how to graph the ordered pair ($^-$3, $^-$4).

Step 1. Start at the origin. Move along the first coordinate axis to $^-$3.

Step 2. Then move parallel to the second coordinate axis to $^-$4.

The ordered pair ($^-$3, $^-$4) gives the coordinates of point B. Point B is the graph of the ordered pair ($^-$3, $^-$4).

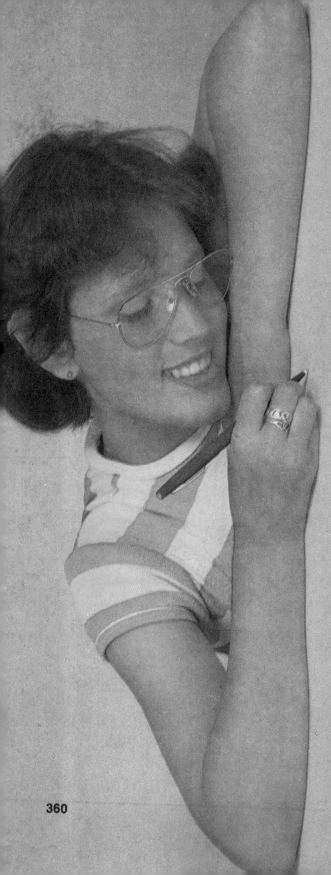

EXERCISES
Give the coordinates of each point.

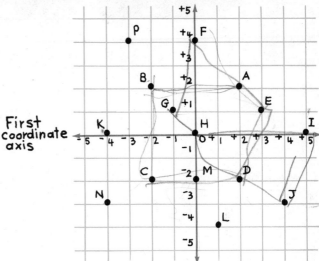

Second coordinate axis

First coordinate axis

1. A 2. B 3. C

4. D 5. E 6. F

7. G 8. H 9. I

10. J 11. K 12. L

13. M 14. N 15. P

Graph the following ordered pairs.
Label each point with its coordinates.

16. $(^+3, \ ^+2)$ 17. $(^+3, \ ^-2)$ 18. $(^-3, \ ^+2)$ 19. $(^-3, \ ^-2)$

20. $(0, 0)$ 21. $(^-4, \ 0)$ 22. $(^-4, \ ^-1)$ 23. $(^-4, \ ^+1)$

24. $(^+4, \ ^-1)$ 25. $(^+4, \ ^+1)$ 26. $(0, \ ^-4)$ 27. $(^+1, \ ^-2)$

28. $(^-3, \ ^+3)$ 29. $(^-2, \ ^-2)$ 30. $(^+3, \ 0)$ 31. $(^+4, \ ^-3)$

32. Copy the triangle on graph paper and give the coordinates of each vertex.

33. Add $^+3$ to the first number of each ordered pair. Graph the new ordered pairs. Connect the points to make a new triangle.

34. Multiply the second number of each original pair by $^-1$. Graph the ordered pairs and draw the triangle.

35. Draw the triangle that you get by multiplying all the original numbers by $^-2$.

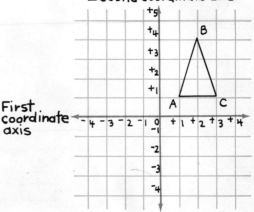

Second coordinate axis

First coordinate axis

CHAPTER CHECKUP

Give each sum. [pages 348–349]

1. $^+6 + {}^+3$
2. $^-5 + {}^+5$
3. $^-3 + {}^-9$
4. $^-6 + {}^+3$

5. $^+5 + {}^-5$
6. $^-1 + {}^-6$
7. $0 + {}^-2$
8. $^+9 + {}^+7$

9. $^+10 + {}^-3$
10. $^+8 + {}^+9$
11. $^-4 + {}^+10$
12. $^-5 + {}^-8$

Give each difference. [pages 350–351]

13. $^-5 - {}^+3$
14. $^-2 - {}^-1$
15. $^+3 - {}^+5$
16. $^-4 - {}^+5$

17. $^+6 - {}^+6$
18. $^-6 - {}^+2$
19. $^+8 - {}^-8$
20. $^-3 - {}^-6$

21. $^-9 - {}^-2$
22. $^+6 - 0$
23. $^-8 - {}^+3$
24. $^+7 - {}^-9$

Give each product. [pages 354–355]

25. $^-6 \times {}^-4$
26. $^+5 \times {}^+5$
27. $^-5 \times {}^+7$
28. $^+10 \times 0$

29. $^+8 \times {}^-6$
30. $^+8 \times {}^+7$
31. $^-4 \times 0$
32. $^-6 \times {}^-9$

33. $0 \times {}^-3$
34. $^-8 \times {}^-9$
35. $^-9 \times {}^+8$
36. $^+6 \times {}^+9$

Give each quotient. [pages 356–357]

37. $^+45 \div {}^-9$
38. $^-49 \div {}^+7$
39. $^-40 \div {}^+8$
40. $^+64 \div {}^-8$

41. $^+36 \div {}^+4$
42. $^+56 \div {}^+7$
43. $0 \div {}^-9$
44. $^-40 \div {}^-8$

45. $^-72 \div {}^+8$
46. $^-81 \div {}^-9$
47. $^-48 \div {}^-6$
48. $^+42 \div {}^+7$

Give the coordinates of each point. [pages 360–361]

49. A
50. B

51. C
52. D

53. E
54. F

55. G
56. H

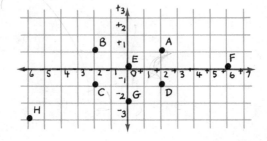

Project

1. You have located points on a coordinate plane by referring to two lines, or axes. Circles around the earth called lines of latitude and longitude are used to locate places on the earth's surface. In an encyclopedia, see what you can learn about latitude and longitude.

2. Use a map in an atlas to find the latitude and longitude of the place where you live. What are the latitude and longitude of the point on the side of the earth opposite the place where you live?

3. The earth is divided into 24 time zones based on the lines of longitude. In an encyclopedia, see what you can learn about time zones. Which time zone do you live in?

CHAPTER REVIEW

Give each sum.

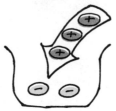  

1. ⁻2 + ⁺3	**2.** ⁺3 + ⁻2	**3.** ⁻2 + ⁻2
4. ⁺5 + ⁻4	**5.** ⁻5 + ⁺4	**6.** ⁻8 + ⁻3
7. ⁺6 + ⁺2	**8.** ⁻7 + 0	**9.** 0 + ⁺6

Give each difference.

10. ⁻8 − ⁻2	**11.** ⁺7 − ⁺2	**12.** ⁺5 − 0
13. ⁺9 − ⁻4	**14.** ⁻7 − ⁻3	**15.** ⁻10 − ⁺8
16. ⁺15 − ⁺7	**17.** ⁺16 − ⁻8	**18.** ⁻12 − ⁺4

> To subtract an integer, add its opposite.

Give each product.

19. ⁺9 × ⁺8	**20.** ⁻6 × ⁻7	**21.** ⁻6 × ⁺8
22. 0 × ⁻7	**23.** ⁺7 × ⁺9	**24.** ⁺5 × ⁻9
25. ⁻6 × ⁺9	**26.** 0 × 0	**27.** ⁻8 × ⁻7

> The product of two integers with the same sign is positive. The product of two integers with different signs is negative.

Give each quotient.

28. ⁺63 ÷ ⁺9	**29.** ⁻56 ÷ ⁺8	**30.** ⁻54 ÷ ⁻6
31. ⁻42 ÷ ⁻6	**32.** ⁺48 ÷ ⁺6	**33.** ⁻36 ÷ ⁺4
34. ⁺32 ÷ ⁻4	**35.** 0 ÷ ⁻8	**36.** ⁻27 ÷ ⁻9

> The quotient of two integers with the same sign is positive. The quotient of two integers with different signs is negative.

CHAPTER CHALLENGE

To get the **output number**, this function machine adds ⁻3 to the **input number**.

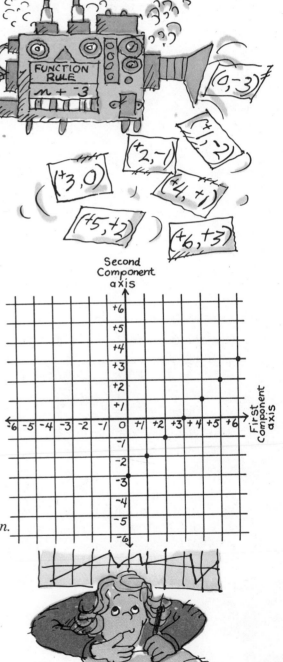

We can describe the function by writing

$$f : n \longrightarrow n + ^-3$$

input number   output number

Read as "f takes n to $n + ^-3$."

To graph a function, we graph the ordered pairs of the function. Here we have graphed some ordered pairs of the function

$$f : n \longrightarrow n + ^-3$$

What do you notice about the points of the graph? What are some other points that belong to the graph of this function?

1. Copy and complete these ordered pairs of the function $f : n \longrightarrow ^-3n$.

    a. $(^-3, ?)$ **b.** $(^+1, ?)$ **c.** $(0, ?)$

    d. $(^-4, ?)$ **e.** $(^-2, ?)$ **f.** $(^+3, ?)$

    g. $(^+2, ?)$ **h.** $(^+4, ?)$ **i.** $(^-1, ?)$

    j. Graph your ordered pairs for $f : n \longrightarrow ^-3n.$

2. Graph some ordered pairs of these functions.

    a. $g : n \longrightarrow ^+2n$ **b.** $h : n \longrightarrow n - ^-4$

    c. $j : n \longrightarrow n^2$

365

13 a b c d 33 a b c d 13 a b c d 3 a b c d 29 a b c d
14 a b c d 34 a b c d 14 a b c d 4 c d 30 a b c d
15 a b c 31 a b c d

MAJOR CHECKUP
Standardized Format

Choose the correct letter.

1. Round 42.0385 to the nearest thousandth.

a. 42.04
b. 42.038
c. 42.039
d. none of these

2. Multiply.

59.2
× 4.83

a. 8.880
b. 2859.36
c. 285.936
d. none of these

3. Divide.

$0.016\overline{)7.568}$

a. 47.3
b. 4.73
c. 473
d. none of these

4. Add.

$8\frac{5}{6}$
$+3\frac{3}{4}$

a. $11\frac{7}{12}$
b. $11\frac{1}{12}$
c. $12\frac{7}{12}$
d. none of these

5. Subtract.

12
$-5\frac{3}{4}$

a. $7\frac{3}{4}$
b. $7\frac{1}{4}$
c. $6\frac{1}{4}$
d. none of these

6. Find the product.

$\frac{3}{8} \times \frac{2}{3}$

a. $\frac{1}{4}$
b. $\frac{9}{16}$
c. 4
d. none of these

7. Give the quotient.

$\frac{5}{6} \div \frac{5}{4}$

a. $\frac{3}{2}$
b. $\frac{25}{24}$
c. $\frac{2}{3}$
d. none of these

8. $33\frac{1}{3}\%$ of 96 = _____?_____

a. 32
b. 64
c. 288
d. none of these

9. 40% of _____?_____ = 54

a. 90
b. 135
c. $21\frac{3}{5}$
d. none of these

10. A bicycle that regularly sells for $96 was put on sale for $80. The percent of discount was

a. 24%
b. 25%
c. 16%
d. none of these

11. How many lines of symmetry does a parallelogram have?

a. 1
b. 2
c. 4
d. none of these

12. Imagine tossing a dime and then tossing a nickel. The probability of getting both tails is

a. $\frac{1}{2}$
b. $\frac{3}{4}$
c. $\frac{1}{4}$
d. none of these

366

Final Test

Add, subtract, multiply, or divide.

1. 296
    58
    341
    + 67

2. 8402
    − 1597

3. 504
    × 261

4. 326)¯18256

Round 59.8956 to the nearest

5. hundredth   6. tenth

Complete.

7. $9.382 + 6.88 =$ ___?___   8. $7.43 - 2.286 =$ ___?___

Multiply or divide.

9.   0.74
     × 0.06

10.   32.1
      × 6.23

11. 0.04)¯3.904

12. 3.02)¯7.7312

Complete.

13. The greatest common factor of 24 and 36 is ___?___.

14. The prime factorization of 48 is ___?___.

15. The least common multiple of 12 and 9 is ___?___.

16. The standard numeral for 4^3 is ___?___.

Complete.

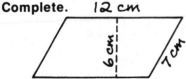

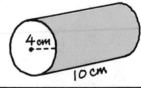

Use 3.14 as an approximation for π.

17. The perimeter is ___?___.

18. The area is ___?___.

19. The surface area is ___?___.

20. The volume is ___?___.

Give each sum or difference in lowest terms.

21. $\frac{1}{3} + \frac{1}{4}$ 22. $\frac{2}{3} - \frac{1}{2}$ 23. $4\frac{3}{5} + 2\frac{1}{2}$ 24. $9\frac{3}{8} - 6\frac{3}{4}$

Continued on the next page

Give each product or quotient.

25. $\dfrac{3}{4} \times \dfrac{2}{5}$ **26.** $\dfrac{5}{6} \div \dfrac{3}{2}$ **27.** $2\dfrac{1}{4} \times 3\dfrac{1}{2}$ **28.** $3\dfrac{1}{2} \div 2\dfrac{2}{3}$

Solve.

29. $\dfrac{n}{4} = \dfrac{5}{8}$ **30.** $\dfrac{5}{n} = \dfrac{3}{8}$ **31.** 25% of 10 = n **32.** 20% of n = 17

Solve.

33. Apples are on sale at 6 for 98¢. How much will 1 apple cost?

34. Oranges are priced at 6 for 89¢. How much will 5 oranges cost?

35. Jim bought a $40 tennis racket on sale for 20% off. What was the sale price of the racket?

36. How much interest will be charged on a loan of $2000 at 8% per year for 6 months?

True or false?

37. An acute angle is an angle that measures 90°.

38. Figures that have the same size and shape are called congruent figures.

39. An isosceles triangle has 1 line of symmetry.

40. A parallelogram has a point of symmetry.

Think about putting these marbles in a sack, mixing, and picking one without looking. Give each probability in lowest terms.

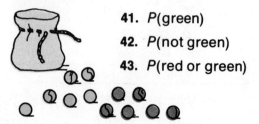

41. P(green)

42. P(not green)

43. P(red or green)

Answer each question about the test data.

Test Scores			
99	90	83	80
99	90	83	76
99	90	83	70
96	86	82	65
95	85	81	50
93	84	81	43
90	84	81	43

44. What is the mean?

45. What is the median?

46. What is the range?

Add, subtract, multiply, or divide.

47. $^{+}8 + {}^{-}9$ **48.** $^{-}3 - {}^{+}7$ **49.** $^{-}9 \times {}^{-}6$ **50.** $^{+}24 \div {}^{-}3$

Skill Test

skill objective	test items			
1 Add two or more numbers	475 +312	296 +352	596 628 +327	3758 5863 +9479
2 Subtract any two numbers	352 −121	462 −139	526 −347	6000 −2382
3 Multiply by a 1-digit number	241 ×2	28 ×3	516 ×6	2371 ×8
4 Multiply by 10 or 100	67 ×10	38 ×100	576 ×10	3241 ×100
5 Multiply by a 2-digit number	431 ×26	358 ×34	544 ×61	8075 ×85
6 Multiply by a 3-digit number	543 ×122	308 ×496	615 ×204	8312 ×426
7 Divide by a 1-digit number	3)252	6)594	8)462	5)4295
8 Divide by a 2-digit number	23)713	45)1080	93)5762	42)8320
9 Divide by a 3-digit number	200)4600	120)960	431)13392	486)2483
10 Add any two decimals	3.51 +2.81	4.75 +2.68	67.5 +9.8	4.832 +.96

	skill objective			test items		
11	Subtract any two decimals		$\begin{array}{r} .483 \\ -.265 \end{array}$	$\begin{array}{r} 2.67 \\ -.88 \end{array}$	$\begin{array}{r} 35.2 \\ -17.8 \end{array}$	$\begin{array}{r} 18.6 \\ -9.83 \end{array}$
12	Multiply by a whole number		$\begin{array}{r} 5.6 \\ \times 3 \end{array}$	$\begin{array}{r} 7.24 \\ \times 8 \end{array}$	$\begin{array}{r} 1.59 \\ \times 12 \end{array}$	$\begin{array}{r} 3.68 \\ \times 142 \end{array}$
13	Multiply by a decimal		$\begin{array}{r} 5.3 \\ \times 2.7 \end{array}$	$\begin{array}{r} .41 \\ \times .08 \end{array}$	$\begin{array}{r} .62 \\ \times .37 \end{array}$	$\begin{array}{r} 1.46 \\ \times 3.8 \end{array}$
14	Divide by a whole number		$3\overline{)85.2}$	$5\overline{)6.25}$	$56\overline{)71.68}$	$200\overline{)4.6}$
15	Divide by a decimal		$.9\overline{)1.08}$	$.06\overline{).192}$	$2.3\overline{)1.334}$	$.46\overline{)1.426}$
16	Divide and round to the nearest tenth		$.6\overline{)5.23}$	$.9\overline{)1}$	$1.6\overline{)59.2}$	$.45\overline{)17.6}$
17	Find an equivalent fraction		$\frac{2}{3} = \frac{?}{12}$	$\frac{5}{8} = \frac{?}{64}$	$\frac{5}{6} = \frac{?}{30}$	$\frac{5}{4} = \frac{?}{32}$
18	Reduce a fraction to lowest terms		$\frac{6}{12}$	$\frac{18}{24}$	$\frac{15}{35}$	$\frac{45}{63}$
19	Compare fractions		< or >? $\frac{3}{7} \bullet \frac{4}{7}$	$\frac{2}{3} \bullet \frac{3}{5}$	$\frac{4}{8} \bullet \frac{4}{7}$	$\frac{4}{7} \bullet \frac{5}{8}$
20	Add fractions		$\frac{1}{8} + \frac{3}{4}$	$\frac{1}{6} + \frac{1}{3}$	$\frac{2}{3} + \frac{2}{5}$	$\frac{3}{4} + \frac{2}{3}$
21	Subtract fractions		$\frac{3}{4} - \frac{1}{8}$	$\frac{1}{3} - \frac{1}{6}$	$\frac{2}{3} - \frac{2}{5}$	$\frac{3}{4} - \frac{2}{3}$
22	Change a fraction to a mixed number		$\frac{7}{2} = ?$	$\frac{8}{3} = ?$	$\frac{15}{4} = ?$	$\frac{23}{8} = ?$

370

	skill objective	test items			

23	Change a mixed number to a fraction	$2\frac{1}{2} = \underline{?}$	$3\frac{2}{3} = \underline{?}$	$5\frac{3}{4} = \underline{?}$	$4\frac{7}{8} = \underline{?}$
24	Add mixed numbers	$3\frac{5}{7}$ $+2\frac{3}{7}$	$4\frac{2}{3}$ $+1\frac{1}{3}$	$12\frac{5}{6}$ $+4\frac{3}{8}$	$5\frac{2}{3}$ $+4\frac{3}{4}$
25	Subtract mixed numbers	$5\frac{2}{7}$ $-1\frac{1}{7}$	$6\frac{2}{9}$ $-3\frac{5}{9}$	$6\frac{3}{4}$ $-4\frac{5}{6}$	$8\frac{2}{3}$ $-3\frac{3}{4}$
26	Multiply fractions	$\frac{2}{3} \times \frac{4}{7}$	$\frac{3}{5} \times \frac{5}{8}$	$\frac{6}{7} \times \frac{5}{3}$	$\frac{12}{15} \times \frac{5}{4}$
27	Find a fraction of a number	$\frac{1}{2}$ of 18	$\frac{2}{3}$ of 21	$\frac{4}{3}$ of 12	$\frac{5}{6}$ of 18
28	Divide fractions	$\frac{3}{4} \div \frac{5}{2}$	$\frac{3}{4} \div \frac{3}{8}$	$\frac{2}{3} \div \frac{3}{4}$	$\frac{5}{7} \div \frac{3}{7}$
29	Simplify fractions	$\dfrac{\frac{2}{3}}{\frac{2}{5}}$	$\dfrac{\frac{3}{4}}{\frac{3}{8}}$	$\dfrac{\frac{2}{3}}{\frac{3}{4}}$	$\dfrac{\frac{5}{9}}{\frac{2}{3}}$
30	Change a fraction to a decimal	$\frac{1}{4} = \underline{?}$	$\frac{2}{5} = \underline{?}$	$\frac{9}{10} = \underline{?}$	$\frac{3}{2} = \underline{?}$
31	Change a mixed number to a decimal	$2\frac{1}{2} = \underline{?}$	$1\frac{3}{4} = \underline{?}$	$2\frac{5}{8} = \underline{?}$	$3\frac{3}{8} = \underline{?}$
32	Change a decimal to a fraction	$0.5 = \underline{?}$	$0.25 = \underline{?}$	$0.65 = \underline{?}$	$0.75 = \underline{?}$
33	Change a decimal to a mixed number	$1.5 = \underline{?}$	$2.75 = \underline{?}$	$1.375 = \underline{?}$	$2.05 = \underline{?}$
34	Change a fraction to a mixed decimal	$\frac{1}{3} = \underline{?}$	$\frac{2}{3} = \underline{?}$	$\frac{5}{6} = \underline{?}$	$\frac{4}{9} = \underline{?}$

	skill objective	test items	
35	Multiply mixed numbers	$3\frac{1}{2} \times 2$ $2\frac{1}{3} \times 3\frac{2}{3}$	$1\frac{1}{4} \times 1\frac{1}{2}$ $1\frac{2}{3} \times 2\frac{3}{4}$
36	Divide mixed numbers	$3\frac{1}{2} \div 2$ $2\frac{1}{3} \div 1\frac{1}{2}$	$2\frac{3}{4} \div 1\frac{1}{3}$ $4\frac{2}{3} \div 2\frac{3}{8}$
37	Solve a proportion	$\frac{5}{3} = \frac{n}{4}$ $\frac{4}{5} = \frac{6}{n}$	$\frac{2}{n} = \frac{3}{8}$ $\frac{n}{5} = \frac{6}{7}$
38	Change a fraction to a percent	$\frac{3}{10} = \underline{?}$ $\frac{1}{4} = \underline{?}$ $\frac{2}{5} = \underline{?}$ $\frac{3}{4} = \underline{?}$	
39	Change a percent to a fraction	$60\% = \underline{?}$ $5\% = \underline{?}$ $25\% = \underline{?}$ $90\% = \underline{?}$	
40	Change a decimal to a percent	$0.1 = \underline{?}$ $0.15 = \underline{?}$ $2.36 = \underline{?}$ $1.7 = \underline{?}$	
41	Change a percent to a decimal	$18\% = \underline{?}$ $12.2\% = \underline{?}$ $65.3\% = \underline{?}$ $8.6\% = \underline{?}$	
42	Change a fraction to a mixed percent	$\frac{1}{3} = \underline{?}$ $\frac{2}{3} = \underline{?}$ $\frac{5}{6} = \underline{?}$ $\frac{5}{9} = \underline{?}$	
43	Find a percent of a number	25% of $28 = n$ $33\frac{1}{3}\%$ of $51 = n$	35% of $50 = n$ $83\frac{1}{3}\%$ of $72 = n$
44	Find the number when a percent is given	10% of $n = 6$ $12\frac{1}{2}\%$ of $n = 16$	75% of $n = 45$ 32% of $n = 8$

	skill objective		test items		
45	Compare integers	**< or >?**			
		$^+3$ ● $^-2$	0 ● $^-5$	$^+6$ ● $^-8$	$^-5$ ● $^-6$
46	Add two integers	$^+8 + {}^+6$	$^-4 + {}^+7$	$^+9 + {}^-3$	$^-5 + {}^-7$
47	Subtract two integers	$^+5 - {}^+2$	$^+6 - {}^-4$	$^-5 - {}^-2$	$^-7 - {}^+3$
48	Multiply two integers	$^+8 \times {}^-3$	$^+2 \times {}^+7$	$^-6 \times {}^-4$	$^-3 \times {}^+7$
49	Divide two integers	$^-8 \div {}^+2$	$^+18 \div {}^-6$	$^+9 \div {}^+3$	$^-28 \div {}^-7$

Extra Practice

Set 1   Give each sum.

1. $9 + 4$ 2. $6 + 8$ 3. $5 + 7$ 4. $4 + 9$ 5. $5 + 9$
6. $9 + 7$ 7. $6 + 6$ 8. $6 + 9$ 9. $3 + 9$ 10. $5 + 6$
11. $5 + 8$ 12. $8 + 9$ 13. $7 + 6$ 14. $8 + 5$ 15. $9 + 8$
16. $9 + 6$ 17. $2 + 9$ 18. $7 + 7$ 19. $9 + 2$ 20. $7 + 9$
21. $8 + 8$ 22. $7 + 8$ 23. $9 + 9$ 24. $9 + 5$ 25. $8 + 7$

Set 2   Add.

1.	43	2.	70	3.	32	4.	41	5.	51	6.	63
	$+26$		$+28$		$+32$		$+35$		$+20$		$+31$

7.	62	8.	33	9.	81	10.	54	11.	73	12.	86
	$+33$		$+62$		$+12$		$+62$		$+55$		$+21$

13.	41	14.	30	15.	43	16.	52	17.	44	18.	35
	53		25		61		33		20		72
	$+12$		$+84$		$+50$		$+24$		$+64$		$+22$

Set 3   Add.

1.	78	2.	36	3.	19	4.	45	5.	39	6.	46
	$+29$		$+38$		$+45$		$+63$		$+82$		$+29$

7.	54	8.	94	9.	58	10.	28	11.	63	12.	57
	$+38$		$+65$		$+58$		$+36$		$+78$		$+95$

13.	75	14.	83	15.	89	16.	79	17.	94	18.	68
	$+67$		$+78$		$+21$		$+32$		$+56$		$+75$

Set 4   Give each difference.

1. $12 - 3$ 2. $12 - 6$ 3. $11 - 9$ 4. $14 - 5$ 5. $12 - 4$
6. $15 - 9$ 7. $13 - 4$ 8. $11 - 7$ 9. $12 - 5$ 10. $13 - 7$
11. $12 - 8$ 12. $14 - 6$ 13. $13 - 5$ 14. $13 - 8$ 15. $16 - 8$
16. $16 - 9$ 17. $13 - 9$ 18. $17 - 8$ 19. $14 - 8$ 20. $15 - 8$
21. $17 - 9$ 22. $11 - 6$ 23. $18 - 9$ 24. $13 - 6$ 25. $14 - 7$

Set 5 Subtract.

1.   65
   −23
	2. 38
	   −15
		3. 65
		   −22
			4. 56
			   −14
				5. 49
				   −23
					6. 78
					   −35

7.   39
   −15
	8. 87
	   −24
		9. 79
		   −32
			10. 88
			   −43
				11. 55
				   −40
					12. 86
					   −32

13.   148
   −82
	14. 184
	   −91
		15. 177
		   −93
			16. 166
			   −84
				17. 156
				   −92
					18. 135
					   −83

Set 6 Subtract.

1.   82
   −23
	2. 75
	   −36
		3. 64
		   −39
			4. 53
			   −16
				5. 45
				   −36
					6. 72
					   −58

7.   76
   −39
	8. 82
	   −46
		9. 60
		   −58
			10. 75
			   −29
				11. 42
				   −18
					12. 93
					   −47

13.   164
   −95
	14. 143
	   −75
		15. 132
		   −58
			16. 120
			   −46
				17. 165
				   −97
					18. 174
					   −86

Set 7 Give each product.

1. 6×4
2. 4×7
3. 6×7
4. 6×6
5. 9×6
6. 8×7
7. 9×5
8. 3×9
9. 8×6
10. 5×6
11. 8×5
12. 8×9
13. 5×5
14. 4×9
15. 8×4
16. 3×7
17. 3×8
18. 3×6
19. 9×8
20. 6×8
21. 8×8
22. 7×6
23. 7×8
24. 5×9
25. 9×7
26. 7×7
27. 9×9
28. 4×5
29. 7×9
30. 6×9

Set 8 Multiply.

1.   23
   ×2
	2. 34
	   ×2
		3. 21
		   ×4
			4. 23
			   ×3
				5. 22
				   ×3
					6. 20
					   ×4

7.   21
   ×6
	8. 42
	   ×3
		9. 30
		   ×5
			10. 42
			   ×4
				11. 82
				   ×2
					12. 61
					   ×8

13.   84
   ×2
	14. 30
	   ×6
		15. 51
		   ×6
			16. 41
			   ×5
				17. 64
				   ×2
					18. 70
					   ×7

Set 9 Multiply.

1. 29 $\times 2$	2. 46 $\times 4$	3. 38 $\times 3$	4. 54 $\times 5$	5. 63 $\times 7$	6. 75 $\times 6$
7. 39 $\times 8$	8. 46 $\times 6$	9. 74 $\times 3$	10. 65 $\times 5$	11. 84 $\times 4$	12. 95 $\times 7$
13. 65 $\times 6$	14. 58 $\times 8$	15. 73 $\times 5$	16. 92 $\times 9$	17. 83 $\times 7$	18. 69 $\times 4$

Set 10 Give each quotient.

1. $18 \div 9$ 2. $40 \div 8$ 3. $15 \div 3$ 4. $24 \div 6$ 5. $21 \div 7$
6. $20 \div 4$ 7. $25 \div 5$ 8. $16 \div 4$ 9. $36 \div 4$ 10. $56 \div 7$
11. $45 \div 9$ 12. $42 \div 6$ 13. $63 \div 9$ 14. $35 \div 7$ 15. $45 \div 5$
16. $56 \div 8$ 17. $24 \div 3$ 18. $27 \div 3$ 19. $54 \div 6$ 20. $72 \div 8$
21. $36 \div 6$ 22. $81 \div 9$ 23. $49 \div 7$ 24. $28 \div 4$ 25. $42 \div 7$

Set 11 Divide.

1. $4\overline{)33}$ 2. $3\overline{)17}$ 3. $2\overline{)19}$ 4. $5\overline{)33}$ 5. $8\overline{)47}$ 6. $7\overline{)23}$

7. $6\overline{)50}$ 8. $9\overline{)37}$ 9. $3\overline{)25}$ 10. $5\overline{)43}$ 11. $6\overline{)40}$ 12. $8\overline{)44}$

13. $9\overline{)70}$ 14. $7\overline{)29}$ 15. $4\overline{)38}$ 16. $6\overline{)46}$ 17. $8\overline{)53}$ 18. $7\overline{)39}$

Set 12 Divide.

1. $3\overline{)69}$ 2. $2\overline{)64}$ 3. $4\overline{)88}$ 4. $3\overline{)66}$ 5. $2\overline{)86}$ 6. $3\overline{)93}$

7. $5\overline{)105}$ 8. $8\overline{)168}$ 9. $7\overline{)217}$ 10. $6\overline{)120}$ 11. $5\overline{)155}$ 12. $9\overline{)279}$

13. $6\overline{)426}$ 14. $8\overline{)488}$ 15. $7\overline{)287}$ 16. $9\overline{)369}$ 17. $5\overline{)350}$ 18. $8\overline{)488}$

Set 13 Divide.

1. $3\overline{)48}$ 2. $4\overline{)56}$ 3. $2\overline{)96}$ 4. $5\overline{)70}$ 5. $7\overline{)84}$ 6. $3\overline{)51}$

7. $7\overline{)98}$ 8. $3\overline{)87}$ 9. $6\overline{)84}$ 10. $5\overline{)75}$ 11. $6\overline{)72}$ 12. $6\overline{)96}$

13. $4\overline{)76}$ 14. $4\overline{)92}$ 15. $8\overline{)96}$ 16. $3\overline{)84}$ 17. $2\overline{)58}$ 18. $5\overline{)60}$

Set 14   Give the standard numeral.

1. eight thousand
2. five thousand one hundred twenty
3. forty-two thousand, nine hundred six
4. nineteen thousand, seven hundred fifty-three
5. three hundred twenty-eight thousand, six hundred seventy-six
6. five million, two hundred twelve thousand, four hundred thirty-seven
7. two hundred forty-two million, six thousand, two hundred eighty-three
8. five billion, two hundred twenty million, two hundred eleven thousand, sixty-six
9. twenty-four billion, nine hundred forty million, five thousand eighty-two
10. seven trillion, one hundred thirty-four million, two hundred forty thousand, twenty

Set 15   Give the next three multiples.

1. 10, 20, 30, ?, ?, ?
2. 140, 150, 160, ?, ?, ?
3. 370, 380, 390, ?, ?, ?
4. 1550, 1560, 1570, ?, ?, ?
5. 200, 300, 400, ?, ?, ?
6. 1600, 1700, 1800, ?, ?, ?
7. 2300, 2400, 2500, ?, ?, ?
8. 4600, 4700, 4800, ?, ?, ?
9. 5000, 6000, 7000, ?, ?, ?
10. 36,000, 37,000, 38,000, ?, ?, ?
11. 125,000, 126,000, 127,000, ?, ?, ?
12. 96,000, 97,000, 98,000, ?, ?, ?

Set 16   Round each number to the nearest hundred, thousand, and million.

1. 6,834,527
2. 9,498,937
3. 9,672,403
4. 12,291,742
5. 233,035,555
6. 456,621,384
7. 789,125,246
8. 919,291,350

Set 17   < or >?

1. 482 ● 483
2. 590 ● 589
3. 800 ● 799
4. 4689 ● 4731
5. 6390 ● 6382
6. 4934 ● 4898
7. 26,428 ● 27,222
8. 8999 ● 10,000
9. 72,958 ● 73,094
10. 85,395 ● 83,595
11. 100,000 ● 99,999
12. 168,749 ● 168,579
13. 298,431 ● 298,341
14. 835,822 ● 843,262
15. 987,342 ● 978,342

377

Set 18 Add.

1. 329 +437	2. 509 +388	3. 625 +158	4. 978 +388	5. 659 +594	6. 746 +896
7. 3565 +828	8. 4836 +565	9. 9024 +889	10. 7477 +3593	11. 6185 +6189	12. 4778 +8696
13. 384 292 +743	14. 567 308 +826	15. 295 762 +547	16. 1835 6916 +2159	17. 7068 9383 +4555	18. 5347 8274 +3339

Set 19 Subtract.

1. 863 −235	2. 752 −259	3. 694 −346	4. 538 −162	5. 453 −360	6. 725 −581
7. 3210 −2483	8. 5632 −1955	9. 9322 −3996	10. 6033 −1588	11. 5014 −2939	12. 7003 −4668
13. 5032 −1486	14. 6233 −2485	15. 9157 −3469	16. 7024 −3299	17. 7335 −2467	18. 5001 −2438

Set 20 Multiply.

1. 23 ×3	2. 41 ×2	3. 52 ×3	4. 64 ×4	5. 83 ×5	6. 90 ×4
7. 142 ×5	8. 238 ×9	9. 196 ×8	10. 370 ×7	11. 415 ×6	12. 467 ×5
13. 4916 ×7	14. 5328 ×2	15. 6742 ×4	16. 2864 ×5	17. 8955 ×8	18. 3780 ×9

Set 21 Give each product.

1. a. 24×10
   b. 24×100
   c. 24×1000

2. a. 57×10
   b. 57×100
   c. 57×1000

3. a. 80×10
   b. 80×100
   c. 80×1000

4. a. 142×10
   b. 142×100
   c. 142×1000

5. a. 200×10
   b. 200×100
   c. 200×1000

6. a. 1242×10
   b. 1242×100
   c. 1242×1000

7. a. 3450×10
   b. 3450×100
   c. 3450×1000

8. a. 8100×10
   b. 8100×100
   c. 8100×1000

Set 22   Multiply.

1. 352
    × 24

2. 592
    × 91

3. 766
    × 48

4. 691
    × 63

5. 829
    × 83

6. 527
    × 38

7. 635
    × 64

8. 863
    × 96

9. 478
    × 27

10. 409
    × 75

11. 742
    × 41

12. 312
    × 53

Set 23   Multiply.

1. 527
    × 123

2. 658
    × 243

3. 492
    × 174

4. 581
    × 325

5. 653
    × 208

6. 842
    × 258

7. 952
    × 333

8. 378
    × 156

9. 834
    × 240

10. 815
    × 524

11. 706
    × 430

12. 674
    × 462

13. 640
    × 306

14. 725
    × 301

15. 534
    × 320

16. 906
    × 254

17. 829
    × 306

18. 935
    × 256

Set 24   Divide.

1. 5)706
2. 8)359
3. 5)592
4. 7)488
5. 4)969

6. 9)5218
7. 6)3961
8. 5)7438
9. 3)9064
10. 9)8213

11. 2)62943
12. 7)71826
13. 8)54391
14. 6)70658
15. 6)42653

Set 25   Divide.

1. 18)7364
2. 34)5294
3. 57)1783
4. 24)9642
5. 42)7538

6. 78)3592
7. 95)6000
8. 45)5783
9. 72)7044
10. 80)6903

11. 45)38216
12. 83)53416
13. 16)29784
14. 64)36952
15. 38)74615

Set 26   Divide.

1. 125)3956
2. 203)7834
3. 138)5916
4. 351)7538
5. 150)2964

6. 522)9678
7. 358)6398
8. 212)9000
9. 534)9008
10. 242)8634

11. 156)29783
12. 618)52006
13. 425)39481
14. 625)62934
15. 481)49538

Set 27   Write in words.

1. 0.8 **2.** 0.08 **3.** 3.1 **4.** 0.31 **5.** 3.01 **6.** 30.1

7. 5.20 **8.** 50.2 **9.** 5.02 **10.** 8.40 **11.** 8.04 **12.** 80.4

Set 28   Write in words.

1. 5.002 **2.** 8.06 **3.** 3.4 **4.** 2.007 **5.** 7.024

6. 8.758 **7.** 45.547 **8.** 8.0005 **9.** 9.0016 **10.** 16.0345

Set 29   < or >?

1. .5 ● .4 **2.** .09 ● .08 **3.** .006 ● .005 **4.** .5 ● .05

5. .003 ● .02 **6.** .09 ● .1 **7.** .2 ● .008 **8.** .5 ● .004

9. 0.75 ● 0.76 **10.** 9.24 ● 9.42 **11.** 7.85 ● 7.58 **12.** 18.79 ● 18.8

13. .599 ● 1 **14.** 2 ● 1.897 **15.** 9.534 ● 9.0541 **16.** 6.375 ● 63.75

17. 56.37 ● 5.637 **18.** 5 ● 5.999 **19.** 8.001 ● 8.01 **20.** 19.02 ● 19.019

Set 30   Round each number to the nearest tenth, hundredth, and thousandth.

1. 16.1158 **2.** 43.2565 **3.** 82.3423

4. 65.8166 **5.** 58.3454 **6.** 9.9998

Set 31   Add.

1. 58.6 + 68.8	**2.** 4.63 + 0.34	**3.** .644 + .378	**4.** 91.2 + 25.9	**5.** 8.92 + 6.16	**6.** 5.39 + 0.53

7. 28.4 + 73.6 **8.** 22.4 + 4.78 **9.** 1.86 + 43

10. 4.16 + 0.379 **11.** 27.6 + 9.28 **12.** 7.88 + 0.594

13. 371 + 0.853 **14.** 8.62 + 5.95 **15.** 0.174 + 6.76

16. 99.7 + 4.89 **17.** 0.145 + 5.57 **18.** 0.0683 + 0.646

Set 32   Subtract.

1. $\begin{array}{r} 95.6 \\ -83.1 \end{array}$ 2. $\begin{array}{r} 8.26 \\ -4.19 \end{array}$ 3. $\begin{array}{r} .516 \\ -.384 \end{array}$ 4. $\begin{array}{r} 72.1 \\ -50.9 \end{array}$ 5. $\begin{array}{r} .462 \\ -.399 \end{array}$ 6. $\begin{array}{r} 9.67 \\ -1.09 \end{array}$

7. $46.6 - 7.4$ 8. $5.38 - 4.1$ 9. $629 - 3.84$

10. $80.2 - 9.3$ 11. $92.8 - 3.56$ 12. $89 - 42.8$

13. $7.3 - 7.18$ 14. $40 - 34.8$ 15. $0.3 - 0.286$

16. $70.6 - 2.93$ 17. $5.6 - 0.278$ 18. $0.82 - 0.007$

Set 33   Add or subtract.

1. $3.89 + 2.67$ 2. $5.08 + 0.284$ 3. $70.6 + 36.9$

4. $59.8 + 0.267$ 5. $0.841 + 78.9$ 6. $5.48 + 29.9$

7. $4.6 + 2.83$ 8. $7.2 + 5.94$ 9. $6 + 4.25$

10. $0.29 - 0.163$ 11. $0.43 - 0.286$ 12. $5.3 - 1.92$

13. $16 - 8.4$ 14. $6.62 - 0.8$ 15. $29 - 7.4$

16. $2.01 - 1.99$ 17. $7.09 - 0.4$ 18. $8.64 - 3.79$

Set 34   Multiply.

1. $\begin{array}{r} 35.8 \\ \times 2.9 \end{array}$ 2. $\begin{array}{r} 4.26 \\ \times 1.4 \end{array}$ 3. $\begin{array}{r} 57.4 \\ \times .35 \end{array}$ 4. $\begin{array}{r} 89.3 \\ \times 6.4 \end{array}$ 5. $\begin{array}{r} 6.52 \\ \times 18 \end{array}$ 6. $\begin{array}{r} 145 \\ \times 2.5 \end{array}$

7. $\begin{array}{r} 3.81 \\ \times 16 \end{array}$ 8. $\begin{array}{r} 25.3 \\ \times .33 \end{array}$ 9. $\begin{array}{r} 5.64 \\ \times 8.1 \end{array}$ 10. $\begin{array}{r} 78.2 \\ \times 60 \end{array}$ 11. $\begin{array}{r} 9.11 \\ \times 2.9 \end{array}$ 12. $\begin{array}{r} 6.03 \\ \times 7.5 \end{array}$

13. $\begin{array}{r} 9.38 \\ \times 1.21 \end{array}$ 14. $\begin{array}{r} 71.5 \\ \times 11.5 \end{array}$ 15. $\begin{array}{r} 6.35 \\ \times 34.6 \end{array}$ 16. $\begin{array}{r} 4.93 \\ \times 2.81 \end{array}$ 17. $\begin{array}{r} 38.5 \\ \times 5.63 \end{array}$ 18. $\begin{array}{r} 5.36 \\ \times 40.2 \end{array}$

Set 35   Multiply.

1. $\begin{array}{r} .23 \\ \times .3 \end{array}$ 2. $\begin{array}{r} .081 \\ \times .7 \end{array}$ 3. $\begin{array}{r} .074 \\ \times .5 \end{array}$ 4. $\begin{array}{r} .49 \\ \times .03 \end{array}$ 5. $\begin{array}{r} .063 \\ \times .08 \end{array}$ 6. $\begin{array}{r} .29 \\ \times .04 \end{array}$

7. $\begin{array}{r} .548 \\ \times .005 \end{array}$ 8. $\begin{array}{r} 70.3 \\ \times .004 \end{array}$ 9. $\begin{array}{r} 9.96 \\ \times .007 \end{array}$ 10. $\begin{array}{r} 78.3 \\ \times .38 \end{array}$ 11. $\begin{array}{r} 914 \\ \times 1.58 \end{array}$ 12. $\begin{array}{r} 59.6 \\ \times 60.8 \end{array}$

Set 36   Divide.

1. $3\overline{)567}$ 2. $2\overline{)586}$ 3. $3\overline{)438}$ 4. $9\overline{)288}$ 5. $7\overline{)329}$

6. $8\overline{)8.56}$ 7. $5\overline{)3.90}$ 8. $6\overline{)4.08}$ 9. $7\overline{)11.2}$ 10. $4\overline{)5.12}$

11. $12\overline{)28.8}$ 12. $15\overline{)9.45}$ 13. $11\overline{)3.85}$ 14. $26\overline{)28.6}$ 15. $35\overline{)94.5}$

16. $73\overline{).1314}$ 17. $55\overline{)4950}$ 18. $36\overline{)26.28}$ 19. $49\overline{)2.793}$ 20. $78\overline{)397.8}$

Set 37   Divide. Round quotients to the nearest tenth.

1. $.3\overline{).386}$ 2. $.5\overline{).348}$ 3. $.6\overline{)2.97}$ 4. $.02\overline{)3.51}$ 5. $.07\overline{)6.28}$

6. $.08\overline{).347}$ 7. $.003\overline{).038}$ 8. $.05\overline{)2.97}$ 9. $.04\overline{).511}$ 10. $.9\overline{).629}$

11. $1.2\overline{)3.482}$ 12. $2.4\overline{)1.356}$ 13. $.31\overline{).9382}$ 14. $.43\overline{).3916}$ 15. $.83\overline{).1374}$

16. $.57\overline{)3.056}$ 17. $.64\overline{).2973}$ 18. $3.9\overline{)5.901}$ 19. $7.8\overline{)2.643}$ 20. $4.2\overline{).3967}$

Set 38   Give the greatest common factor.

1. 8, 12   2. 6, 9   3. 9, 12   4. 12, 16   5. 8, 16   6. 15, 20

7. 9, 15   8. 12, 24   9. 8, 14   10. 24, 48   11. 16, 24   12. 18, 24

13. 15, 30   14. 30, 36   15. 12, 20   16. 15, 25   17. 9, 18   18. 18, 42

Set 39   Give the prime factorization.

1. 4   2. 6   3. 8   4. 9   5. 10   6. 12

7. 14   8. 15   9. 16   10. 18   11. 20   12. 21

13. 22   14. 24   15. 25   16. 26   17. 27   18. 28

Set 40   Give the least common multiple.

1. 2, 5   2. 3, 9   3. 4, 6   4. 4, 8   5. 5, 3   6. 5, 21

7. 4, 7   8. 3, 8   9. 4, 9   10. 2, 10   11. 7, 6   12. 6, 14

13. 18, 12   14. 16, 8   15. 15, 20   16. 8, 10   17. 9, 10   18. 6, 8

19. 1, 10   20. 9, 11   21. 6, 16   22. 12, 5   23. 14, 20   24. 16, 24

Set 41 Solve.

1. $n + 9 = 17$ 2. $n - 6 = 15$ 3. $n - 10 = 13$ 4. $n + 8 = 22$

5. $n - 42 = 35$ 6. $16 + n = 30$ 7. $n - 30 = 16$ 8. $n - 21 = 42$

9. $n - 32 = 15$ 10. $n + 18 = 40$ 11. $n - 14 = 23$ 12. $n + 25 = 40$

13. $16 + n = 35$ 14. $25 + n = 49$ 15. $17 + n = 51$ 16. $n - 18 = 25$

17. $n + 59 = 81$ 18. $n + 38 = 67$ 19. $n - 18 = 25$ 20. $63 + n = 94$

Set 42 Solve.

1. $3n = 12$ 2. $6n = 18$ 3. $5n = 20$ 4. $7n = 56$ 5. $9n = 81$

6. $4n = 36$ 7. $2n = 14$ 8. $6n = 36$ 9. $9n = 45$ 10. $8n = 72$

11. $10n = 40$ 12. $10n = 100$ 13. $12n = 0$ 14. $15n = 30$ 15. $16n = 64$

16. $18n = 72$ 17. $23n = 115$ 18. $15n = 180$ 19. $19n = 190$ 20. $28n = 196$

Set 43 Give the standard numeral.

1. 1^2 2. 5^2 3. 2^2 4. 2^3 5. 1^4 6. 10^2

7. 10^3 8. 4^2 9. 2^4 10. 10^4 11. 1^5 12. 6^2

13. 4^3 14. 2^5 15. 5^3 16. 1^8 17. 3^5 18. 3^3

19. 8^2 20. 2^6 21. 3^4 22. 3^2 23. 5^4 24. 1^9

Set 44 Complete.

1. $3 \text{ m} = \underline{?} \text{ dm}$ 2. $5 \text{ m} = \underline{?} \text{ cm}$ 3. $7 \text{ m} = \underline{?} \text{ mm}$
4. $200 \text{ cm} = \underline{?} \text{ m}$ 5. $4000 \text{ mm} = \underline{?} \text{ m}$ 6. $5.8 \text{ m} = \underline{?} \text{ dm}$
7. $3.9 \text{ cm} = \underline{?} \text{ mm}$ 8. $4.6 \text{ dm} = \underline{?} \text{ cm}$ 9. $5.34 \text{ m} = \underline{?} \text{ dm}$
10. $8.92 \text{ dm} = \underline{?} \text{ mm}$ 11. $3.96 \text{ dm} = \underline{?} \text{ cm}$ 12. $4.83 \text{ m} = \underline{?} \text{ cm}$
13. $5.63 \text{ cm} = \underline{?} \text{ mm}$ 14. $3.82 \text{ m} = \underline{?} \text{ dm}$ 15. $2.96 \text{ cm} = \underline{?} \text{ dm}$
16. $2.94 \text{ cm} = \underline{?} \text{ mm}$ 17. $5.42 \text{ dm} = \underline{?} \text{ cm}$ 18. $384 \text{ mm} = \underline{?} \text{ cm}$
19. $5.39 \text{ mm} = \underline{?} \text{ cm}$ 20. $2.63 \text{ m} = \underline{?} \text{ cm}$ 21. $9.8 \text{ mm} = \underline{?} \text{ dm}$
22. $38 \text{ km} = \underline{?} \text{ m}$ 23. $396 \text{ m} = \underline{?} \text{ km}$ 24. $2.4 \text{ km} = \underline{?} \text{ m}$
25. $52.3 \text{ km} = \underline{?} \text{ m}$ 26. $.74 \text{ km} = \underline{?} \text{ m}$ 27. $.385 \text{ km} = \underline{?} \text{ m}$
28. $8.56 \text{ m} = \underline{?} \text{ cm}$ 29. $.3 \text{ m} = \underline{?} \text{ mm}$ 30. $75.2 \text{ m} = \underline{?} \text{ km}$

Set 45   Give the perimeter (circumference). Use 3.14 as an approximation for π.

1.

34 mm

2.

16 cm

3.
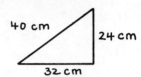
40 cm   24 cm
32 cm

4.
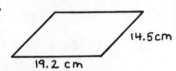
14.5 cm
19.2 cm

5.

3.2 m

6.
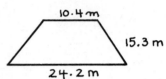
10.4 m   15.3 m
24.2 m

7.
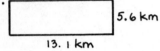
5.6 km
13.1 km

8.
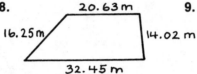
20.63 m
16.25 m   14.02 m
32.45 m

9.

14.2 m

Set 46   Give the area. Use 3.14 as an approximation for π.

1.
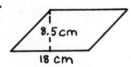
8.5 cm
18 cm

2.

3 m

3.

6 cm
8 cm

4.
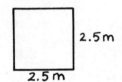
2.5 m
2.5 m

5.
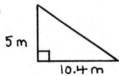
5 m
10.4 m

6.

5 m
4 m
10 m

7.
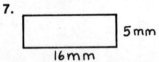
5 mm
16 mm

8.

1.2 m

9.
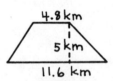
4.8 km
5 km
11.6 km

Set 47   Give the surface area. Use 3.14 as an approximation for π.

1.
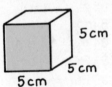
5 cm
5 cm
5 cm

2.
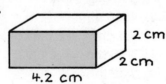
2 cm
2 cm
4.2 cm

3.
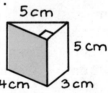
5 cm
5 cm
4 cm   3 cm

4.
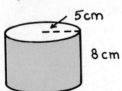
5 cm
8 cm

5.
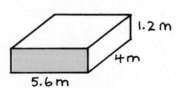
1.2 m
4 m
5.6 m

6.
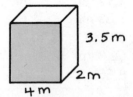
3.5 m
2 m
4 m

Set 48　Find each volume. Use 3.14 as an approximation for π.

1.
5 m
5 m
12 m

2.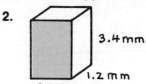
3.4 mm
1.2 mm
1.2 mm

3.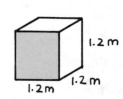
3 m
2 m
2 m

4.
5 m
2 m

5.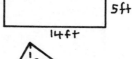
4 m
4.2 m

6.
1.2 m
1.2 m
1.2 m

Set 49　Complete.

1. 3 L = ? mL
2. 2.4 L = ? mL
3. 3.5 L = ? mL
4. 0.24 L = ? mL
5. .356 L = ? mL
6. 2000 mL = ? L
7. 1400 mL = ? L
8. 550 mL = ? L
9. 825 mL = ? L

10. 5 g = ? mg
11. 14 g = ? mg
12. 4000 g = ? mg
13. 5000 g = ? kg
14. 685 g = ? kg
15. 1445 g = ? kg
16. 58 g = ? kg
17. 2.4 kg = ? g
18. .42 kg = ? g

Set 50　Complete.

1. 7 ft = ? in.
2. 3 yd = ? in.
3. 9 yd = ? ft
4. 2 mi = ? ft
5. 4 mi = ? yd
6. 1 mi = ? in.
7. 156 in. = ? ft
8. 138 ft = ? yd
9. 2232 in. = ? yd
10. 40 ft = ? yd ? ft
11. 115 ft = ? yd ? ft
12. 150 in. = ? ft ? in.
13. 205 ft = ? yd ? ft
14. 2 ft 7 in. = ? in.
15. 10 ft 8 in. = ? in.
16. 23 ft 9 in. = ? in.
17. 9 yd 2 ft = ? ft
18. 17 yd 1 ft = ? ft

Set 51　Find each area. Use 3.14 as an approximation for π.

1.
11 ft

2.
5 ft
14 ft

3.
2 yd
5 yd 1 ft

4.
8 in.
1 ft 6 in.

5.
8 ft
16 ft

6.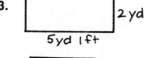
1 ft 1 in.
1 ft 10 in.

7.
7 yd
1 yd 1 ft
9 yd 1 ft

8.
4 ft 8 in.
3 ft
6 ft 8 in.

9.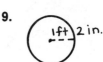
1 ft 2 in.

385

Set 52   Find each volume. Use 3.14 as an approximation for π.

1.
3 ft 4 in.

2.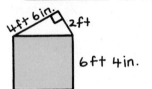
16 in.   34 in.   20 in.

3.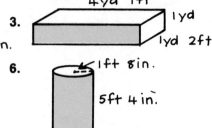
4 yd 1 ft
1 yd
1 yd 2 ft

4.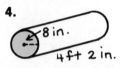
8 in.
4 ft 2 in.

5.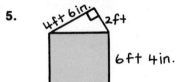
4 ft 6 in.   2 ft
6 ft 4 in.

6.
1 ft 8 in.
5 ft 4 in.

Set 53   Complete.

1. 36 pt = $\underline{?}$ qt

2. 8 qt = $\underline{?}$ gal

3. 24 c = $\underline{?}$ pt

4. 2 gal = $\underline{?}$ pt

5. 6 qt = $\underline{?}$ half-gallons

6. 6 gal = $\underline{?}$ half-gallons

7. 15 qt = $\underline{?}$ gal $\underline{?}$ qt

8. 27 qt = $\underline{?}$ gal $\underline{?}$ qt

9. 23 pt = $\underline{?}$ qt $\underline{?}$ pt

Set 54   Copy and complete.

1. $\frac{1}{2} = \frac{?}{4}$

2. $\frac{1}{3} = \frac{?}{12}$

3. $\frac{2}{3} = \frac{?}{9}$

4. $\frac{5}{6} = \frac{?}{30}$

5. $\frac{3}{4} = \frac{?}{16}$

6. $\frac{3}{2} = \frac{?}{12}$

7. $\frac{5}{2} = \frac{?}{20}$

8. $\frac{4}{4} = \frac{?}{8}$

9. $\frac{7}{8} = \frac{?}{32}$

10. $\frac{1}{3} = \frac{?}{18}$

11. $\frac{1}{4} = \frac{?}{20}$

12. $\frac{3}{5} = \frac{?}{15}$

13. $\frac{1}{2} = \frac{?}{10}$

14. $\frac{3}{8} = \frac{?}{24}$

15. $\frac{3}{4} = \frac{?}{24}$

Set 55   Reduce to lowest terms.

1. $\frac{4}{8}$

2. $\frac{2}{6}$

3. $\frac{4}{6}$

4. $\frac{3}{3}$

5. $\frac{5}{10}$

6. $\frac{2}{8}$

7. $\frac{9}{3}$

8. $\frac{10}{12}$

9. $\frac{12}{3}$

10. $\frac{8}{4}$

11. $\frac{0}{4}$

12. $\frac{2}{10}$

13. $\frac{9}{6}$

14. $\frac{3}{9}$

15. $\frac{10}{10}$

16. $\frac{10}{16}$

17. $\frac{4}{20}$

18. $\frac{15}{12}$

19. $\frac{15}{30}$

20. $\frac{6}{9}$

21. $\frac{5}{20}$

22. $\frac{6}{12}$

23. $\frac{14}{7}$

24. $\frac{0}{6}$

Set 56 $<, =,$ or $>$?

1. $\frac{1}{3} \bullet \frac{1}{2}$

2. $\frac{1}{4} \bullet \frac{1}{5}$

3. $\frac{1}{2} \bullet \frac{6}{12}$

4. $\frac{3}{8} \bullet \frac{1}{3}$

5. $\frac{5}{6} \bullet \frac{15}{18}$

6. $\frac{3}{2} \bullet \frac{2}{3}$

7. $\frac{5}{9} \bullet \frac{1}{2}$

8. $\frac{2}{3} \bullet \frac{5}{8}$

9. $\frac{3}{4} \bullet \frac{5}{6}$

10. $\frac{6}{8} \bullet \frac{3}{4}$

11. $\frac{6}{16} \bullet \frac{3}{8}$

12. $\frac{3}{5} \bullet \frac{6}{10}$

13. $\frac{7}{4} \bullet \frac{5}{2}$

14. $\frac{5}{9} \bullet \frac{9}{5}$

15. $\frac{7}{8} \bullet \frac{5}{6}$

16. $\frac{5}{9} \bullet \frac{2}{3}$

17. $\frac{5}{4} \bullet \frac{5}{3}$

18. $\frac{3}{4} \bullet \frac{4}{3}$

19. $\frac{5}{2} \bullet \frac{15}{6}$

20. $\frac{5}{8} \bullet \frac{5}{6}$

Set 57 Give each sum in lowest terms.

1. $\dfrac{1}{2}$ $+\dfrac{1}{4}$
2. $\dfrac{5}{6}$ $+\dfrac{2}{3}$
3. $\dfrac{3}{3}$ $+\dfrac{2}{2}$
4. $\dfrac{1}{4}$ $+\dfrac{5}{8}$
5. $\dfrac{6}{5}$ $+\dfrac{3}{10}$
6. $\dfrac{5}{12}$ $+\dfrac{1}{4}$
7. $\dfrac{7}{8}$ $+\dfrac{1}{3}$
8. $\dfrac{1}{2}$ $+\dfrac{5}{6}$

9. $\dfrac{3}{2}$ $+\dfrac{2}{3}$
10. $\dfrac{3}{7}$ $+\dfrac{1}{5}$
11. $\dfrac{5}{9}$ $+\dfrac{2}{3}$
12. $\dfrac{1}{2}$ $+\dfrac{1}{3}$
13. $\dfrac{4}{5}$ $+\dfrac{2}{3}$
14. $\dfrac{5}{8}$ $+\dfrac{1}{2}$
15. $\dfrac{3}{5}$ $+\dfrac{1}{3}$
16. $\dfrac{0}{5}$ $+\dfrac{2}{5}$

17. $\dfrac{3}{8}$ $+\dfrac{1}{4}$
18. $\dfrac{2}{3}$ $+\dfrac{3}{4}$
19. $\dfrac{3}{4}$ $+\dfrac{1}{8}$
20. $\dfrac{3}{8}$ $+\dfrac{2}{3}$
21. $\dfrac{5}{6}$ $+\dfrac{7}{10}$
22. $\dfrac{11}{15}$ $+\dfrac{4}{5}$
23. $\dfrac{2}{3}$ $+\dfrac{1}{2}$
24. $\dfrac{7}{3}$ $+\dfrac{7}{4}$

Set 58 Give each difference in lowest terms.

1. $\dfrac{3}{4}$ $-\dfrac{1}{4}$
2. $\dfrac{1}{2}$ $-\dfrac{1}{4}$
3. $\dfrac{5}{9}$ $-\dfrac{1}{3}$
4. 1 $-\dfrac{2}{3}$
5. $\dfrac{2}{3}$ $-\dfrac{1}{3}$
6. $\dfrac{7}{8}$ $-\dfrac{3}{4}$
7. $\dfrac{1}{2}$ $-\dfrac{3}{8}$
8. $\dfrac{3}{10}$ $-\dfrac{1}{5}$

9. $\dfrac{5}{6}$ $-\dfrac{2}{3}$
10. $\dfrac{2}{3}$ $-\dfrac{1}{4}$
11. $\dfrac{7}{4}$ -1
12. $\dfrac{3}{4}$ $-\dfrac{3}{8}$
13. $\dfrac{1}{2}$ $-\dfrac{1}{3}$
14. 2 $-\dfrac{5}{4}$
15. $\dfrac{3}{4}$ $-\dfrac{1}{2}$
16. $\dfrac{7}{2}$ -2

17. $\dfrac{7}{8}$ $-\dfrac{7}{8}$
18. $\dfrac{3}{4}$ $-\dfrac{5}{8}$
19. $\dfrac{7}{9}$ $-\dfrac{0}{3}$
20. $\dfrac{2}{3}$ $-\dfrac{3}{8}$
21. $\dfrac{5}{4}$ $-\dfrac{5}{8}$
22. $\dfrac{3}{4}$ $-\dfrac{2}{3}$
23. $\dfrac{5}{9}$ $-\dfrac{1}{2}$
24. $\dfrac{8}{9}$ $-\dfrac{3}{4}$

Set 59 Copy and complete.

	1.	2.	3.	4.	5.	6.	7.	8.	9.	10.
Fraction	$\dfrac{5}{2}$	$\dfrac{5}{3}$	$\dfrac{23}{4}$	$\dfrac{11}{2}$	$\dfrac{23}{7}$	$\dfrac{15}{4}$	$\dfrac{15}{8}$	$\dfrac{37}{5}$	$\dfrac{18}{4}$	$\dfrac{21}{6}$
Mixed number										

	11.	12.	13.	14.	15.	16.	17.	18.	19.	20.
Fraction										
Mixed number	$5\dfrac{1}{2}$	$3\dfrac{1}{4}$	$2\dfrac{2}{3}$	$3\dfrac{3}{4}$	$2\dfrac{5}{8}$	$1\dfrac{5}{9}$	$3\dfrac{7}{8}$	$5\dfrac{3}{8}$	$6\dfrac{2}{3}$	$8\dfrac{5}{6}$

Set 60 Add.

1. $6\frac{1}{3}$
  $+2\frac{1}{3}$

2. $5\frac{1}{4}$
  $+2\frac{1}{2}$

3. $8\frac{1}{3}$
  $+2\frac{1}{4}$

4. $7\frac{3}{8}$
  $+5\frac{1}{4}$

5. $8\frac{1}{2}$
  $+6\frac{1}{2}$

6. $9\frac{1}{8}$
  $+5\frac{1}{4}$

7. $3\frac{1}{4}$
  $+7\frac{3}{4}$

8. 6
  $+4\frac{2}{5}$

9. $8\frac{7}{8}$
  $+5\frac{1}{4}$

10. $7\frac{5}{8}$
  $+6\frac{1}{2}$

11. $9\frac{3}{4}$
  $+2\frac{1}{2}$

12. $9\frac{3}{4}$
  $+6\frac{3}{8}$

13. $13\frac{2}{3}$
  $+7\frac{2}{3}$

14. $18\frac{3}{8}$
  $+9$

15. $18\frac{2}{5}$
  $+10\frac{3}{4}$

16. $20\frac{1}{6}$
  $+8\frac{1}{3}$

17. $23\frac{5}{9}$
  $+15\frac{2}{3}$

18. $16\frac{7}{8}$
  $+3\frac{3}{8}$

19. $23\frac{3}{5}$
  $+16\frac{1}{2}$

20. $31\frac{1}{3}$
  $+24\frac{2}{9}$

21. $25\frac{1}{2}$
  $+38\frac{3}{4}$

22. $46\frac{3}{4}$
  $+56\frac{2}{3}$

23. $65\frac{1}{4}$
  $+83\frac{1}{8}$

24. $35\frac{3}{4}$
  $+19\frac{5}{8}$

Set 61 Subtract.

1. $6\frac{2}{3}$
  $-3\frac{1}{3}$

2. $5\frac{1}{2}$
  $-2\frac{1}{2}$

3. $8\frac{3}{4}$
  $-6\frac{1}{2}$

4. $9\frac{4}{9}$
  $-2\frac{1}{9}$

5. $9\frac{2}{5}$
  $-3\frac{1}{5}$

6. 8
  $-1\frac{1}{3}$

7. $9\frac{4}{5}$
  $-6\frac{3}{5}$

8. $5\frac{7}{9}$
  $-2\frac{4}{9}$

9. $6\frac{2}{3}$
  $-3\frac{1}{6}$

10. $7\frac{3}{4}$
  $-4\frac{5}{8}$

11. $9\frac{3}{4}$
  $-2\frac{7}{8}$

12. $8\frac{3}{4}$
  $-5\frac{7}{8}$

13. $14\frac{1}{3}$
  $-5\frac{2}{3}$

14. $17\frac{1}{8}$
  $-8\frac{3}{4}$

15. $15\frac{3}{5}$
  $-5\frac{7}{10}$

16. $19\frac{1}{2}$
  $-4\frac{3}{4}$

17. 21
  $-9\frac{3}{5}$

18. $18\frac{1}{4}$
  $-6\frac{3}{5}$

19. $24\frac{5}{9}$
  $-17\frac{2}{3}$

20. 44
  $-19\frac{5}{8}$

21. $32\frac{1}{6}$
  $-18\frac{1}{8}$

22. 21
  $-13\frac{2}{3}$

23. $25\frac{1}{3}$
  $-16\frac{1}{2}$

24. $27\frac{2}{3}$
  $-18\frac{3}{4}$

Set 62 Give each product in lowest terms.

1. $\dfrac{1}{3} \times \dfrac{1}{3}$ 2. $\dfrac{2}{5} \times \dfrac{2}{5}$ 3. $\dfrac{4}{7} \times \dfrac{2}{5}$ 4. $\dfrac{2}{3} \times \dfrac{4}{4}$ 5. $\dfrac{5}{8} \times \dfrac{0}{6}$ 6. $\dfrac{5}{9} \times \dfrac{3}{10}$

7. $\dfrac{3}{7} \times \dfrac{1}{8}$ 8. $\dfrac{1}{2} \times \dfrac{3}{8}$ 9. $\dfrac{1}{2} \times \dfrac{1}{2}$ 10. $\dfrac{1}{4} \times \dfrac{2}{2}$ 11. $\dfrac{2}{3} \times \dfrac{3}{10}$ 12. $\dfrac{3}{4} \times \dfrac{4}{3}$

13. $\dfrac{1}{4} \times \dfrac{1}{2}$ 14. $\dfrac{7}{4} \times \dfrac{4}{10}$ 15. $\dfrac{3}{4} \times \dfrac{8}{5}$ 16. $\dfrac{2}{3} \times \dfrac{3}{7}$ 17. $\dfrac{5}{8} \times \dfrac{7}{5}$ 18. $\dfrac{1}{5} \times \dfrac{1}{4}$

19. $\dfrac{2}{3} \times \dfrac{3}{3}$ 20. $\dfrac{3}{4} \times \dfrac{8}{7}$ 21. $\dfrac{2}{3} \times \dfrac{3}{2}$ 22. $\dfrac{4}{3} \times \dfrac{9}{2}$ 23. $\dfrac{5}{8} \times \dfrac{8}{5}$ 24. $\dfrac{3}{5} \times \dfrac{10}{9}$

Set 63 Compute.

1. $\dfrac{1}{2}$ of 18 2. $\dfrac{2}{3}$ of 27 3. $\dfrac{2}{3}$ of 12 4. $\dfrac{5}{9}$ of 36 5. $\dfrac{7}{4}$ of 36

6. $\dfrac{5}{2}$ of 10 7. $\dfrac{3}{8}$ of 24 8. $\dfrac{1}{3}$ of 21 9. $\dfrac{5}{7}$ of 14 10. $\dfrac{1}{5}$ of 20

11. $\dfrac{3}{5}$ of 35 12. $\dfrac{9}{8}$ of 24 13. $\dfrac{7}{8}$ of 56 14. $\dfrac{5}{4}$ of 40 15. $\dfrac{3}{4}$ of 40

16. $\dfrac{5}{8}$ of 16.8 17. $\dfrac{1}{4}$ of 12.8 18. $\dfrac{4}{9}$ of 19.8 19. $\dfrac{5}{6}$ of 73.8 20. $\dfrac{2}{5}$ of 12

Set 64 Give the reciprocal of each number.

1. $\dfrac{1}{2}$ 2. $\dfrac{1}{4}$ 3. $\dfrac{1}{3}$ 4. $\dfrac{1}{5}$ 5. $\dfrac{2}{3}$ 6. $\dfrac{3}{4}$ 7. $\dfrac{3}{8}$ 8. $\dfrac{5}{8}$

9. $\dfrac{7}{8}$ 10. 1 11. 2 12. 3 13. 4 14. 5 15. 6 16. 7

17. $\dfrac{7}{2}$ 18. $\dfrac{7}{4}$ 19. $\dfrac{5}{6}$ 20. $\dfrac{5}{9}$ 21. $\dfrac{4}{9}$ 22. $\dfrac{5}{2}$ 23. $\dfrac{11}{6}$ 24. $\dfrac{12}{5}$

Set 65 Give the quotient in lowest terms.

1. $\dfrac{1}{2} \div \dfrac{2}{3}$ 2. $\dfrac{4}{9} \div \dfrac{1}{3}$ 3. $\dfrac{3}{2} \div \dfrac{3}{4}$ 4. $\dfrac{3}{4} \div \dfrac{1}{8}$ 5. $\dfrac{9}{5} \div \dfrac{3}{8}$ 6. $\dfrac{5}{6} \div \dfrac{1}{2}$

7. $\dfrac{1}{8} \div \dfrac{9}{5}$ 8. $\dfrac{1}{5} \div \dfrac{5}{4}$ 9. $3 \div \dfrac{2}{3}$ 10. $\dfrac{1}{3} \div \dfrac{2}{3}$ 11. $\dfrac{3}{5} \div \dfrac{3}{8}$ 12. $5 \div \dfrac{5}{3}$

13. $\dfrac{3}{10} \div \dfrac{1}{5}$ 14. $\dfrac{5}{8} \div \dfrac{1}{4}$ 15. $6 \div \dfrac{3}{8}$ 16. $\dfrac{3}{10} \div \dfrac{3}{4}$ 17. $\dfrac{1}{2} \div \dfrac{7}{2}$ 18. $\dfrac{7}{4} \div \dfrac{3}{2}$

19. $\dfrac{5}{8} \div 2$ 20. $\dfrac{3}{8} \div 5$ 21. $\dfrac{1}{4} \div \dfrac{7}{8}$ 22. $\dfrac{2}{3} \div \dfrac{1}{6}$ 23. $\dfrac{2}{5} \div 4$ 24. $\dfrac{0}{4} \div \dfrac{1}{2}$

Set 66   Simplify.

1. $\dfrac{\frac{1}{2}}{\frac{1}{4}}$ 2. $\dfrac{\frac{7}{8}}{\frac{1}{3}}$ 3. $\dfrac{\frac{5}{2}}{\frac{3}{4}}$ 4. $\dfrac{\frac{1}{2}}{\frac{5}{6}}$ 5. $\dfrac{\frac{6}{5}}{\frac{3}{10}}$ 6. $\dfrac{\frac{3}{2}}{\frac{2}{3}}$ 7. $\dfrac{\frac{3}{5}}{\frac{1}{3}}$ 8. $\dfrac{\frac{3}{8}}{\frac{1}{4}}$

9. $\dfrac{\frac{4}{5}}{\frac{2}{3}}$ 10. $\dfrac{\frac{1}{4}}{\frac{5}{8}}$ 11. $\dfrac{\frac{5}{6}}{\frac{2}{3}}$ 12. $\dfrac{\frac{5}{8}}{\frac{1}{2}}$ 13. $\dfrac{\frac{2}{3}}{\frac{3}{4}}$ 14. $\dfrac{\frac{5}{12}}{\frac{1}{4}}$ 15. $\dfrac{\frac{3}{8}}{\frac{3}{4}}$ 16. $\dfrac{\frac{1}{2}}{\frac{1}{3}}$

17. $\dfrac{\frac{3}{4}}{\frac{1}{8}}$ 18. $\dfrac{\frac{3}{7}}{\frac{1}{5}}$ 19. $\dfrac{\frac{3}{8}}{\frac{2}{3}}$ 20. $\dfrac{\frac{5}{6}}{\frac{7}{10}}$ 21. $\dfrac{\frac{5}{9}}{\frac{2}{3}}$ 22. $\dfrac{\frac{2}{3}}{\frac{1}{2}}$ 23. $\dfrac{\frac{7}{3}}{\frac{7}{4}}$ 24. $\dfrac{\frac{5}{9}}{\frac{5}{3}}$

Set 67   Copy and complete.

	1.	2.	3.	4.	5.	6.	7.	8.	9.	10.
Fraction or Mixed Number	$\frac{1}{5}$	$\frac{7}{20}$	$\frac{3}{8}$	$\frac{3}{5}$	$\frac{7}{8}$	$1\frac{1}{4}$	$1\frac{1}{2}$	$2\frac{3}{10}$	$2\frac{4}{5}$	$3\frac{1}{2}$
Decimal										

	11.	12.	13.	14.	15.	16.	17.	18.	19.	20.
Fraction or Mixed Number										
Decimal	0.25	0.3	0.5	0.625	0.8	1.1	1.5	1.75	2.4	2.6

Set 68   Change to a mixed decimal.

1. $\frac{1}{3}$ 2. $\frac{1}{6}$ 3. $\frac{5}{7}$ 4. $\frac{2}{3}$ 5. $\frac{1}{9}$ 6. $\frac{10}{3}$ 7. $\frac{5}{6}$ 8. $\frac{5}{9}$

9. $\frac{11}{6}$ 10. $\frac{7}{3}$ 11. $\frac{4}{9}$ 12. $\frac{2}{9}$ 13. $\frac{5}{3}$ 14. $\frac{4}{3}$ 15. $\frac{10}{9}$ 16. $\frac{7}{6}$

17. $\frac{13}{6}$ 18. $\frac{1}{11}$ 19. $\frac{1}{18}$ 20. $\frac{5}{18}$ 21. $\frac{2}{11}$ 22. $\frac{7}{18}$ 23. $\frac{11}{18}$ 24. $\frac{5}{11}$

Set 69 Give each product.

1. $4\frac{1}{2} \times 2$
2. $2\frac{1}{3} \times 7$
3. $7\frac{1}{4} \times 6$
4. $6\frac{1}{3} \times 5$
5. $3\frac{1}{4} \times 4$

6. $2\frac{2}{3} \times 2\frac{1}{2}$
7. $3\frac{1}{4} \times 3\frac{1}{3}$
8. $3\frac{3}{4} \times 4\frac{1}{4}$
9. $1\frac{3}{8} \times 1\frac{1}{4}$
10. $2\frac{1}{5} \times 1\frac{1}{4}$

11. $4\frac{2}{3} \times 3\frac{1}{2}$
12. $1\frac{1}{5} \times 2\frac{3}{4}$
13. $1\frac{1}{2} \times 1\frac{1}{2}$
14. $2\frac{3}{8} \times 3\frac{1}{4}$
15. $4\frac{2}{3} \times 1\frac{3}{4}$

16. $1\frac{3}{4} \times 1\frac{1}{6}$
17. $3\frac{1}{3} \times 2\frac{1}{5}$
18. $2\frac{1}{9} \times 2\frac{1}{4}$
19. $3\frac{2}{3} \times 2\frac{1}{2}$
20. $2\frac{1}{4} \times 2\frac{3}{4}$

Set 70 Give each quotient.

1. $1\frac{1}{4} \div 1\frac{1}{4}$
2. $3\frac{1}{2} \div 1\frac{3}{4}$
3. $5 \div 1\frac{1}{2}$
4. $7\frac{1}{3} \div 2\frac{1}{4}$
5. $7\frac{2}{3} \div 4$

6. $2\frac{2}{9} \div 1$
7. $9\frac{1}{2} \div 3\frac{1}{2}$
8. $3\frac{3}{4} \div 3$
9. $0 \div 5\frac{1}{3}$
10. $3 \div 6\frac{2}{3}$

11. $6\frac{2}{3} \div 8\frac{3}{4}$
12. $2\frac{7}{8} \div 7\frac{2}{3}$
13. $8\frac{1}{2} \div 2\frac{1}{8}$
14. $8\frac{1}{4} \div 4\frac{2}{3}$
15. $9\frac{1}{3} \div 2\frac{3}{5}$

16. $4\frac{5}{8} \div 6\frac{3}{4}$
17. $4\frac{1}{2} \div 3\frac{1}{6}$
18. $5\frac{1}{4} \div 5\frac{4}{5}$
19. $6\frac{1}{3} \div 7\frac{1}{5}$
20. $6\frac{3}{5} \div 8\frac{2}{3}$

Set 71 Solve.

1. $\frac{2}{3} = \frac{x}{9}$
2. $\frac{5}{9} = \frac{20}{x}$
3. $\frac{5}{8} = \frac{x}{96}$
4. $\frac{24}{x} = \frac{3}{5}$

5. $\frac{3}{8} = \frac{5}{x}$
6. $\frac{7}{6} = \frac{8}{x}$
7. $\frac{8}{x} = \frac{5}{6}$
8. $\frac{9}{x} = \frac{3}{7}$

9. $\frac{6}{1} = \frac{8}{x}$
10. $\frac{3}{4} = \frac{x}{5}$
11. $\frac{8}{5} = \frac{7}{x}$
12. $\frac{x}{11} = \frac{7}{8}$

13. $\frac{12}{x} = \frac{4}{3}$
14. $\frac{x}{14} = \frac{11}{2}$
15. $\frac{15}{x} = \frac{3}{2}$
16. $\frac{17}{x} = \frac{5}{7}$

17. $\frac{9}{8} = \frac{x}{6}$
18. $\frac{8}{3} = \frac{x}{9}$
19. $\frac{13}{x} = \frac{4}{5}$
20. $\frac{16}{x} = \frac{9}{5}$

Set 72 Solve.

1. $\frac{2}{4} = \frac{n}{2}$
2. $\frac{5}{6} = \frac{n}{12}$
3. $\frac{n}{9} = \frac{4}{3}$
4. $\frac{5}{6} = \frac{11}{n}$

5. $\frac{8}{3} = \frac{13}{n}$
6. $\frac{3}{2} = \frac{5}{n}$
7. $\frac{3}{12} = \frac{1}{n}$
8. $\frac{7}{2} = \frac{9}{n}$

9. $\frac{n}{11} = \frac{3}{8}$
10. $\frac{7}{8} = \frac{n}{4}$
11. $\frac{n}{14} = \frac{7}{4}$
12. $\frac{20}{24} = \frac{n}{12}$

13. $\frac{6}{7} = \frac{9}{n}$
14. $\frac{n}{18} = \frac{5}{4}$
15. $\frac{3}{n} = \frac{4}{7}$
16. $\frac{5}{9} = \frac{8}{n}$

Set 73　Copy and complete.

	1.	2.	3.	4.	5.	6.	7.	8.	9.	10.
Fraction	$\frac{9}{100}$	$\frac{17}{100}$	$\frac{33}{100}$							
Decimal				.43	.57	.59				
Percent							21%	37%	83%	97%

	11.	12.	13.	14.	15.	16.	17.	18.	19.	20.
Fraction	$\frac{1}{4}$	$\frac{1}{2}$	$\frac{3}{4}$	$\frac{3}{5}$						
Decimal					.8	.4	.2			
Percent								30%	85%	90%

Set 74　Copy and complete.

	1.	2.	3.	4.	5.	6.	7.	8.	9.	10.
Decimal	0.34	3.4	0.034	0.65	6.5	0.065	0.43	0.671	1.251	2
Percent										

	11.	12.	13.	14.	15.	16.	17.	18.	19.	20.
Decimal										
Percent	17.2%	1.72%	172%	38.6%	4.2%	42%	156.2%	7%	70%	.7%

Set 75　Copy and complete.

	1.	2.	3.	4.	5.	6.	7.	8.	9.	10.
Fraction	$\frac{1}{3}$	$\frac{1}{6}$	$\frac{2}{3}$	$\frac{5}{6}$	$\frac{1}{8}$	$\frac{3}{8}$	$\frac{4}{3}$	$\frac{7}{6}$	$\frac{5}{8}$	$\frac{9}{8}$
Percent										

	11.	12.	13.	14.	15.	16.	17.	18.	19.	20.
Fraction	$\frac{1}{16}$	$\frac{3}{16}$	$\frac{5}{16}$	$\frac{7}{16}$	$\frac{9}{16}$	$\frac{7}{5}$	$\frac{5}{3}$	$\frac{7}{4}$	$\frac{6}{5}$	$\frac{5}{2}$
Percent										

Set 76   Solve.

1. 25% of 80 = n
2. 50% of 72 = n
3. 20% of 60 = n
4. 40% of 10 = n
5. 100% of 63 = n
6. 150% of 8 = n
7. 125% of 20 = n
8. $33\frac{1}{3}$% of 15 = n
9. $12\frac{1}{2}$% of 40 = n
10. 25% of 28 = n
11. 75% of 78 = n
12. 60% of 90 = n
13. 200% of 12 = n
14. 500% of 30 = n
15. 50% of 30 = n
16. 5% of 30 = n
17. 30% of 60 = n
18. 60% of 30 = n

Set 77   Solve.

1. 6% of 100 = n
2. 50% of 39 = n
3. 20% of 45 = n
4. 12% of 25 = n
5. 175% of 12 = n
6. 8% of 50 = n
7. 125% of 200 = n
8. $37\frac{1}{2}$% of 24 = n
9. 25% of 48 = n
10. $87\frac{1}{2}$% of 40 = n
11. 10% of 60 = n
12. 150% of 52 = n
13. $12\frac{1}{2}$% of 40 = n
14. 200% of 19 = n
15. $16\frac{2}{3}$% of 42 = n
16. 40% of 8 = n
17. $83\frac{1}{3}$% of 24 = n
18. $33\frac{1}{3}$% of 37 = n

Set 78   Solve.

1. 4% of n = 2
2. 75% of n = 12
3. 9% of n = 9
4. 50% of n = 13
5. 100% of n = 29
6. $66\frac{2}{3}$% of n = 18
7. $33\frac{1}{3}$% of n = 23
8. 25% of n = 31
9. 10% of n = 8
10. 42% of n = 21
11. $12\frac{1}{2}$% of n = 19
12. $83\frac{1}{3}$% of n = 25
13. $62\frac{1}{2}$% of n = 25
14. 80% of n = 74
15. 200% of n = 39
16. $16\frac{2}{3}$% of n = 43
17. 20% of n = 18
18. $37\frac{1}{2}$% of n = 12

Set 79   Compute the unit price (cents per gram).
Round to the nearest hundredth of a cent.

1. 39 g for 78¢
2. 100 g for 60¢
3. 60 g for 54¢
4. 40 g for 92¢
5. 120 g for 84¢
6. 165 g for 43¢
7. 65 g for 48¢
8. 58.5 g for 52¢
9. 95.5 g for 75¢
10. 62.5 g for 56¢
11. 68.75 g for 64¢
12. 200 g for 72¢

Set 80   Compute the prices.

1. 2 for 89¢
   a. 1 costs ?
   b. 3 cost ?

2. 3 for 71¢
   a. 1 costs ?
   b. 2 cost ?

3. 4 for 57¢
   a. 1 costs ?
   b. 3 cost ?

4. 3 for 79¢
   a. 1 costs ?
   b. 4 cost ?

5. 5 for 83¢
   a. 1 costs ?
   b. 4 cost ?

6. 4 for 95¢
   a. 1 costs ?
   b. 5 cost ?

7. 2 for 93¢
   a. 1 costs ?
   b. 5 cost ?

8. 3 for $1.13
   a. 1 costs ?
   b. 5 cost ?

9. 4 for $1.93
   a. 1 costs ?
   b. 3 cost ?

10. 2 for $1.19
    a. 1 costs ?
    b. 7 cost ?

11. 3 for $2.15
    a. 1 costs ?
    b. 8 cost ?

12. 5 for $2.74
    a. 1 costs ?
    b. 7 cost ?

Set 81   Copy and complete.

	1.	2.	3.	4.	5.	6.	7.	8.	9.	10.
Regular Price	$80	$60	$50	$18	$43	$62	$73	$81	$56	$42
Percent of Discount	10%	15%	12%	18%	25%	32%	30%	50%	$33\frac{1}{3}\%$	$66\frac{2}{3}\%$
Sale Price										

	11.	12.	13.	14.	15.	16.	17.	18.	19.	20.
Regular Price	$18.50	$16.75	$23.40	$26.80	$52.40	$36.75	$81.50	$72.30	$65.45	$72.48
Percent of Discount	10%	20%	15%	30%	50%	$37\frac{1}{2}\%$	$33\frac{1}{3}\%$	$66\frac{2}{3}\%$	$62\frac{1}{2}\%$	$12\frac{1}{2}\%$
Sale Price										

Set 82 Copy and complete.

	Principal	Rate	Time	Interest
1.	$100	6%	1 year	
2.	$300	9%	2 years	
3.	$150	8%	$1\frac{1}{2}$ years	
4.	$275	8%	6 months	
5.	$450	10%	8 months	
6.	$600	9%	9 months	
7.	$1000	$8\frac{1}{2}$%	3 months	
8.	$850	10%	2 months	
9.	$1125	10%	4 months	
10.	$3600	$9\frac{1}{2}$%	18 months	
11.	$2100	$8\frac{1}{4}$%	$2\frac{1}{2}$ years	
12.	$8000	$9\frac{3}{4}$%	$1\frac{3}{4}$ years	

Set 83 Complete.

Event

Toss this die.

1. $P(1) = $ _?_
2. P(even number) $= $ _?_
3. $P(2) = $ _?_
4. P(not 2) $= $ _?_
5. P(odd number) $= $ _?_
6. P(prime number) $= $ _?_
7. P(number less than 2) $= $ _?_
8. P(number greater than 3) $= $ _?_
9. P(factor of 12) $= $ _?_
10. P(multiple of 2) $= $ _?_

Set 84   Complete.

First Event
Spin this spinner:

7. $P(3, blue) = \underline{?}$
9. $P(number > 3, red) = \underline{?}$

Second Event
Then (without looking)
pick a marble:

1. $P(1, red) = \underline{?}$
2. $P(2, green) = \underline{?}$
3. $P(odd, red) = \underline{?}$
4. $P(odd, blue) = \underline{?}$
5. $P(even, blue) = \underline{?}$
6. $P(even, red) = \underline{?}$
8. $P(odd, green) = \underline{?}$
10. $P(number < 3, green) = \underline{?}$

Set 85   Find the range, mean, and median.

1. 3, 5, 8, 8, 10, 11, 14
2. 5, 6, 9, 9, 11, 12
3. 32, 38, 46, 49, 50
4. 26, 32, 34, 41, 42, 42, 46
5. 68, 69, 70, 71, 72
6. 39, 43, 56, 57, 65
7. 45, 45, 45, 45, 45, 45
8. 83, 86, 86, 89, 90, 91
9. 126, 124, 132, 128, 130
10. 153, 162, 147, 165, 147

Set 86   < or >?

1. $^{+}5 \bullet ^{+}4$
2. $^{-}5 \bullet ^{+}4$
3. $^{-}5 \bullet ^{-}4$
4. $^{+}5 \bullet ^{-}4$
5. $^{+}9 \bullet ^{-}8$
6. $^{+}6 \bullet ^{+}5$
7. $^{-}9 \bullet ^{-}8$
8. $^{-}5 \bullet ^{+}4$
9. $^{-}14 \bullet ^{+}16$
10. $^{+}9 \bullet ^{-}12$
11. $^{+}1 \bullet 0$
12. $0 \bullet ^{-}1$
13. $^{+}12 \bullet ^{-}13$
14. $^{+}12 \bullet ^{+}13$
15. $^{-}12 \bullet ^{+}13$
16. $^{-}12 \bullet ^{-}13$
17. $^{+}18 \bullet ^{+}19$
18. $^{+}32 \bullet ^{+}33$
19. $^{-}16 \bullet ^{-}15$
20. $^{+}12 \bullet ^{-}12$
21. $^{-}36 \bullet ^{+}35$
22. $^{-}13 \bullet ^{+}13$
23. $^{-}23 \bullet ^{-}24$
24. $^{-}18 \bullet ^{+}19$

Set 87   Give each sum.

1. $^{+}5 + ^{+}9$
2. $^{+}9 + ^{-}5$
3. $^{-}8 + 0$
4. $^{-}5 + ^{-}6$
5. $^{+}9 + ^{+}3$
6. $^{-}9 + ^{-}5$
7. $^{-}6 + ^{-}6$
8. $^{+}9 + 0$
9. $^{-}15 + ^{+}11$
10. $^{-}11 + ^{-}3$
11. $^{+}8 + ^{-}9$
12. $^{-}9 + ^{+}13$
13. $^{+}11 + ^{-}11$
14. $^{-}1 + ^{-}10$
15. $^{+}7 + ^{+}9$
16. $^{-}14 + ^{+}14$
17. $^{+}13 + ^{+}5$
18. $^{-}19 + 0$
19. $^{-}13 + ^{+}13$
20. $^{+}13 + ^{-}20$
21. $^{-}16 + ^{+}16$
22. $0 + 0$
23. $^{+}12 + ^{-}5$
24. $^{+}11 + ^{+}9$

Set 88   Give each difference.

1. $^{+}6 - ^{+}4$
2. $^{+}6 - ^{-}4$
3. $^{+}7 - 0$
4. $^{-}5 - ^{+}7$
5. $0 - ^{-}6$
6. $^{-}5 - ^{-}3$
7. $^{-}3 - ^{+}9$
8. $^{+}12 - ^{+}5$
9. $^{-}2 - ^{-}6$
10. $^{-}9 - ^{+}8$
11. $^{+}8 - ^{+}3$
12. $^{-}8 - ^{-}2$
13. $^{+}3 - ^{-}9$
14. $0 - 0$
15. $^{+}12 - ^{-}3$
16. $^{-}2 - ^{-}9$
17. $^{+}3 - ^{+}8$
18. $^{-}4 - ^{+}11$
19. $^{-}9 - ^{-}4$
20. $^{+}4 - ^{-}6$
21. $^{-}4 - ^{+}6$
22. $^{+}13 - ^{-}6$
23. $^{+}6 - ^{+}14$
24. $^{-}1 - ^{-}5$

Set 89 Give each product.

1. $^+5 \times {}^+4$
2. $^+7 \times {}^-3$
3. $^-8 \times {}^-8$
4. $^-6 \times {}^+6$
5. $^-6 \times {}^+2$
6. $0 \times {}^-4$
7. $^+5 \times {}^+7$
8. $^-4 \times {}^+3$
9. $^-3 \times {}^-9$
10. $^+9 \times {}^-9$
11. $^-5 \times {}^-8$
12. $^-9 \times {}^-5$
13. $^-7 \times {}^+9$
14. $^+6 \times {}^+4$
15. $^+5 \times {}^-9$
16. $^-8 \times {}^-9$
17. $^+9 \times {}^+8$
18. $^+7 \times {}^-7$
19. $^-4 \times {}^-8$
20. $^+8 \times {}^-9$
21. $^-9 \times {}^-6$
22. 0×0
23. $^+6 \times {}^-8$
24. $^+6 \times {}^+9$

Set 90 Give each quotient.

1. $^+24 \div {}^-6$
2. $^+56 \div {}^-7$
3. $^-32 \div {}^+8$
4. $^-27 \div {}^-3$
5. $^-35 \div {}^+7$
6. $^-36 \div {}^-6$
7. $0 \div {}^-7$
8. $^+32 \div {}^+8$
9. $^+36 \div {}^+4$
10. $^-8 \div {}^-8$
11. $^+48 \div {}^-6$
12. $^-45 \div {}^-9$
13. $^-36 \div {}^+9$
14. $^+48 \div {}^+6$
15. $^-54 \div {}^+6$
16. $^-21 \div {}^+3$
17. $^+49 \div {}^-7$
18. $^-28 \div {}^-4$
19. $^+63 \div {}^-9$
20. $0 \div {}^+9$
21. $^+81 \div {}^+9$
22. $^+72 \div {}^-9$
23. $^-48 \div {}^-8$
24. $^+64 \div {}^-8$

Glossary

acute angle An angle whose measure is less than 90°.

addend A number used in an addition problem.

adding 0 property The sum of any number and zero is that number.

$$29 + 0 = 29$$

angle A figure formed by two rays with the same endpoint.

arc Part of a circle.

area The number of unit squares that cover a figure.

associative property of addition Changing the grouping of the addends does not change the sum.

$$(9 + 4) + 6 = 9 + (4 + 6)$$

associative property of multiplication Changing the grouping of the factors does not change the product.

$$(7 \times 25) \times 4 = 7 \times (25 \times 4)$$

average The average of 4, 5, 5, 7, and 9 is 6. To find the average, add the numbers and divide by the number of numbers.

axes Two perpendicular lines used as a reference for graphing number pairs (ordered pairs).

The horizontal line is the first coordinate axis and the vertical line is the second coordinate axis.

bisect To cut into halves.
The segment is bisected.

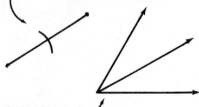

The angle is bisected.

budget A plan for using money.

canceling Dividing a numerator and a denominator in the product of two fractions by a common factor before multiplying.

$$\frac{4\cancel{6}}{15} \times \frac{1}{\cancel{6}3}$$

Celsius temperature (°C) The metric temperature scale in which 0°C is the freezing point of water and 100°C is the boiling point of water.

centimeter A metric unit of length. One centimeter is one hundredth of a meter.

circle A curved plane figure with all points a given distance from the center.

circumference The distance around a circle.

common denominator A common denominator for $\frac{1}{2}$ and $\frac{1}{3}$ is 6, because $\frac{1}{2} = \frac{3}{6}$ and $\frac{1}{3} = \frac{2}{6}$. A common denominator is a common multiple of the denominators of two fractions.

common factor 2 is a common factor of 4 and 6, because 2 is a factor of 4 and a factor of 6.

common multiple 30 is a common multiple of 5 and 6, because it is a multiple of 5 and a multiple of 6.

commutative property of addition Changing the order of the addends does not change the sum.

$$23 + 89 = 89 + 23$$

commutative property of multiplication Changing the order of the factors does not change the product.

$$19 \times 54 = 54 \times 19$$

complex fraction A fraction in which either the numerator or the denominator or both are fractions.

$$\frac{\frac{6}{7}}{\frac{2}{3}} \qquad \frac{8}{\frac{3}{4}} \qquad \frac{\frac{5}{2}}{6}$$

composite number A whole number other than 0 having more than two factors.

4, 6, 8, 9

1, 2, 4   1, 2, 3, 6

congruent figures Figures that have the same size and shape.

conversion fraction A fraction equivalent to 1 that is multiplied by a measurement to convert the measurement from one unit to another unit.

$$2 \text{ ft} \times \frac{12 \text{ in.}}{1 \text{ ft}} = 24 \text{ in.}$$

coordinates A pair of numbers that locates a point on a grid.

corresponding parts In congruent figures, the parts that fit are called corresponding parts.

cube A rectangular solid with all edges the same length.

customary system The system of measurement that uses foot, quart, pound, and Fahrenheit temperature.

cylinder A three-dimensional figure formed by two congruent circular regions in parallel planes and a "curved" rectangular region.

decagon A polygon with ten sides.

decimal A number written in our place-value system with a decimal point before the tenths place.

degree A unit for measuring angles. This is a 1° (1 degree) angle.

denominator In $\frac{2}{3}$, the denominator is 3.

diameter The distance across a circle through its center.

difference The answer to a subtraction problem.

digits The basic symbols used to write numerals in a place-value system. In our base ten system the digits are 0, 1, 2, 3, 4, 5, 6, 7, 8, and 9.

discount An amount subtracted from the regular price of an item.

distributive property of multiplication A product can be written as the sum of two products.

$$3 \times (10 + 2) = (3 \times 10) + (3 \times 2)$$

dividend The number that is divided.

$$3\overline{)18} \qquad 18 \div 3 = 6$$
dividend

divisor The number that one divides by.

$$4\overline{)36} \qquad 36 \div 4 = 9$$
divisor

down payment The first amount paid when buying on an installment plan.

equally likely outcomes Outcomes such that each has the same chance of occurring.

equation A sentence with an equals sign, such as $3 \times 9 = 27$.

equilateral triangle A triangle with all sides congruent.

equivalent fractions Fractions for the same number. $\frac{1}{2}, \frac{2}{4}$, and $\frac{3}{6}$ are equivalent fractions.

error of measurement The difference between the measurement of a quantity and the quantity itself.

even number A multiple of 2.

expanded numeral A numeral used to show the place value of each digit in a standard numeral.

$$248 = 200 + 40 + 8$$

exponent An exponent tells the number of factors.

exponent
$$2^3 = \underbrace{2 \times 2 \times 2}_{3 \text{ factors}}$$

factors Numbers used in a multiplication problem.

$$\begin{array}{r} 8 \leftarrow \text{factor} \\ \times 6 \leftarrow \text{factor} \\ \hline 48 \leftarrow \text{product} \end{array}$$

formula A general rule expressed by using symbols.

$$A = l \times w$$

function A set of number pairs of which no two first numbers are the same.

Function rule
$n \rightarrow n + 3$
(0, 3)
(1, 4)
(2, 5)

gram A metric unit of weight (mass). One gram is one thousandth of a kilogram.

graph A picture used to show numerical information.

greatest common divisor The greatest factor of each of two or more whole numbers.

greatest common factor (GCF) The greatest number that is a factor of each of two or more numbers.

4 is the GCF of 8 and 12.

greatest possible error Half of the unit used in making the measurement.

hectare A metric unit of area. One hectare is 10,000 square meters.

heptagon A polygon with seven sides.

hexagon A polygon with six sides.

installment buying A way of buying expensive items. You pay part of the cost (the down payment) when you get the item and then agree to pay a certain amount each month for a certain number of months.

integers The numbers . . ., ⁻5, ⁻4, ⁻3, ⁻2, ⁻1, 0, ⁺1, ⁺2, ⁺3, ⁺4, ⁺5, ...

interest A payment for the use of money.

intersecting lines Lines that meet at a point.

intersection of sets
The intersection of set A and set B, $A \cap B$, is the set of all elements that belong to both A and B.

$A = \{0, 1, 2, 3\}$
$B = \{2, 3, 4, 5\}$
$A \cap B = \{2, 3\}$

isosceles trapezoid
A trapezoid with 2 congruent sides.

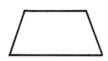

isosceles triangle A triangle with two congruent sides.

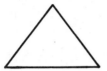

kilogram A unit of weight (mass) in the metric system. A kilogram is 1000 grams.

kiloliter A unit of volume in the metric system. One kiloliter is 1000 liters.

kilometer A unit of length in the metric system. A kilometer is 1000 meters.

kite A quadrilateral with 2 pairs of congruent sides.

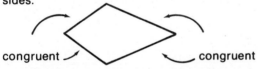

congruent   congruent

least common denominator The least common multiple of the denominators of two or more fractions.

least common multiple The least (smallest) common multiple of two or more numbers. The least common multiple of 6 and 15 is 30.

line of symmetry If a figure can be folded along a line so the two parts of the figure match, the fold line is a line of symmetry.

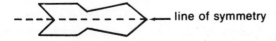
line of symmetry

liter A unit of volume in the metric system.

mean The average of a set of numbers.

median The median of a set of numbers is a number such that half of the numbers in the set are less and half are greater.

$\{63, 68, 74, 81, 86\}$

The median is 74.

median of a triangle A segment joining a vertex of a triangle with the midpoint of the opposite side.

meter A unit of length in the metric system. A meter is 100 centimeters.

metric system An international system of measurement that uses meter, liter, gram, and Celsius temperature.

midpoint The point that bisects a segment.

milligram A metric unit of weight (mass). One milligram is one thousandth of a gram.

milliliter A metric unit of volume. One milliliter is one thousandth of a liter.

millimeter A metric unit of length. One millimeter is one thousandth of a meter.

mixed number A number that has a whole-number part and a fraction part. $2\frac{3}{4}$ is a mixed number.

multiple A product. 0, 4, 8, 12, 16, 20, and so on, are multiples of 4.

multiplying by 1 property The product of any number and 1 is that number.

$8 \times 1 = 8$

multiplying by 0 property The product of any number and 0 is 0.

$24 \times 0 = 0$

nonagon A polygon with nine sides.

number line A line with its points labeled with numbers.

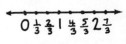

number pair An ordered pair of numbers.

(5, 6), (8, 2)

numeral A name or symbol for a number.

Numerals for ten:
10, 2 × 5, 12 − 2

numerator In $\frac{2}{3}$, the numerator is 2.

obtuse angle An angle whose measure is greater than 90°.

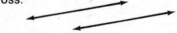

octagon A polygon with eight sides.

odd number A whole number that is not divisible by 2. The numbers 1, 3, 5, 7, 9, 11, and so on, are odd.

odds The ratio of the number of ways that an outcome can occur to the number of ways that the outcome cannot occur.

opposites Two numbers are opposites if their sum is 0.

$$^-3 + {}^+3 = 0$$
opposites

origin The point where axes intersect.

outcome A possible result.

parallel lines Lines in a plane that do not cross.

parallelogram A quadrilateral with opposite sides parallel.

pentagon A polygon with five sides.

percent (%) Percent means per hundred. 5% is a percent. It equals $\frac{5}{100}$.

perimeter The distance around a figure. The sum of the lengths of the sides.

The perimeter is 9 cm.

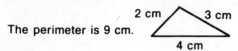

2 cm 3 cm
4 cm

perpendicular bisector A line that bisects and is perpendicular to a segment.

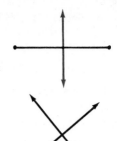

perpendicular lines Lines that intersect to form right angles.

pi The number that is the ratio of the circumference of a circle to its diameter. It is represented by the Greek letter π and is approximately equal to $\frac{22}{7}$ or 3.14.

place value A system for writing numbers in which the value of a digit is determined by its position.

plane A flat surface that extends endlessly in all directions.

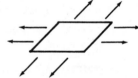

point of symmetry If a figure fits itself after a half-turn about a point, the point is a point of symmetry of the figure.

polygon A plane figure made up of segments.

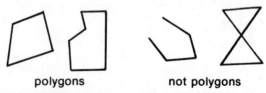

polygons   not polygons

prime factorization Writing a composite number as a product of prime numbers. The prime factorization of 18 is 2 × 3 × 3.

prime number 2, 3, 5, 7, 11, 13, and so on, are prime numbers. They cannot be obtained by multiplying smaller whole numbers.

principal An amount of money on which interest is paid.

prism A three-dimensional figure with two congruent parallel faces that are polygons and with the remaining faces parallelograms.

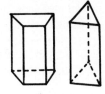

probability of an outcome The ratio of the number of ways that an equally likely outcome can occur to the total number of ways that all the equally likely outcomes can occur.

probability of picking black = $\frac{3}{5}$.

proportion An equation stating that two ratios are equal.

$$\frac{5}{8} = \frac{30}{48}$$

protractor An instrument used for measuring angles.

pyramid A three-dimensional figure with a face (known as the base) that is any polygon and with all other faces, which are triangles, sharing a common vertex.

quadrilateral A polygon with four sides.

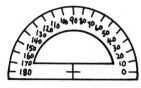

quotient The answer to a division problem.

radius The distance from the center of a circle to the circle.

range The highest and lowest numbers in a set of numbers. Can also be thought of as the difference of the highest and lowest numbers.

{8, 13, 23, 27, 42, 51, 55}

The range is from 8 to 55, or 47.

rate A comparison by division of two quantities.

$$\frac{87 \text{ kilometers}}{2 \text{ hours}}$$

ratio A comparison of two quantities by division. In a quadrilateral, the ratio of sides to diagonals is 4 to 2, 4 : 2, or $\frac{4}{2}$.

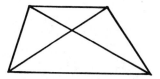

ray A part of a line that has one endpoint. This is ray *AB*.

A •━━━━━━━━━━━━━━━━━━━▶ B

reciprocal Two numbers are reciprocals if their product is 1.

$$\frac{3}{4} \times \frac{4}{3} = 1$$

↑   ↑
reciprocals

rectangle A parallelogram with four right angles.

rectangular prism A prism whose faces are rectangles.

reduced to lowest terms A fraction such that the greatest common factor of its numerator and denominator numbers is 1.

$\frac{5}{6}$ is in lowest terms.

remainder In a division problem the number that is "left over." When it is added to the product of the divisor and quotient, the sum is the dividend.

$$\begin{array}{r} 3 \\ 8\overline{)29} \\ -24 \\ \hline 5 \leftarrow \text{remainder} \end{array}$$

repeating decimal A decimal in which a digit or a group of digits repeats forever.

$$0.3333\ldots \qquad 1.47474747\ldots$$

rhombus A parallelogram with 4 congruent sides.

right angle An angle whose measure is 90°.

round a number To replace a number by another one that is easier to use. You round a number to the nearest ten by choosing the nearest multiple of ten. (5 is rounded up.)

$$13 \rightarrow 10 \qquad 27 \rightarrow 30 \qquad 45 \rightarrow 50$$

You round a number to the nearest hundred by choosing the nearest multiple of one hundred.

$$487 \rightarrow 500 \qquad 1238 \rightarrow 1200 \qquad 550 \rightarrow 600$$

sample A small group, chosen from a larger group, that is examined carefully in order to make predictions about the larger group.

scale drawing A drawing of an object such that the ratio of a unit of length on the drawing to a unit of length on the object is fixed.

scalene triangle A triangle with no congruent sides.

scientific notation A notation for writing a number as the product of a number between 1 and 10 and a power of ten.

$$186.3 = 1.863 \times 10^2$$

segment A part of a line that has two endpoints.

set A collection of things.

solve an equation Find the numbers that make an equation true.

square A rectangle with four congruent sides.

statistics A branch of mathematics that studies numerical facts as a basis for drawing general conclusions and making predictions.

standard numeral A numeral written in its simplest place-value form. 248

subset Set A is a subset of set B, $A \subseteq B$, if all the members of A are also members of B.

$$A = \{0, 2, 4\} \qquad B = \{0, 1, 2, 3, 4, 5\}$$
$$A \subseteq B$$

substitute Replace a variable with a numeral.

$$7a + 3$$
$$\downarrow$$
$$7 \cdot 6 + 3$$

surface area The total area of the surface of a three-dimensional figure.

terms (of a fraction) The numerator and denominator numbers of a fraction.

trapezoid A quadrilateral with two parallel sides.

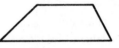

triangular prism A prism with two triangular faces in parallel planes.

union of sets The union of set A and set B, $A \cup B$, is the set of all elements in either A or B.

$$A = \{3, 5, 7\} \qquad B = \{1, 2, 3\}$$
$$A \cup B = \{1, 2, 3, 5, 7\}$$

unit A fixed quantity used as a standard for measuring length, area, volume, weight, etc.

variable A symbol, usually a letter, that holds the place for a number.

$$8x + 19 = 23$$

vertex The point at the "corner" of an angle, plane figure, or solid figure.

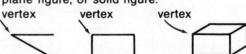

volume The measure of the space inside a three-dimensional figure. A cube is used as a unit.

whole number Any of the numbers 0, 1, 2, 3, 4, and so on.

Index

Symbols

{ }	set
∅	the empty set
⊆	is a subset of
∪	union
∩	intersection
<	is less than
>	is greater than
(a, b)	number pair
%	percent
.34	.34343434 . . .
⁺6	positive 6
⁻6	negative 6
P(2)	the probability of the outcome 2

′	foot
″	inch
≈	is approximately equal to
π	pi
°	degree
$a : b$	the ratio of $a : b$
≅	is congruent to
$\overline{AB}$	segment AB
$\overrightarrow{AB}$	ray AB
△	triangle
‖	is parallel to
⊥	is perpendicular to

Formulas

$P = 4s$	Perimeter of a square
$P = 2l + 2w$	Perimeter of a rectangle
$C = \pi d$	Circumference of a circle
$A = lw$	Area of a rectangle
$A = s^2$	Area of a square
$A = bh$	Area of a parallelogram
$A = \frac{1}{2} bh$	Area of a triangle
$A = \frac{1}{2} h(b_1 + b_2)$	Area of a trapezoid
$A = \pi r^2$	Area of a circle
$V = lwh$	Volume of a rectangular prism
$V = Bh$	Volume of a prism
$V = \pi r^2 h$	Volume of a cylinder
$I = prt$	Interest